The Battleship
FUSO 扶桑

ANATOMY OF THE SHIP

The Battleship
FUSO 扶桑

Naval
Institute
Press

JANUSZ SKULSKI

In memory of the lost crew of HIJMS Fuso

Frontispiece: The 1st Fleet (Blue Fleet) during the Grand Manouevre in Hiroshima Bay on 14 October 1919. Here *Fuso* leads *Hyuga*, *Ise Aki* and *Seetsu*.

CONTENTS

ACKNOWLEDGEMENTS

I would like to express my deep gratitude to my Japanese friends and the authorities of the Imperial Japanese Navy history and research department, who provided most valuable assistance in this project. In particular, I would like to thank (in alphabetical order): Hasegawa Toichi, Izumi Kozo, Kamakura Takumi, Kawamoto Koichi, Mizutani Kiyotaka, Tsukamoto Hideki and Uchiyama Mutsuo. Without their priceless help in uncovering sources, translating information, and offering advice and direction, it would have been impossible to write this book. Also, special thanks to 'G F' society members.

PREFACE

THIS portrait of HIJMS *Fuso* is the third comprehensive monograph of a Japanese ship that I have written for the Conway 'Anatomy of the Ship' series. The wartime career of this battleship – the first 'superdreadnought' designed and built in Japan – is well known from the history books, but close study of the details of the ship has shown that she was a somewhat unusual unit. The extent of the preserved material on the *Fuso* – official drawings, photographs and other information – has always been thought to be rather modest, but after lengthy research, intensive study, and the help and consultation of my Japanese friends, I have been able to prepare a precise reconstruction of the ship, showing her various appearances over the course of several modernisations.

This present work contains almost 900 detailed drawings, and includes, I can boldly say, all the information that could possibly be obtained from official Japanese sources and photographs. Unfortunately, however, the condition of the Imperial Japanese Navy's archives is woefully inadequate in comparison with British and American naval records. Most of the Imperial Navy's documents were lost during or after the Second World War. Hence, it has been impossible to find, for instance, the drawings of *Fuso*'s engine machinery or the precise details of the hull structure. As was the case with my last monograph on the heavy cruiser *Takao*, it is therefore unlikely that the scope of this book will be expanded in the future. I am delighted to say, however, that, rather unexpectedly, and thanks to the extreme kindness of my contacts in Japan, I have recently received new material on HIJMS *Yamato* that was not previously available to the public, which will hopefully enhance and develop information on *Yamato* and her sister ships *Musashi* and *Shinano* already available in my previous book in the 'Anatomy of the Ship' series.

Janusz Skulski
November 1997

INTRODUCTION

THE Battle of Tsushima in May 1905 between Russia and Japan – the first major battle fought by fleets of armoured battleships – was the earliest sign of the revolutionary changes that were about to occur in the design of capital ships and the increase in weapon power. The revolution began in 1906 when the leading naval power of the day – the Royal Navy – commissioned into service the first of the new generation 'all-big-gun' battleships, HMS *Dreadnought*. Although the introduction of the *Dreadnought* rendered every other battleship in the world obsolete, and caused worldwide excitement, it was not entirely unexpected. Designs for armoured ships with single-calibre armament had begun to emerge several years earlier in other countries, including Japan. As early as 1903, the Japanese had started to develop a 17,000-ton armoured cruiser armed with eight 305mm guns. Only the weak economic situation in the country prevented the project from being realised.

At this time, the planned development and modernisation of the Imperial Japanese Navy was known as the '6 + 6' Fleet Programme, meaning the number of capital ships (six battleships and six armoured cruisers) in service at any one time. According to this plan, new units were to replace ships that were ten years old or were lost. The Japanese government decided, as part of its National Defence Policy, that from 1907 the role of the Imperial Japanese Navy was to expand, and that the '6 + 6' Fleet Programme should become the '8 + 8' Programme, with eight of the latest battleships and eight of the latest armoured cruisers in service as capital ships, and auxiliary warships to support them. However, economic difficulties delayed the implementation of the programme.

The commissioning of *Dreadnought* forced the Japanese to change their plans and start construction of ships to the new design. One of the first effects of this was that the Imperial Navy decided to complete the armoured cruisers *Satsuma* and *Aki*, which were in the process of being built (work on them had started in 1905), as 'dreadnoughts'. *Aki* was an innovation in that she was fitted with turbine propulsion, making her, according to many sources, seven months ahead of *Dreadnought*. In turn, in 1909–11 the battleships *Settsu* and *Kawachi* were also built as 'dreadnoughts' in Japanese naval yards. They turned out to be very good units, although they were inferior in dimensions to contemporary British and US battleships.

In the years leading up to the outbreak of the First World War, competition among navies intensified. Japan responded by ordering the construction of the 'superdreadnought' battle-cruiser *Kongo* from the British shipbuilding firm Vickers; three further ships of this class – *Hiei*, *Haruna* and *Kirishima* – were also built in Japan. In 1911, the Imperial Japanese Navy submitted an urgent request to the government to implement the '8 + 8' Fleet Programme. But the government, whilst acknowledging the need to develop Japanese sea power, concluded that due to the country's economic hardship only four new battleships could be built.

In the financial year 1911, as part of its Third Naval Development Programme, the Japanese government approved the building of a new 'superdreadnought' battleship. Designated Battleship No 3, this vessel had its keel-laying ceremony at Kure Kaigun Kosho (Kure Naval Base) shipyard on 11 March 1912. One and half years later, on 20 November 1913, the keel of a sister ship, Battleship No 4 (later *Yamashiro*), was laid in Yokosuka Naval Yard. On 28 March 1914, Battleship No 3 was launched, and the following year, on 8 November 1915, she was commissioned as HIJMS *Fuso* (an early Chinese designation for Japan). Her weight of 30,600 tons in normal condition (standard condition) made her the largest battleship in the world at that time.

Earlier in 1915, the building of the next two battleships of the class – No 5 (later *Ise*) and No 6 (later *Hyuga*) – had begun. They were subsequently called 'improved *Fuso*-class battleships'. The main differences between these ships and *Fuso* was that their main gun turrets (No 3 and No 4) were fitted abaft the funnels and that the calibre of their secondary guns was changed from 15cm (6in) to 14cm (5.5in). [Note: the official designation of gun calibres in the Imperial Japanese Navy was in full centimetres, although real calibres were in inches.]

During her twenty-nine years of service, *Fuso* was modernised several times. Her major modernisation, which created her characteristic silhouette, began in 1930 and initiated the programme of major modernisations for all the Imperial Japanese Navy's 'superdreadnoughts'. Following their major modernisations, *Fuso* and *Yamashiro* were unusual among the Imperial Japanese Navy's ships because of their high and complicated tower bridges – known as 'pagoda towers' – which were a record-breaking 44m above the waterline. The various stages of *Fuso*'s first major modernisation lasted six years until 1936, while the second lasted from 1937 to 1941. Later modernisations were essentially limited to additional light anti-aircraft guns and the installation of radar. After the Battle of Midway in June 1942, during which the Imperial Japanese Navy lost four aircraft carriers, there was a plan to convert *Fuso* and *Yamashiro* into battleship-carriers, each with a short flight-deck aft. In the event, however, *Ise* and *Hyuga* were converted.

During the Second World War, *Fuso* and *Yamashiro* mostly operated together, as they had done before the war. The twin battleships even sank together – only fifty minutes apart – in the Battle of Surigao Strait in October 1944. *Fuso* went down with all her crew, while only about ten sailors were saved from *Yamashiro*.

TABLE 1: 'Superdreadnoughts' built at the same time as *Fuso*

NAME (Nation)	DATE: Keel-laying Commission	DISPLACEMENT: Trial (tons) Full (tons)	ARMAMENT: Main Secondary	HORSEPOWER Speed (kts)	DIMENSIONS: Loa x beam x draught (m)
Fuso (Japan)	11.03.1912 08.11.1915	30,600 35,900	12–356mm 16–152mm	40,000 23	205.1 x 28.7 x 8.7
Queen Elizabeth (UK)	27.10.1912 19.01.1915	29,150 33,750	8–381mm 16–152mm	75,000 25	195 x 27.6 x 9.3
Nevada (US)	04.11.1912 11.03.1916	27,500 28,900	10–356mm 21–127mm	23,300 20.5	177.8 x 29 x 9.9
Provence (France)	21.05.1912 01.03.1916	23,936 28,500	10–340mm 22–138mm	29,000 20	166 x 26.9 x 9.8
Caio Duilio (Italy)	24.02.1912 10.05.1915	22,694 25,200	13–305mm 16–152mm	32,000 21.5	176.1 x 28 x 9.5
König (Germany)	??.10.1911 09.08.1914	25,390 29,560	10–305mm 14–152mm	31,000 21	175.4 x 29.5 x 9.2
Gangut (Russia)	03.06.1909 21.10.1914	23,370 25,580	12–305mm 16–120mm	42,000 23	182.9 x 26.9 x 8.3

D E S I G N

Before the start of the superdreadnought battleship project – which had the official code 'A 64' – a team of Imperial Navy architects went to Britain to assist in the construction of the Japanese 'superdreadnought' battle-cruiser *Kongo*, which was being built at Vickers' shipyard. While they were there, they offered their skills and expertise to a British battle-cruiser project based on the *Lion* class. The value and importance of the Japanese contribution to the British project was clearly significant, for the British designers adopted many of the features of the *Kongo* in the battle-cruiser *Tiger*.* The exchange of design knowledge worked both ways: the Japanese constructors who went on to design the battleships of the *Fuso* class thus had access to the latest British project studies. But instead of copying what they had seen in Britain, they developed their own battleship that was to be superior to all contemporaries. This determination to build ships better than those of other countries eventually culminated in the building of the most powerful battleships in the world: the superbattleships of the *Yamato* class.

When she was commissioned in 1915, HIJMS *Fuso* had a standard displacement of 29,330 tons and was armed with twelve 36cm (14in) 45-calibre Type 41 guns as the main armament, and sixteen 15cm (6in) 50-calibre Type 41 single gun mounts, as the secondary armament. The 36cm guns were in six twin turrets, although studies had also been carried out on triple and even quadruple turrets. The arrangement of these turrets was very carefully examined. Many ideas were worked out before the final arrangement was accepted: two turrets superimposed at forecastle deck level, one between the two funnels, another between the second funnel and the rear superstructure, and two superimposed at quarterdeck level.

* Note: Recent research by John Campbell and John Roberts suggests that the revised layout of HMS *Tiger* may already have been settled, and the armour arrangements are very different.

TABLE 2: Characteristics of HIJMS *Fuso*

	1915	1935
Length overall	205.130m	212.750m
Length waterline	202. 692m	210.312m
Length between perpendiculars	192.024m	192.024m
Beam (max)	28.650m	33.080m
Draught	8.690m	9.690m
Displacement (standard)	29,330 tons	—
Displacement (trial)	30,600 tons	34,700 tons
Displacement (full load)	35,900 tons	39,154 tons
Shaft horsepower	40,000hp	75,000hp
Max shaft horsepower	—	76,889hp
Speed	23kts	24.7kts (24.75kts max)
Fuel capacity	4,000 tons (coal) 1,000 tons (oil)	5,100 tons (oil)
Radius of action	8,000nm at 14kts	11,800nm at 16kts
Propulsion plant	4 steam turbines	4 steam turbines
Armour:	102–305mm side belt 32–51mm deck 279–76mm main turrets 305–203mm barbettes 152mm casemate	102–305mm side belt 51–130mm 279–114mm main turrets 305–203mm barbettes 152mm casemate
Weight of armour	8,587.6 tons	12,199.4 tons
Armament:	12–36cm 16–15cm 5–8cm (from 1917)	12–36cm 16–15cm (after 1938 14–15cm) 8–12.7cm 16–13.2mm quadruple mountings
Torpedo tubes	6–533mm (below waterline)	—
Aircraft	—	3 floatplanes, 1 catapult
Crew	1,193	1,396

CAREER SUMMARY

11 March 1912:	Keel laid in dry dock at the Kure Kaigun Kosho (naval shipyard)
28 March 1914:	Launched
8 November 1915:	Commissioned and registered at the Kure-Chinjufu (naval district)
13 December 1915:	Attached to 1st Squadron of 1st Fleet
9 April 1917:	Departs from Sasebo Naval Base for operations off the coast of China
29 April 1917:	Returns to Kure Naval Base
27 February 1918:	Departs from Makou and cruises in Chinese waters
3 March 1918:	Returns to Sasebo Naval Base
1 December 1918:	Goes into first reserve
1 August 1919:	Attached to 1st Squadron of 1st Fleet
29 August 1920:	Departs from Tateyama for guard duty off coast of USSR
7 September 1920:	Returns to Otaru
1 December 1921:	Goes into first reserve
9–22 September 1923:	Assists in rescue operation following great earthquake near Tokyo
1 July 1924:	Captain Mitsumasa Yonai assumes command
1 November 1924:	Captain Mitsukichi Takahashi assumes command
1 December 1924:	Attached to 1st Squadron of 1st Fleet
30 March 1925:	Departs from Sasebo Naval Base and operates around Qinhuangdao off China
April 1925:	Returns to Lüshun port
30 March 1926:	Departs from Nakajou Bay and operates around Amoy off China
5 April 1926:	Returns to Makou
20 April 1926:	Departs from Jilong and cruises around Quindao off China
26 April 1926:	Returns to Terashima Channel
1 December 1926:	Goes into first reserve
1 December 1927:	Attached to 1st Squadron of 1st Fleet
29 March 1928:	Departs from Ariake-Bay and operates around Zhoushan Quindao off China
2 April 1928:	Returns to Jilong
7 April 1928:	Departs from Jilong and cruises off Hong Kong
15 April 1928:	Returns to Makou
10 December 1928:	Goes into first reserve
12 April 1930:	Main modernisation starts at Yokosuka Naval Yard; bulges are fitted to the hull and the machinery is replaced
15 May 1930:	Goes into third reserve
26 September 1932:	Arrives at Kure Naval Base for second phase of modernisation: twin 12.7cm HA gun, 13.2mm machine guns, shell-room equipment, etc. fitted
1 March 1933:	Goes into second reserve
12 May 1933:	Completion of modernisation. *Fuso* leaves Kure Naval Base for trial at sea
16 August 1933:	Departs from Tateyama and operates around Marshall Islands
21 August 1933:	Arrives Kisarazu
15 November 1933:	Attached to 1st Squadron of 1st Fleet; Captain Koshiro Otani assumes command
16 September 1934:	Enters dry dock at Kure Naval Base for second phase of main modernisation; enlargement of stern starts
1 November 1934:	Captain Seiichiro Iwamura assumes command

March 1935:	Second phase of modernisation completed
29 March 1935:	Departs from Sasebo Naval Base and operates off Anmagundo off China
4 April 1935:	Returns to Terashima Channel
1 November 1935:	Captain Ninnichi Kusaka assumes command
13 April 1936:	Departs from Terashima Channel and operates around Quindao
22 April 1936:	Returns to Terashima Channel
4 August 1936:	Departs from Kure and operates around Amoy
7 August 1936:	Returns to Makou
1 December 1936:	Attached to Guard Fleet in Kure and assigned to training duties
26 February 1937:	Start of the second modernisation at Kure Naval Base shipyard: twin 25mm machine guns mounted, stern reinforced, 10m rangefinder fitted on the top of tower bridge
1 December 1937:	Captain Hiroki Abe assumes command
31 March 1938:	Second modernisation complete; departs from Kure Naval Base
1 April 1938:	Captain Ruitaro Fujita assumes command
15 November 1938:	Attached to No 1 Squadron of No 1 Fleet; Captain Fukui Kiku assumes command
22 March 1939:	Departs from Kagoshima and operates in northern Chinese waters
2 April 1939:	Returns to Terashima Channel
15 December 1939:	Goes into third reserve; second phase of second modernisation starts: replacement of aircraft equipment to stern deck, AA defence platform on top of tower bridge
10 April 1941:	Attached to 2nd Squadron of 1st Fleet
15 September 1941:	Captain Mitsuo Kinoshita assumes command
8 December 1941:	Pacific War starts; *Fuso* departs from Hashirajima as support for task force attacking Pearl Harbor
13 December 1941:	Returns to Hashirajima due to lack of US counter-attack against the task force
21 February 1942:	Arrives at Kure Naval Base for exchange of gun barrels
25 February 1942:	Departs from Kure Naval Base
18 April 1942:	Sails from Hashirajima for counter-attack against the US task force bombing Tokyo with carrier-based bombers – the 'Doolittle Raid'; returns to Hashirajima after failing to catch the enemy task force
29 May 1942:	Sails from Hashirajima to support strike force attacking Midway
16 June 1942:	Returns to Yokosuka
22 June 1942:	Departs from Yokosuka
24 June 1942:	Arrives at Hashirajima
15 November 1942:	Transferred to Military Academy for service as training ship (until 15 January 1943)
5 December 1942:	Captain Keizo Yoshimura assumes command
1 June 1943:	Captain Shinzo Tsuruoka assumes command
18 July 1943:	Enters dry dock at Kure Naval Base; Type 21 radar, and twin and single 25mm machine gun mountings fitted
24 July 1943:	Departs from Kure Naval Base
18 August 1943:	Sails from Inland Sea and heads towards Truk Naval Base
23 August 1943:	Arrives at Truk for training
17 October 1943:	Departs from Truk and prepares to attack US task force in Battle of Marshall Islands
19 October 1943:	Arrives at Borneo
23 October 1943:	Departs from Borneo and sails to Truk Naval Base

26 October 1943:	Arrives at Truk
1 February 1944:	Departs from Truk with other capital ships to avoid US air raid
4 February 1944:	Arrives at Palau
16 February 1944:	Departs from Palau with other capital ships due to threat of air raids and fuel problem
21 February 1944:	Arrives at Lingga harbour for training
23 February 1944:	Captain Masami Ban assumes command
25 February 1944:	Attached to Grand Fleet
8 April 1944:	Departs from Lingga harbour and sails to Singapore
13 April 1944:	Enters dry dock in Singapore
25 April 1944:	Leaves dry dock
27 April 1944:	Departs from Singapore and sails to Lingga harbour
11 May 1944:	Departs from Lingga harbour
14 May 1944:	Arrives at Tawi-Tawi, Borneo
30 May 1944:	Departs from Tawi-Tawi to participate in operation 'Kon'
31 May 1944:	Arrives at Davao
2 June 1944:	Sails for Biaku Island
3 June 1944:	Returns to Davao following breakdown of operation 'Kon'
5 June 1944:	Arrives at Davao
17 June 1944:	Departs from Davao and sails to Mararagu; on alert for operation 'A'
20 June 1944:	Departs from Mararagu for Davao
1 July 1944:	Departs from Davao for Tarakan, arriving 2 July
8 July 1944:	Departs from Tarakan with 4th Destroyer Fleet
15 July 1944:	Arrives at Kure Naval Base
2 August 1944:	Enters dry dock at Kure; Type 13 and Type 22 radar and additional 25mm and 13.2mm machine guns fitted
14 August 1944:	Departs from Kure Naval Yard
10 September 1944:	Together with *Yamashiro*, is attached to 2nd Squadron of 2nd Fleet
23 September 1944:	Departs from Kure
4 October 1944:	Arrives at Lingga Roads to prepare for Operation 'Sho Go' – Battle of the Philippine Islands
18 October 1944:	Departs from Lingga Roads and sails to Brunei
20 October 1944:	Arrives in Brunei
22 October 1944:	Departs from Brunei with 3rd Squadron of 1st Fleet (1st Fleet commanded by Admiral Takeo Kurita; 3rd Squadron by Admiral Nishimura) to participate in Battle of Leyte Gulf. 3rd Squadron consists of seven warships: *Yamashiro* (Admiral Nishimura's flagship), *Fuso* (under the command of Admiral Masami Ban), heavy cruiser *Mogami* and the destroyers *Michishio*, *Asagumo*, *Yamagumo* and *Shigure*. Nishimura's fleet sails to Surigao Strait
24 October 1944:	Attacked by US aircraft carriers
25 October 1944:	At 04:21hrs, under bombardment from torpedoes and shells from US battleships and cruisers, *Fuso* sinks in Surigao Strait with the loss of all her crew
31 August 1945:	*Fuso* is formally deleted from the Navy List

THE LOSS OF HIJMS *FUSO*

The final moments of HIJMS *Fuso* and her sister ship HIJMS *Yamashiro* – the most tragic of all the Japanese battleships, indeed of all the world's lost super–dreadnoughts – have to this day been shrouded in mystery. There are two versions of the last phase of the engagement in Surigao Strait: the Japanese version claims that *Fuso* sank fifty minutes after *Yamashiro* as a result of gunfire from battleships and cruisers of Rear-Admiral Oldendorf's fleet; the second version, propagated by US publications, claims that the positions of *Fuso* and *Yamashiro* in the battle were reversed, *Fuso* sinking first. Following extensive research, it seems that the Japanese version of the events is the most accurate.

On 14 August 1944, *Fuso* left Kure naval shipyard after undergoing minor repairs and having additional AA machine guns (total number then being ninety-five 25mm guns and ten 13.2mm guns) and Type 13 and Type 22 radar fitted. These modifications were carried out as part of the Japanese preparations for the decisive Battle of the Philippine Islands against the US naval forces. In September 1944, *Fuso*, together with her twin *Yamashiro*, was assigned to the 3rd Squadron of the 1st Fleet, commanded by Admiral Takeo Kurita. Admiral Kurita ordered Vice-Admiral Shoji Nishimura to take command of 3rd Squadron. Admiral Kurita himself commanded both 1st Squadron (the battleships *Yamato*, *Mushashi*, *Nagato*, the heavy cruisers *Atago*, *Takao*, *Maya*, *Chokai*, the light cruiser *Noshiro* and nine destroyers) and 2nd Squadron (the battleships *Kongo*, *Haruna*, the heavy cruisers *Kumano*, *Suzuya*, *Tone*, *Chikuma*, the light cruiser *Yahagi* and six destroyers).

At 08:00hrs on 22 October, the 1st and 2nd squadrons left Brunei. A few hours later, sometime in the afternoon, Admiral Nishimura's 3rd Squadron also left the base. The squadron sailed south of Palawan island across the Sulu Sea, and headed towards the southern entrance of Surigao Strait, through which it would reach Leyte Gulf. At 09:18hrs on 24 October, *Fuso* was hit by a torpedo from an aircraft from a US aircraft carrier, but was not seriously damaged. During the night of 24 October, both 3rd Squadron and 4th Fleet, commanded by Admiral Kiyohide Shima, and some 40 nautical miles behind Nishimura's fleet, sailed across the Mindanao Sea and around Bohoul Island, so that, in the early hours of 25 October, they could speed towards Leyte Gulf from Surigao Strait as Kurita's fleet approached from the north.

However, the US 7th Fleet was waiting for the Japanese warships. On both sides of the southern entrance of the strait, thirty-nine US torpedo boats and three groups of destroyers were arranged. On the northern entrance, six battleships – the USs *California*, *Tennessee*, *Mississippi*, *West Virginia*, *Maryland* and *Pennsylvania* – and three heavy cruisers, two light cruisers and nine destroyers were in position. These US warships, under the command of Rear-Admiral Jesse B Oldendorf, were placed to 'Cross the T' against the Japanese ships. Nishimura's fleet – which had been fighting enemy torpedo boats since 23:00hrs and had arrived at the southern entrance of Surigao Strait at 01:20hrs – took the following formation: the destroyers *Michishio* and *Asagumo* led the line, the destroyers *Yamagumo* and *Shigure* were arranged on both sides of the central formation, which was made up by *Fuso* and *Yamashiro*, and the heavy cruiser *Mogami* followed at the rear.

At 03:00hrs on 25 October 1944, the first squadron of US destroyers began to attack the Japanese ships, launching 27 torpedoes from both sides of the straits, before escaping under cover of a smokescreen. *Yamashiro* was hit by between two and four torpedoes. Admiral Nishimura radioed to his other ships that he had been torpedoed and ordered them to go forward and attack the enemy. This order left the captain of *Fuso*, Admiral Masami Ban, in command of 3rd Squadron. At 03:23hrs, a second squadron of US destroyers attacked the Japanese with torpedoes. *Fuso* was hit by two torpedoes, but was able to maintain her speed. *Michishio*, however, was stopped in her tracks by the bombardment, *Asagumo* lost her bow, and

Yamagumo was sunk. *Fuso* continued to go forward with *Mogami* and *Shigure*, but she lost her position and escorts as she turned to avoid enemy torpedoes. She then turned back to search for *Yamashiro*, but failed to find her twin, which had sunk following an internal explosion. *Fuso* turned back towards Leyte Gulf again and sailed forward. The Japanese ships were still having their 'T' crossed by the US battleships.

At 03:53hrs, the US battleships and cruisers opened fire from the direction of Leyte Gulf. Shell after shell rained down on *Fuso* and *Mogami*. Despite this heavy bombardment, and fire spreading along her hull, *Fuso* continued to steam ahead, trying to counter-attack by firing from her forward turrets. At 03:55hrs, *Mogami* launched several torpedoes before turning south to escape. At the same time, *Fuso* began to turn to port. It is not known whether this turn was the result of a loss of control caused by damage or to position herself so that all twelve main guns could be fired at the US fleet.

With her flank thus exposed, *Fuso* was hit by many – it is not clear how many – 406mm (16in), 356mm (14in), and smaller-calibre shells. Her forward 44m-high 'pagoda tower' toppled under the shelling as if it were a simple sandcastle knocked down by a wave. A third squadron of US destroyers then approached from the north and launched torpedoes. After what was either a huge explosion in her shell room or a direct torpedo hit, at 04:19hrs *Fuso* overturned and began to sink by the stern. At 04:21hrs, she vanished below the water, taking her entire crew, including her captain, Admiral Masami Ban, down with her.

HULL

In its shape and system of armour protection, *Fuso*'s hull was partly based on the battle-cruisers of the *Kongo* class. However, since *Fuso* was built as a battleship, she had thicker side armour, as well as thicker lower underwater armour as protection against diving shells. She also had an innovatory anti-torpedo bulkhead situated at a

maximum 0.48m from the ship's side, in the middle part of the hull (on *Kongo* this was a maximum 0.24m). The side armour, along with deck armour, enclosed the ship's vitals in an armoured citadel, with No 1 main barbette in front and No 6 turret barbette behind. To preserve the buoyancy of the ship in case of damage, the hull was divided into 737 watertight compartments – 574 underneath the armour deck (upper deck) and 163 above.

PROTECTION

When *Fuso* was completed in 1915, her armour was typical for a 'pre-Jutland' battleship. Her armoured belt was 305mm thick, while under the waterline it was 102mm thick. Horizontal armour was 51mm (UD) and 32mm (FD); casemate was 152mm. Main gun turrets were 279-76mm front, 228.6mm side and rear wall, 114.3mm roof, 305mm barbetter. The conning tower was 351mm sides and 152mm roof. During her main modernisation in 1930–33, 51 x 102mm armour was added to the protection of the shell room and machinery room. To improve the underwater protection, a 64 x 76mm longitudinal bulkhead was created and some extra plates were added to cover the partly original hull plating. Although armour weight increased from an original 8,587.6 tons to 12,199.4 tons – about 31.2% of total weight – the improved protection was still arranged in the original manner, including the horizontal protection, and it was not enough to withstand 14in shells. Bulges were added, not only for underwater protection, but also to compensate for the increase in weight. After *Fuso*'s first reconstruction, the upper edge of the bulge reached only the middle deck. After her 1935 modifications, it reached to the upper deck. At the same time, the maximum beam of the hull was increased to 33.08m, 4.43m wider than the original beam.

MACHINERY

The installation of six main gun turrets on the centreline caused complications in the arrangement of *Fuso*'s boilers and engine compartments. In 1915, her machinery was almost the same as the

Kongo class battle-cruisers, but its arrangement was different: No 1 and No 2 boiler rooms were arranged below the fore funnel, No 3 and No 4 boiler rooms were arranged abaft No 3 main gun turret, and forward and aft engine rooms were arranged abaft No 4 main gun turret. *Fuso* had 40,000hp output and a planned maximum speed of 22.5kts. She had eight double-ended boilers and sixteen single-ended boilers. These were 'Miyahara-shiki' (Miyahara-type) boilers, in which both coal and oil could be burnt. One thousand tons of heavy oil and 4,000 tons of coal gave the ship an 8,000nm radius of action. *Fuso* had two Brown-Curtis high-, medium- and low-pressure turbines, a combination of which drove the shafts: inner shafts were driven by the high- and low-pressure turbines, while the outer ones were driven by the medium-pressure turbines.

During the modernisation of 1930–33, *Fuso*'s machinery was replaced. She received six new boilers: four of the 'Ro-go Kanpon shiki' type and two of the 'Ha-go Kanpon shiki' type, using only oil fuel. All her new boilers were arranged in the original aft boiler room. The number of funnels was reduced to one, in the position of the former second funnel. The main engine was also replaced by four newly-developed turbines called 'Kanpon shiki', which had an increased output of 75,000hp (in trials 76,889hp). Oil capacity was 5,100 tons, giving a maximum radius of action of 11,800nm at 16 knots, the greatest of all the Japanese battleships after modernisation.

ARMAMENT

Main armament

The battleships of the Fuso class were conceived and designed by the Imperial Japanese Navy as super-dreadnought battleships to operate with the super-dreadnought battle-cruisers of the Kongo class. The designers also took into account the US Navy battleships of the Nevada class, which were then being built. Consequently, studies were carried out on 34, 36 and 38cm guns, with barrel lengths of 42, 45 and 50 calibres, in twin, triple and quadruple turrets. Finally, the Imperial Navy adopted the 36cm 45-calibre twin-gun turret based on the

Vickers-type turrets imported from Britain for the construction of the battle-cruisers of the Kongo class built in Japan. The most important result of this decision was the subsequent standardisation of Japanese ship armament.

Construction of the gun barrel

The construction of the gun barrel for the Fuso class was known as 'layered wound wire'. The barrel consisted of many tubes. Wire was wound around the rifled inner tubes and another hardened tube was pulled over this wire. Another wire was then wound around this tube and a further hardened outer tube was pulled over this. The outer tubes, which had an internal diameter slightly smaller than the inner tubes, were then heated. The outer tube was then shrunk by water cooling, making the barrel very strong. The winding wire became a flat steel belt, 6.3mm wide and 1.6mm thick. The number of rifling grooves was 84 while the pitch was 28 calibres per rotation. The breech was of the screw type. The name of this gun was 41 Shiki (Type 41), meaning the type of the breech.

Construction of turret mounting

The gun barrel was mounted on the gunslide in the gun cradle and pivoted up and down the trunnion bracket axis by hydraulic power. Cabinet, turntable, shell-loading-platform equipment and shell cage all moved as one by hydraulic power. Rollers on the roller path supported the weight of the turret as well as acting as bearings. Shells and cordite charges were loaded on the central shell carrier in the shell room and then carried to the working chamber. In the working chamber, the shells and cordite charges were loaded by a hydraulic ram onto rails and into the gun-loading cage, which was then lifted to the fixed gun-loading position of +5°. The breechblock was opened, and the shell loaded by hydraulic ram, followed by two cordite charges and then another two cordite charges.

Recuperation and recoil mechanism

Upon firing, the gun barrel recoiled in the opposite direction to that of the shell's flight. The force of this recoil was decreased by a recuperator cylinder. A recoil piston and cylinder then returned the gun barrel to its former position for its next loading. The recuperator cylinder was fixed on the gun cradle, and the recuperator piston rod was fixed on the gunslide. The recoil cylinder was also fixed on the gun cradle, while the recoil piston rod was fixed on the gunslide. Like the loading system, this recuperation and recoil mechanism was driven by water hydraulics. There were some problems with the hydraulic system, however. Due to the small capacity of the pumps, when firing a volley from the main battery, the cycle time of firing, recoiling and carrying ammunition became too long. Therefore, alternate firing (firing a salvo from half of the main guns, then firing from the other guns) was often adopted. The crew in the working chamber often had to wear raincoats to protect themselves from leaking water pipes.

Comparison between Vickers-type and 41-Shiki turrets

The twin 36cm 41-shiki turret of *Fuso* was slightly different from similar turrets on *Ise* and *Hyuga*. The turrets for *Kongo* and *Kirishima* were imported from Britain and the later turrets were built in Japan based on those British designs. The turret on *Fuso* was known as Type 41-improved Vickers, and the main differences between the original British and the Japanese turrets were s follows.

The guns of the Vickers turret could be elevated from –3° to +33°, while the guns in the *Fuso* could only be elevated from 0° to +30°. Maximum firing-range of the Vickers guns was 28,600m, while that of the Japanese guns was 27,800m (*Hyuga*). Shells and cordite charges were able to be loaded in Vickers turrets at an elevation angle of –3° to +25°; in the *Fuso* turret they were loaded at the fixed angle of +5°. The Vickers turret was equipped with 254mm armour on the front surface, 76mm armour on the roof and 228mm armour on the barbette. The 41-Shiki turret was equipped with 280mm armour on the front surface, 115mm armour on the roof and 305mm armour on the barbette. The weight of the rotating turret structure was 607 tons for the Vickers turret and 615 tons for the 41-Shiki turret. Both the firing cycle – 1.5 shell per minute per gun – and the muzzle velocity – 770m/sec – were the same for Vickers and 41-Shiki guns.

Modernisation of the 41-Shiki turret in 1930–33 main refit

During *Fuso*'s modernisation, the elevation of her guns was increased from –5° to +43°, and the range was extended to 35,450m. The recuperation and recoil mechanism was changed from hydraulics to compressed air. Upon firing, the recoil of the gun barrel compressed the air in the recoil cylinder, and the increased air pressure then pushed the gun barrel back to its normal position. The air pressure in the recoil cylinder was usually 100–150 atmospheres after filling in its normal position. This change enabled the firing of a salvo without the delay in the firing cycle that had occurred previously. The barrel construction was also changed from the 'wirewound' design to that of '*Autofrettage*' which used self-shrinking inner tubes. '*Autofrettage*' was the name of a technique of manufacturing gun barrels developed by the French company Schneider. The Imperial Japanese Navy had bought the patent for the technique in 1924 and had adopted it in the modernisation of its ships' main armaments.

TABLE 3: Main gun data

Designation	41-Shiki (Type 41) 36cm (14in) 45-calibre
Calibre of bore	355.6mm (14in)
Length in calibres	45
Length overall	16,469mm
Length of bore	16,002mm (45 calibres)
Chamber length	2,007.7mm
Rifling length	13,706mm
No of grooves	84
Dimensions of grooves	3,048mm deep x 8,865mm
Lands	4,435mm
Pitch of rifling	1 rotation per 28 calibres
Distance between gun axes	2,286mm
Weight of gun (including breech mechanism)	86,000kg (84.6 tons)
Weight of Type 91 AP projectile	673.5kg
Muzzle velocity for Type 91 AP	775m/sec
Weight of HE and incendiary projectile	625kg
Muzzle velocity for HE and incendiary	805m/sec
Weight of propellant charge	142.3kg
Working pressure	3,020kg/cm²
Maximum elevation/maximum range for Type 91 AP projectile	30°/27,800m (1915-1930) 43°/35,450m (after 1933)
Life of barrel	280 rounds

TABLE 4: Gun mount data

Weight of revolving (rotating) part	615 tons
Roller path diameter	7,772mm
Distance between gun axes	2,286mm
Maximum elevation/ maximum depression	+30°/0° (1915-1930) +43/-5° (after 1933)
Maximum elevating speed	5°/sec
Maximum training speed	3°/sec
Firing cycle	30–40 sec at maximum elevation

In the arrangement of *Fuso* and *Yamashiro*, the No 3 and No 4 turrets and the shell rooms for each mounting were positioned separately. This was partly because of difficulties arising from the protection of the shell rooms and partly because of the reduction in space and problems of hull construction caused by the anti-heat sections adjoining the boiler and engine rooms. Furthermore, the arrangement of the superstructure and the equipment on the forecastle deck was restricted by the main gun mount turrets. On the 'improved *Fuso* class' – battleships *Ise* and *Hyuga* – the No 3 and No 4 main gun mount turrets were superimposed abaft the second funnel.

Projectiles

1. Capped 91-Shiki (Type 91) Hibo Tetsukodan – armour-piercing shell; weight 673.5kg, length 1,524.7mm.

2. HE (high-explosive) 91-Shiki Tsûjôdan; weight 625kg, length 1,210mm.

3. 3-Shiki Sankaidan common shell (incendiary or fragmentation shell); weight 625kg, length 1,210mm. The shell was filled with 480 incendiary tubes and 192 stays, together with 672 fragments. The time of the shell burst was controlled by a fuze, the incendiary tubes igniting about half a second later and burning for five seconds at 3,000°C, giving a flame about 5m long. All incendiary tubes and stays exploded in a cone about 20° towards any incoming aircraft or land targets. This type of shell was used after 1939.

The propellant charge had a total weight of 142.3kg, consisting of four 35.575kg cordite (85 DC type) bags with a 225g black powder igniter on each one.

Secondary armament

As secondary armament, *Fuso* was equipped with sixteen 15cm 50-calibre Vickers-type guns. These were the same type as fitted in the battle-cruisers of the *Kongo* class. All guns were in the casemates at upper deck level. The casemates were protected by a 90mm armour shield, and the whole battery by 152mm vertical armour. The casemates had a horizontal angle of rotation of 130° and a maximum elevation angle of +15°. In 1933, after main modernisation, the maximum elevation angle was increased to +30° and the trunnion bracket was raised 450mm to allow the barrel to recoil further. The casemates, and the edge of the forecastle deck covering them, were also changed. In the 1937-1938 modernisation, the forward pair of casemates were removed, reducing the number of guns to fourteen. After the battleship's draught had been increased by 1m during her main modernisation of 1930–33, the poor positioning of these casemates meant that at high speed the guns were flooded with sea water.

Projectiles used were HE shell, Type 4 common shell, anti-submarine shell and illuminating shell. The propellant charge was one cordite bag with a 60g black powder igniter.

High-angle guns

In 1918, *Fuso* was fitted with her first anti-aircraft guns, in five 8cm gun mounts. The 8cm HA guns were installed on both sides of the forward superstructure, on both sides of the second funnel structure and on the port side of the rear superstructure. Probably at the turn of the 1920s, three additional 6.5mm 'Shu-type' machine guns were fitted; these were subsequently replaced by 'Sannen-shiki' guns. The arrangement of these machine guns is not mentioned in the preserved material.

TABLE 5: Secondary gun data

Designation	41-Shiki (Type 41) 15cm (6in) 50-calibre gun
Calibre of bore	152.4mm (6in)
Length in calibres	50
Length overall	7,875.8mm
Length of bore	7,620mm (50 calibres)
Chamber length	949.36mm
Rifling length	6,584.4mm
No of grooves	42
Dimensions of grooves	1.27mm deep x 7.62mm
Lands	3.78mm
Pitch of rifling	1 rotation per 30 calibres
Weight of gun (including breech mechanism)	8,360kg (8.23 tons)
Weight of projectile	45.36kg
Muzzle velocity	850–855m/sec
Propellant charge	12.4kg (37 DC type cordite)
Working pressure	2,870–2,900kg/cm²
Maximum elevation/ maximum range	+15°/14,100m (1915- 1930) +30°/15,000m+ (after 1933)
Life of barrel	500–600 rounds

TABLE 6: 8cm HA gun data

Designation	8cm (3in) 40-calibre 3rd-Year type (1914)
Calibre of bore	76.2mm (3in)
Length in calibres	40
Length overall	3,203mm
Length of bore	3,048mm (40 calibres)
Chamber length	390mm
Chamber volume	2057–2100cm²
Rifling length	2,608.5mm
No of grooves	24
Dimensions of grooves	1.0mm deep x 5.905mm
Lands	4.07mm
Pitch of rifling	1 rotation per 28 calibres
Weight of gun (including breech mechanism)	600kg (0.59 tons)
Weight of projectile	5.67–5.99kg
Muzzle velocity	680–685m/sec
Weight of propellant charge	0.89–0.93kg
Working pressure	2,220–2,300kg/cm²
Maximum elevation/maximum range	75°/10,800m
Ceiling (maximum vertical range)	7,200m/75°
Life of barrel	1,200–2,000 rounds

12.7cm (5in) 40-calibre HA gun

After the main modernisation, the heavy anti-aircraft armament consisted of four twin 12.7cm gun mounts fitted on both sides of the forward and rear superstructures. Of particular interest is the fact that the 12.7cm guns on the rear superstructure were positioned 20 metres above the waterline. Such a high position for heavy AA guns – a world record – only ever occurred in *Fuso* and *Yamashiro*.

TABLE 7: 12.7cm HA gun data

Designation	Type 89 Model A-1 12.7cm (5in) 40-calibre twin HA gun mount
Calibre of bore	127mm (5in)
Length in calibres	40
Length overall	5,284mm
Length of bore	4,930mm (40 calibres)
Chamber length	534mm
Chamber volume	9,000cm^3
Rifling length	4,450.1mm
No of grooves	36
Dimensions of grooves	1.52mm deep x 6.63mm
Lands	4.45mm
Pitch of rifling	1 rotation per 28 calibres
Weight of gun (including breech mechanism)	3,060kg
Weight of projectile	23.05kg
Muzzle velocity	725m/sec
Weight of propellant charge	3.98kg 21 DC
Assembled round weight	34.32kg
Working pressure	2,530kg/cm^2
Breech mechanism	Horizontal sliding
Barrel construction	Monoblock, autofrettaged, radially expanded
Maximum firing rate	14 rounds/min
Effective firing rate	11–12 rounds/min
Maximum range	14,800m
Ceiling (maximum vertical range)	9,440m
Maximum elevation	+90°
Maximum depression	–8°
Life of barrel	800–1,500 rounds
Total weight of twin mount	20.3 tons
Maximum training speed	6°/sec
Maximum elevation/depression speed	12°/sec

12.7cm ammunition

Each shell weighed 23.05kg, with a length of 43.68cm. Each was fitted with a brass cartridge containing 3.98kg of 21 DC powder. The length of assembled round was 970.8mm, the cartridge being 583mm.

Shells

1. HE Tsûjôdan common shell, containing 1.778kg of Shimose (picric acid) explosive. In anti-aircraft firing it had an effective destruction radius of 18.8m.
2. 3-Shiki Sankaidan common incendiary shell, containing 43 incendiary tubes and 23 stays. Its effective burst diameter was about 54m in anti-aircraft firing.
3. Illuminating shell 'B₁' 'Shomeidan B₁', containing 1.1kg of illuminating powder. Maximum range was 14,500m, effective range 8,000m. Illumination was 680,000 candlepower.
4. Time exercise shell 'Jigen Enshudan'.
5. Exercise shell 'Enshudan', not fused.

Light anti-aircraft armament

In 1933, four quadruple 13.2mm machine-gun mounts were fitted in *Fuso* – one each on the forward and rear platforms of the 'pagoda tower' superstructure and one on both sides of the funnel. At first it was planned to install 40mm Ho shiki machine-gun mounts, but this project was given up and the 13.2mm machine guns were adopted instead. These were a Japanese version of the French Hotchkiss gun. Also in 1933, two 7.7mm (0.303in) Lewis gas-operated, air-cooled machine guns were fitted in the forward part of the signalling platform of the 'pagoda tower'. In August 1944, during a short dry docking in Kure Naval Base, *Fuso* was equipped with ten single 13.2mm machine-gun mounts – five each on the forward and stern decks. Weight of a single mount was 113–213kg, a quadruple mount was 1,163kg.

TABLE 8: 13.2mm machine gun data

Designation	93-Shiki 13.2mm (0.52in)
	76-calibre quadruple gun mount
Calibre of bore	13.2mm (0.52in)
Length in calibres	76
Length overall	1,597mm
Length of bore	1,003mm (76 calibres)
Barrel construction	Monoblock
Breech mechanism	Gas operated
No of grooves	8
Dimensions of grooves	0.15mm deep
Pitch of rifling	1 rotation per 32 calibres
Weight of barrel	19.8kg
Weight of breech	22kg
Total weight of gun	41.8kg
Weight of quadruple mount	1,163kg
Weight of projectile	44.5–51.8g
Muzzle velocity	805m/sec
Weight of propellant charge	15g
Working pressure	3,000kg/cm^2
Maximum firing rate	475 rounds/min
Standard firing rate	450 rounds/min
Effective firing rate	250 rounds/min
Maximum range	6,500m at 50° elevation
Ceiling (maximum vertical range)	4,500m at 85° elevation
Maximum AA fighting range	2,500m
Effective AA fighting range	1,000m
Maximum elevation	+85°
Maximum depression	–4°

13.2mm ammunition

Ammunition consisted of 30-round magazines, weight of round 118.5g.
Projectiles

1. Incendiary, weight 49.6g, weight of round 116.7g (filled with 3.5g of phosphor.
2. Common, weight 44.5g, weight of round 126g (filled by 50% pentrit and 50% hexogen).
3. Tracer, weight 46g, weight of round 113g.
4. AP, weight 51.8g, weight of round 118.5g.
5. Exercise, weight 51.8g, weight of round 118.5g.

Supply was 2,500 rounds per barrel.

Arrangement of 25mm machine guns

During the first phase of her second modernisation at Kure Naval Base – February 1937 to March 1938 – *Fuso*'s quadruple 13.2mm machine-gun mounts were removed and eight twin 25mm machine-gun mounts were fitted instead for use as light anti-aircraft armament. Two mounts were fitted on an enlarged platform in front of the 'pagoda tower' superstructure and two on a new platform behind. The remaining four mounts were fitted on both sides of the funnel on superstructure platforms. In July 1943, seventeen single and two twin 25mm machine guns were fitted. In August 1944, seventeen single, six twin and eight triple 25mm machine guns were added. Five single 25mm machine-gun mounts were fitted on transportable-type mounts (that is, they were not fixed to the deck). These movable guns do not appear on the August 1944 general plan and profile drawings, reproduced later; all the fixed single, twin and triple mounts are shown, however. The triple 25mm machine-gun mounts were arranged as follows: two on a platform fitted on the conning tower roof, two on both sides of No 3 main gun turret on the forecastle deck, two on the rear platforms of the funnel superstructure (they replaced the two twin 25mm machine guns), and two on the roof of No 5 main gun turret.

The number of 25mm machine guns was as follows:

Date	Mounts	Total
31 March 1938	8 twin	16
24 July 1943	17 single, 10 twin (8+2)	37
14 August 1944	39 single (17+17+5),	
	16 twin (10+6), 8 triple	95

TABLE 9: 25mm machine gun data

Designation	96-Shiki 25mm (0.984in) 60-calibre gun
Calibre of bore	25mm (0.984in)
Length in calibres	60
Length overall	2,420mm
Length of bore	1,500mm (60 calibres)
Length of rifling	1,350mm
Barrel construction	Monoblock
Breech mechanism	Gas operated
No of grooves	12
Dimensions of grooves	0.25mm deep x 3.58mm
Lands	2.96mm
Pitch of rifling	1 rotation per 25.2 calibres
Weight of barrel	43kg
Weight of breech	72kg
Total weight of gun	115kg
Total weight of single mount	785kg
Total weight of twin mount	1,100kg
Total weight of triple mount	1,800kg
Muzzle velocity	900m/sec
Maximum bore pressure	2,700kg/cm^2
Life of barrel	15,000 rounds
Maximum firing rate	260 rounds/min
Standard firing rate	220–240 rounds/min
Effective firing rate	110–120 rounds/min
Maximum range	7,500m at 50° elevation
Ceiling (maximum vertical range)	5,250m at 80° elevation
Maximum AA fighting range	3,500m
Effective AA fighting range	1,500m
Maximum elevation	+80°
Maximum depression	–10°
Maximum training speed	18°/sec
Maximum elevation speed	12°/sec

.25mm ammunition

Ammunition consisted of 15-round magazines.

Projectiles

1. Common Tsûjôdan, weight 243.2g, filled with 13.2g of trotyl.
2. Incendiary common Shoi Tsûjôdan, weight 250.7g.
3. AP Tetsukôdan.
4. Tracer Eiryôdan.

The round cartridge contained 102g of powder, the overall weight of the round was about 680g. One of the five shells was a tracer round. The normal ammunition supply was 2,000 rounds per barrel. The twin mounting had a seven-man crew, and the triple mounting a crew of nine.

Torpedo armament

As completed, six 53.3cm single torpedo tubes were fitted below the waterline, in frame spaces 39–40, 86–88 and 180–182 (three on each side). The torpedo armament was removed during modernisation in 1930–33.

FIRE-CONTROL ARRANGEMENTS

In the years 1912–23, the standard fire-control system (Housenshiki Souchi Seishiki) – used throughout the Imperial Japanese Navy – was changed three times. *Fuso*'s fire-control arrangements consequently changed as follows: on 19 January 1912, the 'standard gun-firing command and communication system' for battleships and armoured cruisers was adopted; on 3 March, the 'standard battle communication system' replaced the previous one; on 24 April 1923, another new system was brought in: the 'standard gun-firing command system'. The introduction of this system initiated a series of minor modernisations during the transitional period between the Taisho era and the early Showa era, which, with small supplements, was in force until the end of the Second World War.

Five elements made up the system:

1. Fire-control centre (Shageki Shikisho) in conning position.
2. Directors (Hoiban Shageki Sochi).
3. Searchlights.
4. Firing equipment (Shageki Shiki Yougu).
5. Communication network (Tsûshin Keitou).

The system was designed to be suitable for both day and night fighting, and to be able to fire at multiple targets on either beam. The overall requirement also determined the method of protecting the system, which was to be waterproof and vibration-proof. A spare system was also to be provided.

It was determined that the fire-control centre (Shageki shikisho) of battleships and battle-cruisers should be divided into:

Main battery 14in control position (Shuho shikisho)

Back-up main battery 14in control position (Shuho Yobi shikisho)

Turret control position (Hoto shikisho)

Secondary battery 14in control position (Fukuho shikisho)

Back-up secondary battery control position (Fukuho Yobi shikisho)

Secondary battery multiple-target control position (Fukuho Bunka shikisho)

Anti-aircraft-gun control position (Kôkûho shikisho).

It was also determined that the conning position (Hatsurei sho) should be divided into three parts: one for the main battery, one for the secondary battery and one for the telephone switchboard room. The target-tracking position (Sokuteki sho) should be divided into two: one for the main battery and one for the secondary battery. The standard areas for all platforms and positions was also determined. The main-battery command platform (Shuho shikisho), for example, should be 16m² and the main-battery conning position (Hatsureisho) should be 23m². The main battery control position (Shuho shikisho) should be higher than 38m above the waterline. The conning position (Hatsureisho) should be arranged in a protection area under the forward bridge structure and should be both soundproof and heatproof. The communication equipment between the conning position and the conning tower should also be protected. Air-conditioning equipment should keep the temperature in the conning position below 30°C. The target-tracking position (Sokuteki sho)

should be arranged near the upper gun-control position on the forward superstructure. All the necessary equipment for measuring target movements and positions was to be fitted in the target-tracking position, which should be rainproof and windproof. It was determined that the observation and reporting of the fall of shot should be done from an observation platform (Kansoku sho), which was to be divided into a rear superstructure observation platform (Kosho kansoku sho) and a transverse observation platform (Ido kansoku sho). A radio receiver was to be fitted on the observation platform to receive information of the fall of shot from captive balloons and aircraft.

It was decided that battleships were to have a total of three gunnery directors for the main battery: one in the main-battery control position, one in the back-up main battery control position, and one on the forward superimposed 14in turret. They were also to have six directors for the secondary battery. One was mounted on each side of the secondary battery control position, and two on each side of the back-up secondary battery control position. Two AA directors were required, one mounted on either side of the anti-aircraft-gun platform.

The searchlight system was to be divided into the signalling lamps (Shido tou) and searchlights (Tansho tou). It was determined that signal lamps were to be operated from the searchlight control position (Shyosha shikisho) and that the searchlight was to be operated from the central searchlight control position (Tou gun shikisho). Battleships were to have two signal lamps and six or eight searchlights. The searchlight control position was to be fitted on the forward bridge structure and the back-up searchlight control position was to be fitted in the superstructure conning position. The signal lamp command equipment was to be fitted in both the searchlight control position and the back-up position. The central control position was located in the secondary battery control position and the secondary battery central control position. The searchlight command equipment was to be fitted in the central searchlight control position.

The standard gun-firing equipment included:

Rangefinder

Target-speed measuring equipment

Range communication equipment

Target-direction measuring equipment

Target-speed-and-direction measuring equipment

Equipment for observing the fall of shells

Communication equipment for relaying information on
the fall of shot

The communication system was to be divided into visual type and sound type (which included telephone and voice pipe).

This standard fire-control system was altered in March 1932, but in essence the improved system did not significantly differ from the original one. It did, however, develop the Japanese battleship forward superstructures of the Showa era into the very complicated and high 'pagoda masts' or 'pagoda towers'.

AIRCRAFT EQUIPMENT

The first Japanese battleship to launch aircraft was *Fuso*'s sister ship, *Yamashiro*. In March 1922, she launched the British Sparrow Hawk and Sopwith Camel fighters from a launching platform fitted on No 2 gun turret. This was only an experiment, not an advanced trial. The first Japanese battleship equipped with a catapult was *Nagato*. In 1925, she was fitted with an imported German Heinkel-type catapult on the roof of No 2 turret, but this was removed after a short time. From June 1926, *Nagato* was the first Japanese battleship to carry aircraft equipment as standard. In 1924, *Fuso* was equipped with a launch platform on No 2 turret (just like *Yamashiro*), but it was soon removed. Unfortunately, no photographs of this platform have survived. For a longer period *Fuso* was equipped with captive balloons for spotting the fall of shells, since balloons were then more useful than aircraft. The Imperial Japanese Navy bought its balloons from Britain.

During her main modernisation in 1930–33, *Fuso* was fitted with aircraft equipment as standard. At the same time, aircraft crew and staff were assigned to the ship. A type Kure Shiki 2 Go 4 Gata catapult was mounted on No 3 main gun turret. This was later modernised, becoming catapult type Kure Shiki 2 Go 3 Gata. At 17.53m long, this type was approximately 2m shorter than the typical catapult. *Fuso* was the only Japanese battleship fitted with this size of catapult. She was also equipped with three reconnaissance floatplanes, which were stowed on the forecastle deck – one on the catapult and the other two on trolleys. Each trolley was moved, by a system of ropes, blocks and winches, via rails and ramps onto the elevator, which then lifted the trolley to the catapult loading level. The floatplane was moved onto the catapult from the trolley, and the other two aircraft were in turn moved via the rails and ramps to the elevator.

After launching the first floatplane, the catapult cradle was withdrawn to a small platform situated forward of the funnel's superstructure (on vegetable store compartment roof). No 3 turret, with catapult, turned round to receive the next aircraft. The elevator had four poles and its engine room was fitted directly on the forecastle deck, therefore it was necessary to use ramps from the bow and stern sides. Fitted on the rear wall of the 'pagoda tower' bridge, a 20m derrick (crane) lifted the aircraft from the sea on the port side and directly onto trolleys and the catapult.

This method of operating the floatplane catapult was complicated and time consuming, so in *Yamashiro* (her main modernisation was carried out later) the aircraft equipment and catapult were moved to the stern. During the second phase of *Fuso*'s modernisation in 1934–35, part of the stern was lengthened by 7.6m, with a bulge attached on the port side to house the crane's motor room. During the second phase of *Fuso*'s second modernisation in 1940–41, her new 19.5m Kure Shiki 2 Go 3 Gata catapult, rails with turntables, aircraft crane and linoleum covering of the aircraft deck were all fitted.

TABLE 10: *Fuso*'s floatplanes 1933–44

Nakajima E4N2, Navy Type 90-2 reconnaissance floatplane
Three planes were fitted between May 1933 and February 1937.

Length	8.869m
Span	10.976m
Height	3.967m
Maximum speed	232km/h
Powerplant	460hp at 1,500m, 9-cylinder air-cooled Nakajima 'Jupiter' radial engine, driving two-blade propeller
Armament	2–7.7mm machine guns and 2–30kg bombs
Crew	2

Nakajima E8N2, Navy Type 95 reconnaissance floatplane
Allied codename 'Dave'
Three planes were fitted between May 1938 and February 1942.

Length	8.81m
Span	10.98m
Height	3.84m
Wing area	26.5m²
Maximum speed	300km/h at 3,000m
Cruising speed	185km/h
Powerplant	580hp 9-cylinder air-cooled Nakajima Kotobuki 2 Kai radial engine, driving two-blade propeller
Weight empty	1,320kg
Weight loaded	1,900kg
Armament	2–7.7mm machine guns and 2–30kg or 2–60kg bombs
Range	890km
Crew	2

Mitsubishi F1M2, Navy 'Type 0' reconnaissance floatplane (from 1943)
Allied codename 'Pete'

Length	9.5m
Span	11.0m
Height	4.0m
Wing area	29.54m²
Maximum speed	370km/h
Cruising speed	193km/h
Powerplant	875hp 14-cylinder air-cooled Mitsubishi Zuisei 13 radial engine, driving three-blade propeller
Armament	3–7.7mm machine guns and 2–60kg bombs (or as experiment 1–250kg bomb)
Range	740km
Crew	2

RADAR EQUIPMENT

During *Fuso*'s short stay in dry dock at the Kure Naval Base shipyard between 18 and 24 July 1943, Type 21 air-search radar was fitted on the top of her pagoda tower, on the roof of the main 10m rangefinder. During her next stay in dry dock at Kure Naval Base, between 2 and 14 August 1944, Type 13 and Type 22 radar were fitted. The Type 22 surface-search radar antennas were located on both sides of the air-defence command platform on the tower bridge. The Type 13 air search radar antennas were mounted on both sides of the funnel. This was an unusual mounting for Japanese battleships, and was unique to *Fuso*.

TABLE 11: Characteristics of radar

Type 21 air-search radar (21 Go dentan Kai 2)

Antenna	'Mattress' type
Transmitter	Oscillating circuit with two T-310 tubes
Receiver	Detector type UN-953 RE 3
Power output	5kW maximum
Wave length	1.5m
Pulse length	10 microseconds
Pulse rate	1,000/sec
Maximum detection range:	Aircraft group 100km
	Single aircraft 70km
	Range error ±1–2km
	Bearing error 5–8°
Minimum detection range	5km

Type 13 air-search radar (13 Go dentan)

Antenna	Ladder type, boardside array, separated set for transmission and reception; each set four steps of two elements
Transmitter	Type 2C Oscillating circuit with two T-311 tubes
Receiver	Detector type UN-954
Power output (maximum)	10kW
Wave length	2.0m
Pulse length	10 microseconds
Pulse rate	500/sec
Maximum detection range:	Aircraft group 100km
	Single aircraft 50km
	Range error ±2–3km
	Bearing error ±10°
Minimum detection range	5km
Weight of set	110kg

Type 22 surface-search radar (22 Go dentan Kai 3)

Antenna	Two horns, the upper for reception, the lower for transmission
Transmitter	Water-cooled Magnetron Type M-312-A
Receiver	Autodyne circuit with crystal detector and Magnetron Type M–60-S as local oscillator
Wave length	10cm
Power output	2kW
Maximum detection range:	

	Battleships	35km
	Cruisers	20km
	Destroyers	17km
	Range error	±0.7km
	Bearing error	±5°
	Weight of set	320kg

Crew needed to operate all of these sets was 4–6 men, 2–3 to operate radar and 2–3 to operate telephone.

SEARCHLIGHTS

The number of Tansho tou searchlights (used to search and illuminate targets) ranged from eleven (two 90cm and nine 110cm) in 1915 to six (110 cm) in 1944. The searchlight types changed as the ship was modernised. Their arrangement is shown on the general plans and drawings reproduced later. Two 60cm Shido tou searchlights, mainly used for signalling, were fitted above the signal platform of the superstructure.

TABLE 12: 110cm Su-shiki and 92-Shiki searchlights data

	Su shiki (used from 1933)	92 Shiki (used from 1938)
Diameter (mirror)	110cm	110cm
Tension (V)	75	76–82
Current (A)	150	200
Power (kW)	11,250	16,400 maximum
Light intensity (candela/m²)	9,000 (blue-white light)	12,800 (blue-white light)
Elevation	–15° to +100°	–10° to +100°
Inherent scatter angle	1°50'	1°30'
Maximum range	6,000m	8,000m
Effective range	5,000m	6,000m+
Concentrated light of two	8,000m	10,000m

BOATS

Fuso was equipped with the following boat types:

Boat	Dimensions: loa x b (m)	Weight (tons)	Power (hp)	Speed (kts)	Max men on board	No of boats
17m steam pinnace	17.0 x 3.3	21.0	–	–	100	2 (1915–30)
						1 (1933–35)
17m motor pinnace	17.0 x 3.3	21.0	150	10.5	100	1 (1933–35)
						2 (1935–37)
11m motorboat	11.0 x 2.7	5.7	60	10.0	30	1 (1933–44)
12m motor launch	12.0 x 3.0	9.0	30	7.0	110	2
9m cutter	9.0 x 2.45	1.5	–	–	45	4
8m (27ft)sampan	8.0 x 1.9	0.9	–	–	25	1
6m (20ft)sampan	6.0 x 1.5	0.47	–	–	15	1

The arrangement of the boats on *Fuso*'s deck is shown in the general plans. Note that she was using two types of 17m motor pinnace (two types of rear cabin) in the years 1933–37. At anchorage and during trials, some or all of her 9m cutters and sampans could be on davits. When sailing or during war, all her boats were on deck. The 17m motor pinnaces were used only until 1937. During the period 1936–39, *Fuso* occasionally carried barges and pontoons on the forecastle deck on both sides of the rear superstructure for use as artillery targets during exercises.

MODERNISATIONS OF HIJMS FUSO

As fitted, *Fuso* was equipped with twelve 36cm guns in six twin turrets as main battery and sixteen single 15cm guns in casemate mounts as secondary battery. Small guns mounted on the main turret roofs had been planned, but this was abandoned. Before the completion of *Fuso*, her sternwalk was removed (on *Yamashiro* this survived until 1930). The foremast was a tripod type with a high topmast. The firing observation platform was positioned on the upper part of the foremast, and the upper searchlight platform – with two 90cm and two 60cm searchlights – was positioned under this on the foremast starfish. Another searchlight platform – with two 110cm searchlights – was situated in the middle of the tripod. The navigation bridge and conning tower were positioned at the base of the foremast. *Fuso* had two 1.5m rangefinders on the navigation bridge, and two 3.5m rangefinders on the conning tower. On the roof of No 2 main gun turret a self-traversable type 4m rangefinder was fitted. Main gun turrets No 3, No 4 and No 5 were each equipped with a 4.5m turret rangefinder. A tripod aft mast with topmast made up the rear superstructure. Beyond the tripod an auxiliary conning tower was positioned and on the base of the superstructure the aft searchlight platform – with 110cm searchlights– was fitted.

1917 In the second half of 1917, a gun-firing system director was fitted on the foremast observation platform (Kansuku sho).

1918 On 1 December 1918, *Fuso* went into first reserve. During the ship's reserve period, five 8cm HA anti-aircraft guns were mounted as her first anti-aircraft armament. They were fitted to the shelter deck on both sides of the forward superstructure, on platforms alongside the second funnel (replacing the 110cm searchlights, which were moved to the forward superstructure middle searchlight platform).

1919 Firing command platform (Shageki shikisho) and equipment were attached to the lower part of the forward superstructure.

1922–23 On 1 December 1922, *Fuso* once again went into first reserve. In 1923, modifications were carried out to increase the main gun elevation angle and the 4.5m rangefinders were replaced by 8m rangefinders.

1924 The forward superstructure underwent full-scale modernisation. The command platform (Shiki sho), lookout platform (Mihari sho), and target-tracking platform (Sokuteki sho) were added to the superstructure, making it look like a castle. At this time, for a short period, an aircraft-launch platform was fitted on No 2 main gun turret.

1925 Early in 1925, *Fuso*'s characteristic funnel cap was added to the forward funnel to remedy the problems of smoke that had arisen with the new superstructure form.

1926–27 Anti-torpedo net equipment was removed from both sides of the hull. The command platform (Shirei sho) was added to the forward superstructure. Some minor modernisations were made to the superstructure before beginning the main modernisation.

1930–33 On 12 April 1930, *Fuso*'s main modernisation began at Yokosuka Naval Yard, continuing from 26 September 1932 at Kure Naval Base. On 12 May 1933, the main modernisation was completed, and was classified as the prototype for the Imperial Japanese Navy's 'second modification plan'. The modernisations were applied to the whole ship and entailed:

1. Improving the horizontal protection and the underwater protection (bulges).
2. Replacing the main engine turbines and boilers.
3. Modernising the superstructures.
4. Improving the weapons.
5. Fitting aircraft equipment.

The changes arising from points 1, 2, 4 and 5 were described above.

The forward superstructure – 'pagoda tower' bridge – underwent major changes. From the top were fitted:
– Type 'Bu shiki' 6m double rangefinder tower (level XIV)
– Main-battery gun-firing platform (Syuho shageki sho) (level XIII)
– Main-battery command platform (Syuho shikisyo sho) (level XII)
– Upper lookout platform (Yobi mihari sho) (level XI)
– Searchlight command platform (Shosha shiki sho) (level X)
– Secondary gun-firing command platform (Fukuho shageki sho) (level IX)
– Battle bridge (level VII)
– Forward searchlight platform (Zenbu tansyoto) (level VII)
– Signal platform (Shingo sho), lower lookout platform (Kabu mihari sho) and anti-aircraft gun command platform (Kokakuho shiki sho) (level VI)
– Navigation bridge (level V)
– Communication command platform, spare secondary-battery command platform (Tsushin shikisho, Fukuho yobi shiki sho) (level IV)
– Conning platform (level III)
– Lower bridge (level II)
– Shelter deck (level I)

The tripods of the fore- and aft masts were used as structural supports for the fore and aft superstructures. The middle structure and funnel were changed. The rear superstructure was also completely rebuilt to hold the auxiliary main and secondary gun command stands and the 12.7cm HA gun platform.

1934–35 From 16 September 1934 to March 1935, *Fuso* underwent the second phase of her main modernisation at the Kure Naval Base shipyard. The hull stern was enlarged by 7.62m to give the hull an overall length of 212.75m. The upper part of the side bulges was enlarged and raised so that the upper edge of the bulge reached upper deck level (before it had reached only to main deck), which increased the ship's speed slightly. The main 6m rangefinder was replaced by an 8m rangefinder on top of the 'pagoda tower'. The top of the rear superstructure was also modernised. The forward 110cm-searchlight platform was lowered from the funnel superstructure to improve aircraft handling.

1937–38 From 26 February 1937 to 31 March 1938, the first phase of *Fuso*'s second modernisation took place at the Kure Naval Base shipyard. A new 10m rangefinder was fitted on the top of the 'pagoda tower' bridge, changing some of its details. Two 3.5m rangefinder towers were removed from level IX and replaced by two machine-gun fire directors. Two other machine-gun fire directors were fitted on both sides of the funnel. Eight twin 25mm machine guns were added instead of the quadruple 13.2mm machine guns. These mounts were arranged on the new, larger platform on the conning tower, on the new aft platform on level VII of the tower bridge, on both sides of the funnel superstructure (in the position of the removed 13.2mm machine guns) and on the new platforms on the rear part of the funnel superstructure. No 1 and No 2 casemate turrets of the 15cm secondary gun (from starboard and port) were removed, as were the starboard auxiliary anchor and its equipment and the 17m pinnace cradles. The rear mast was shortened.

1940–41 On 15 December 1940, *Fuso* went into Category 3 Reserve. From 19 December until April 1941, she underwent the second phase of her second modernisation. An anti-aircraft-defence control position was added on top of the forward superstructure. The height of the pagoda tower bridge was lowered by about 2m. An emergency damage-control system was added, and the ship's aircraft equipment, with a new 19.5m catapult, was transferred to the stern deck.

1942 In February 1942, at the Kure Naval Base shipyard, the gun barrels were replaced, and a degaussing coil was added around the hull.

1943 In July 1943, while she was in dry dock at Kure Naval Base, *Fuso* had the Type 21 air-search radar, and two twin and seventeen single 25mm machine guns added. The covers from four protected lookout positions (levels IX and X) were removed.

1944 In August 1944, again while she was in dry dock at Kure Naval Base shipyard, *Fuso* had the Type 13 air-search radar and the Type 22 surface-search radar fitted. Also fitted were twenty-two single, six twin and eight triple 25mm machine-gun mounts, and ten single 13.2mm machine-gun mounts. She then had ninety-five 25mm machine guns and ten 13.2mm machine guns (the total number of machine guns she would have at the time of her final battle). The side scuttles under the upper deck level were blanked off.

COMPLEMENT

Fuso's crew in 1915 was 1,198 officers and men. In 1935, this number was 1,396 officers and men. The official size of crew in the following years, right up to October 1944, is unknown as the documentation has not survived. We can suppose, however, that with installation of a larger number of machine guns, radar installations, etc, at the time of her loss the crew was probably higher, perhaps around 1,800–1,900 officers and men.

COLOUR SCHEMES

1. Warship grey was used for painting the hull above the waterline, the superstructures, all the metal decks, the gun turrets, the topside fittings, the boat's external sides and cabins, and the decks of the open boats. The colour of the Imperial Japanese Navy's ships varied in shade but was based on regulation colours and was made according to a standard paint mixture formula consisting of 75 per cent white, 15 per cent black, 6 per cent brown and 4 per cent blue.

2. A reddish-brown was used for the hull below the waterline and consisted of 65 per cent brown, 20 per cent red, 10 per cent black and 5 per cent white. Between 1915 and 1930, this colour was also used for painting the underwater part of the hull of the 17m steam pinnace.

3. A dark green was used for a short period of *Fuso*'s service on the hull below the waterline. Unfortunately, it is not possible to determine precisely when this anti-corrosive varnish was used. After 1933, it could only have been used experimentally.

4. Black was used for the upper parts of the funnels, masts and the target barge with pontoons.

5. White was used in wartime for the 10m rangefinder tower on the top of the 'pagoda tower' bridge, for the small stripes on the black paint on the rear mast, and for the inscriptions on the boats and target barge.

6. Gold was used for the chrysanthemum crest on the bow and part of the ship's name 'FU' written in hiragana (the cursive from of kana, the Japanese syllabary) on the ship's sides.

7. The deck was unpainted teak. A natural wood colour was also used on the inside surfaces of the boats, on the decks of the motor-boats, and on the gratings.

8. White canvas was used for blast bags, reel covers, windscreen on the tower bridge platforms (levels IV, V, IX, X, XI and XII), railings of searchlight platforms, etc. Light brown or grey canvas replaced the white in wartime.

9. A dark yellowish-brown (pale 'milk chocolate shade') linoleum was used for covering the surface of the 'aircraft deck' – stern part of the upper deck after 1940. The linoleum sheets were 2m wide, and the contact edge of the sheets were joined by 30mm-wide brass strips.

The grey, black and white varnishes were semi-gloss in finish.

AIRCRAFT COLOURS

1933–37 The E4N2 floatplanes were painted light grey with a black inscription in katakana (the square form of kana) of the ship's name (fu-sa-u in archaic transcription) and the numeral 1-3 on the upper and lower surfaces of the wings and on body. Red was used for the 'Hinomaru' (hi-no-maru, the rising sun flag), the fin and tailplane, and for the stripes on the floats under the propeller. The cowling was black (see illustrations).

1938–44 The (E8N2 and F1M2) floatplanes were painted sea green N-1 on the upper surfaces, gull grey N-2 on the lower surfaces. On the FlM2, orange stripes were painted on the wings' leading edges. Both planes had red-and-white stripes on the floats under the propellers. 'Hinomaru' was red with white borders over a green background. All versions had white stripes on the upper surface of the tailplanes for the rear gunner (5° angle space).

The keel-laying ceremony of No 3 battleship, the future HIJMS *Fuso*, in the dry dock of the Kure Kaigun Kosho (Kure Naval Base) on 11 March 1912. (*Shizuo Fukui collection*)

Stern view of *Fuso* shortly before being launched. The sternwalk was removed before commissioning. (*Maru Special*)

Fuso's launching ceremony on 28 March 1914, during which a ceremonial ball filled with confetti was broken over the ship. (*Shizuo Fukui collection*)

Fuso in 1916. Note the canvas-pipe vents around second funnel. *(Shizuo Fukui collection)*

Fuso during her full-speed trials in the Western Inland Sea on 24 August 1915. *(Shizuo Fukui collection)*

The 1st Fleet (Blue Fleet) during the Grand Manoeuvre in Hiroshima Bay on 14 October 1919. Here, *Fuso* leads *Hyuga*, *Ise Aki* , and *Settsu*.
(Shizuo Fukui collection)

Aerial view of *Fuso* in 1920.
(Maru Special)

View of *Fuso* in 1920, looking from the bow towards the main gun turrets and the foremast with tower bridge. *(Maru Special)*

View from the stern deck towards No 5 and No 6 main 36cm-gun turrets and the rear superstructure. The constructions above the main gun turrets are derricks for moving the 8cm exercise gun fitted to the main gun barrels. *(Maru Special)*

View from midship to the rear mainmast tower structure. Visible on the deck are the 17m steam pinnace cradles and mushroom vents. *(Maru Special)*

View of *Fuso* in 1920, showing No 3 turret and the rear funnel. On the deck is a 6m sampan. *(Maru Special)*

Stern view of *Fuso* 1920. Visible on both sides of the second funnel are two of the ship's five 8cm HA guns; a third such gun is visible on the port side behind the 17m steam pinnace cradles. *(Maru Special)*

Fuso in 1921. *(Shizuo Fukui collection)*

Fuso's sister ship *Yamashiro* during aircraft-launch trials in March 1922. For a short time in 1924 *Fuso* had a similar launch platform fitted on the roof of her No 2 gun turret. *(Maru Special)*

Fuso in 1925 after her first modernisation. Note the rebuilding of the fore superstructure, including the characteristic cap on the fore funnel. *(Maru Special)*

Fuso's No 5 and No 6 gun turrets during firing exercises on 17 October 1924. *(Sekai-no Kansen)*

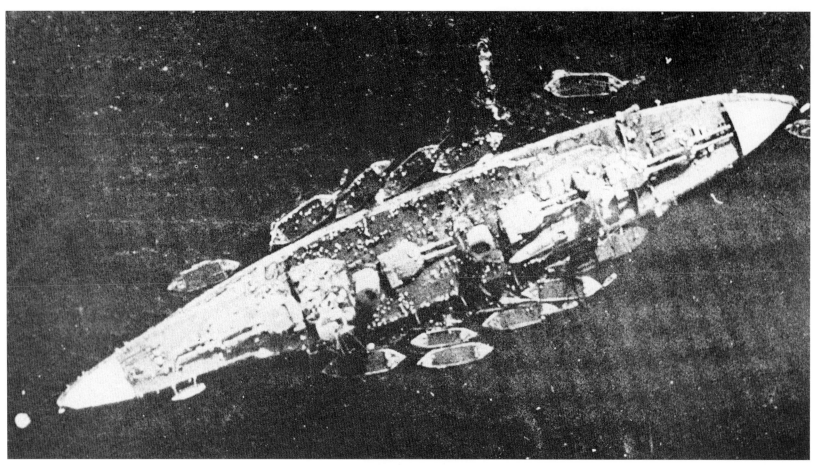

Aerial view of *Fuso* during coal loading.
(Shizuo Fukui collection)

Fuso on 14 February 1925 in the Tsukumo
Straits. *(Shizuo Fukui collection)*

Fuso in February–March 1928 off Mitajiri. Note the captive balloon and the removal of the anti-torpedo net equipment. *(Maru Special)*

Port view of *Fuso* off Sukumo on 10 May 1933, during trials following the first phase of her main modernisation.
(Shizuo Fukui collection)

Fuso in dry dock at Kure Naval Base on 28 April 1933, undergoing the final stages of the first phase of her main modernisation.
(Shizuo Fukui collection)

A detail of the previous photograph.

Starboard view of *Fuso*, 1933/4.
(Source unknown)

Fuso during manoeuvres off
Honsiu on 15–20 August 1933.
(Sekai-no Kansen)

Fuso underway in 1933.
(Source unknown)

Fuso in 1934. *(Maru Special)*

A detail of the previous photograph. *(Maru Special)*

A similar view, but of the author's model of the pagoda tower. *(Author's collection)*

View of the lower part of *Fuso*'s pagoda tower and main guns in 1934. *(Shizuo Fukui collection)*

View from the signal platform of the pagoda tower towards the stern. Clearly visible on the left, above the 110cm searchlights and covered with canvas, is the platform of the aircraft-catapult cradle; on the right is an E4N2 floatplane. *(Shizuo Fukui collection)*

View of *Fuso*'s catapult and an E4N2 floatplane off the Liao Tung Peninsula on 25 September 1934. *(Shizuo Fukui collection)*

Fuso's pagoda tower in 1934/5 from the author's model. *(Author's collection)*

Fuso off Sukumo during trials following the second phase of her main modernisation in January 1935. (Shizuo Fukui collection)

Port side view of Fuso on 11 February 1935. (Source unknown)

Fuso in 1935.
(Sekai-no Kansen)

Stern view of *Yamashiro*. Clearly visible is the form of *Yamashiro*'s stern, which is identical to that of *Fuso*, after it has been lengthened.
(Source unknown)

Fuso in Tokyo Bay in October 1935. *(Maru Special)*

View of *Fuso*'s stern deck off Bungo Straits on 21 May 1936. *(Sekai-no Kansen)*

View of *Fuso* in the Naval Review
of 1936. *(Source unknown)*

Fuso and *Yamashiro* (right) during manoeuvres in 1935–36. *(Source unknown)*

Yamashiro (left) *Fuso* (centre) and *Haruna* (right) in 1935–36. *(Source unknown)*

戦艦「扶桑」航跡静かなり

● 大改装により生れ変わった戦艦「扶桑」の特異な艦影と艦内風景！

▲扶桑艦上の90式2号水偵。大改装で主缶を換装し、1番煙突が撤去されたあとの、3番砲塔上にカタパルトを装備した。その左舷に水偵3機の搭載施設や移動用軌条を設けたが、スペースの余裕がなく、かなり窮屈であった。のちにカタパルトは艦尾へ移された

◀扶桑[...]
3機の[...]
上の90[...]
に14イ[...]
角測距[...]

▼大分[...]
上から[...]
突の周[...]
ートル[...]
っていた

軍艦 ●メモリアル

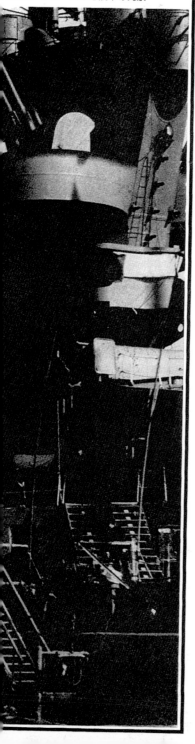

View from *Fuso*'s stern towards No 5 and No 6 turrets and the rear tower superstructure with twin 12.7cm HA gun on 21 May 1936. *(Source unknown)*

Fuso during the Naval Review of 1936, with details of her floatplanes. *(Source unknown)*

No 2 36cm-gun turret on the
author's model.
(Author's collection)

View of No 2 turret, lower part of
superstructure and forecastle
deck, on the author's model.
(Author's collection)

View from *Fuso*'s No 4 turret in 1936–37. At this time the boats were covered with canvas; anti-splinter protection was provided by sheafs of sisal rope. *(Maru)*

Judo and Kendo classes on *Fuso*'s
stern deck. *(Maru)*

Aerial views of *Fuso* in April 1938, after completion of the first phase of her second modernisation. *(Sekai-no Kansen)*

View from the top of *Fuso's* pagoda tower towards her funnel and the upper stands of her rear tower with mainmast. Visible on the port side of the rear superstructure is the target barge, with pontoons on the starboard side. On the horizon is *Kongo*. This photograph was taken on 26 January 1939 in Sukumo Bay.
(Shizuo Fukui collection)

Fuso after her second modernisation, undergoing damage-
control trials at Kure Naval Base on 20 April 1941.
(Source unknown)

Stern view of *Fuso* on 20 April 1941.
(Maru Special)

A view from *Nagato* of the 1st Squadron in the Western Inland Sea on 5 May 1942. *Fuso* leads, followed by *Yamashiro*, *Ise* and *Hyuga*. (*Shizuo Fukui collection*)

The last view of *Fuso* at Brunei 20–22 October 1944. From left to right: *Fuso*, *Musashi*, *Mogami* and *Yamashiro*. (*Sekai-no Kansen*)

The pagoda tower model, based on *Fuso*'s appearance in 1934-5, was initially constructed as a simplified study model which the author then completed adding authentic details confirmed through research. *(Author's collection)*

The author's 1:133 scale model of *Fuso*'s pagoda tower during construction. Note the 3mm steel wire being used as the axis and support of the model. *(Author's collection)*

A rear view of the author's model of the pagoda tower, which was constructed using cardboard, plywood, pear-tree wood, 0.1mm thick steel plating, wires and paper. *(Author's collection)*

Lower part of the pagoda tower with 152mm guns visible. *(Author's collection)*

A rear view of the upper part of the pagoda tower. *(Author's collection)*

Port view of pagoda tower. *(Author's collection)*

Starboard view of pagoda tower. *(Author's collection)*

Front view of the superstructure and No 2 gun
turret barrels of the model.
(Author's collection)

Pagoda tower, superstructure and No 2 gun
platform. *(Author's collection)*

T H E   D R A W I N G S

A   GENERAL ARRANGEMENT

A1   The battleship HIJMS *Fuso* as completed, November 1915 (1:500 scale)

A1/1   External profile (boats are omitted – boat arrangement
shown on drawing A4/2); grey colours on drawing
indicate black painted surfaces

A1/1

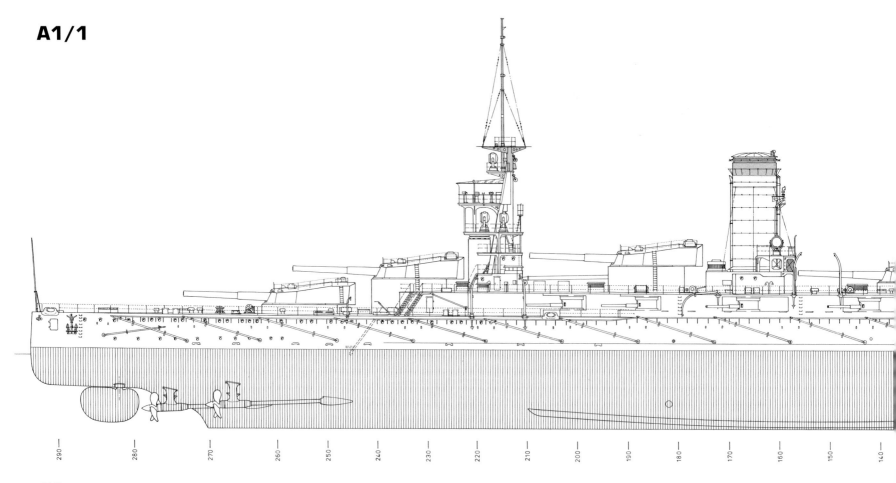

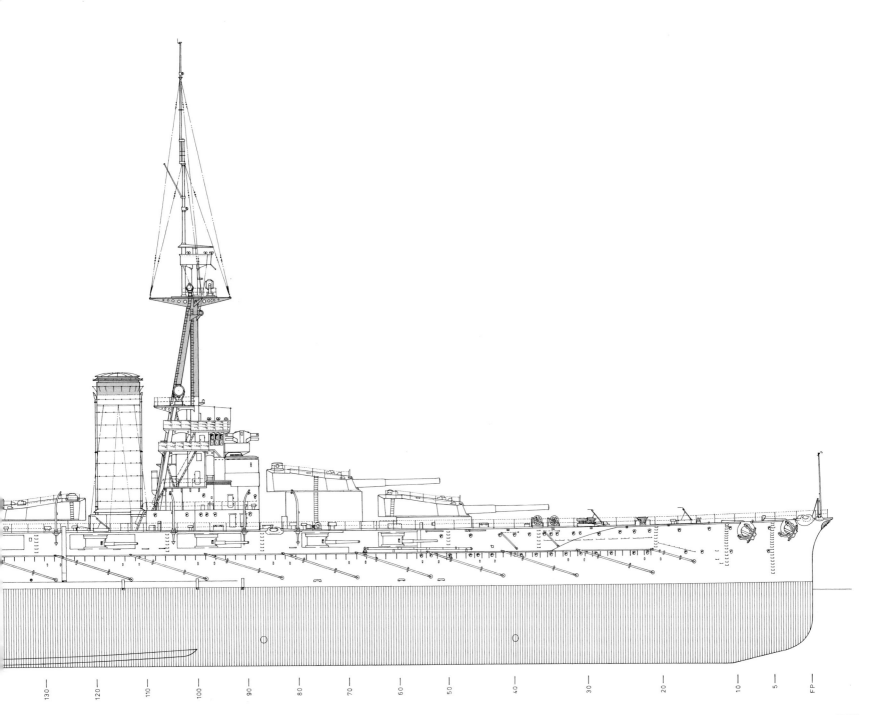

A2 Fuso in August 1919 (1:400 scale)

A2/1 Starboard elevation of forward superstructure
A2/2 Front elevation of forward superstructure
A2/3 Plan (detail) with No 2 and No 3 36cm gun
      turrets, forward superstructure and fore funnel
A2/4 Plan of shelter and lower bridge decks
A2/5 Plan of upper bridge deck

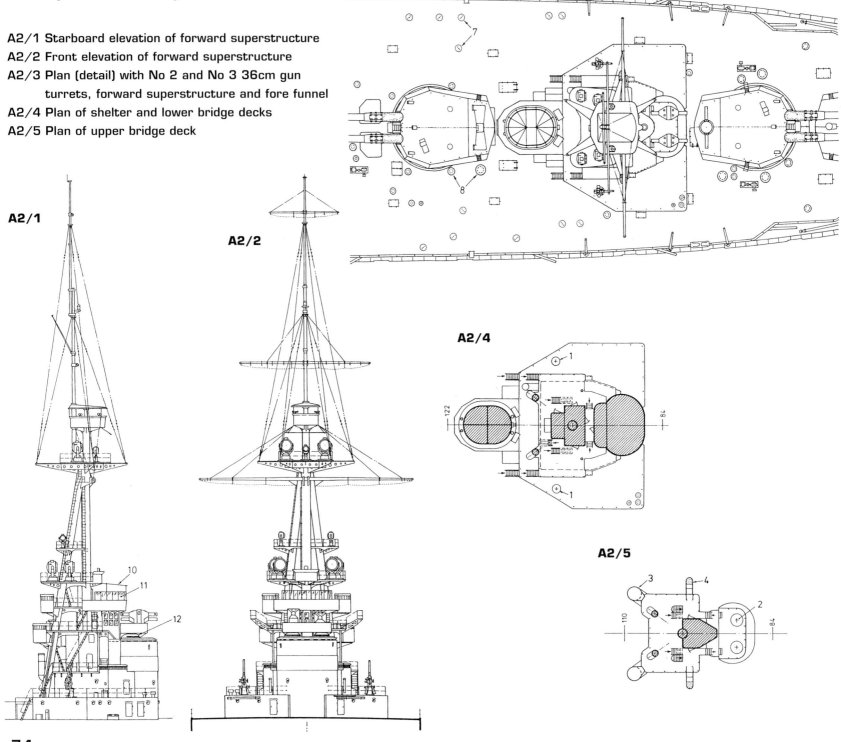

A2/3

A2/1

A2/2

A2/4

A2/5

A2/6 Compass bridge
     platform
A2/7 Signal and middle
     searchlight platform
A2/8 Foremast signal
     searchlights platform
A2/9 Upper searchlight
     platform on foremast
     starfish, under the firing
     observation platform
1 8cm HA gun position
2 3.5m rangefinder position
3 Protected observation stand

4 Signalling positions
5 110cm searchlight position
6 60cm signal searchlight position
7 90cm searchlight position
8 Mushroom vents
9 Anti-torpedo net shelf
10 Coal scuttle
11 Glass windscreen
12 Observation dome on roof of
conning tower
13 Tent (canvas) support

A3 Rear superstructure 1915–24 (1:400 scale)

A3/1 View from bow
A3/2 Rear view
A3/3 Port side profile (detail)
A3/4 Lower bridge deck with roof of vents
A3/5 Middle platform
A3/6 Searchlights platform
A3/7 Lookout platform
A3/8 Searchlight platform (upper)
A3/9 Upper platform on after mast starfish

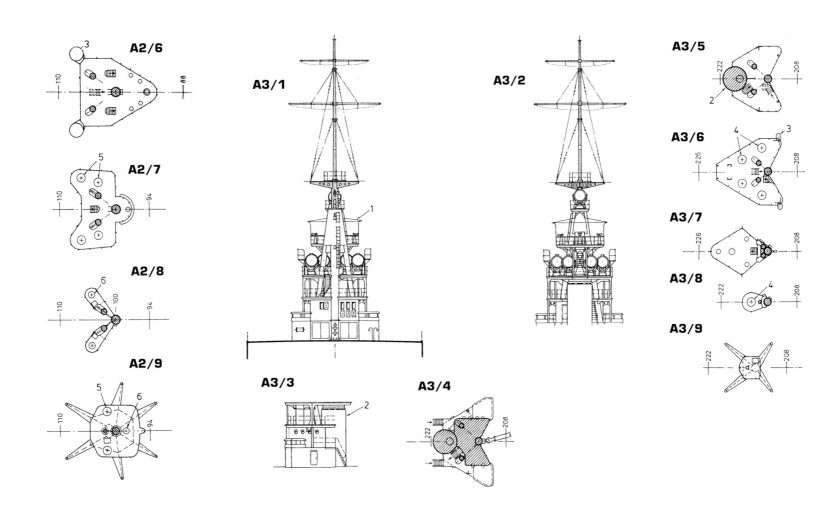

75

A4 Fuso in early 1925

A4/1 Plan (1:500 scale)

A4/1

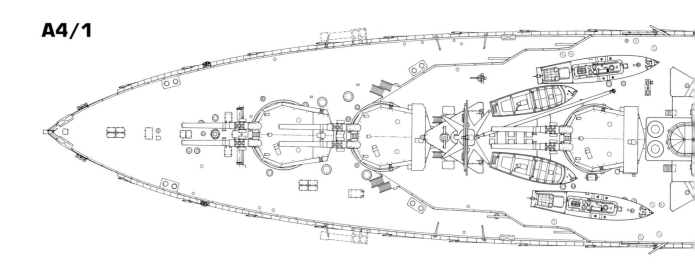

A4/2 External profile
(to provide a clear view
of superstructures,
the boats have been
omitted) (1:500 scale)

A4/2

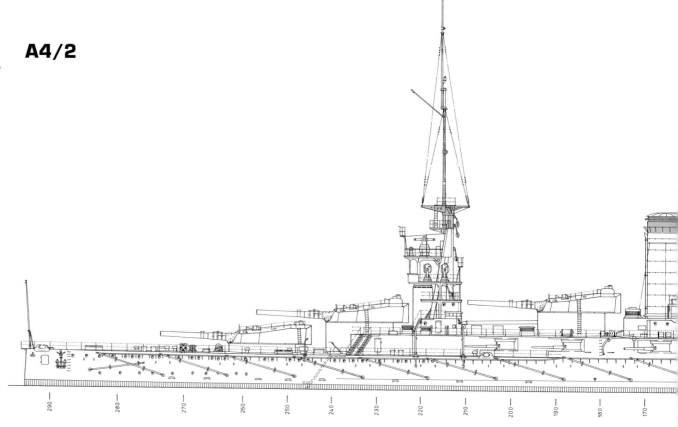

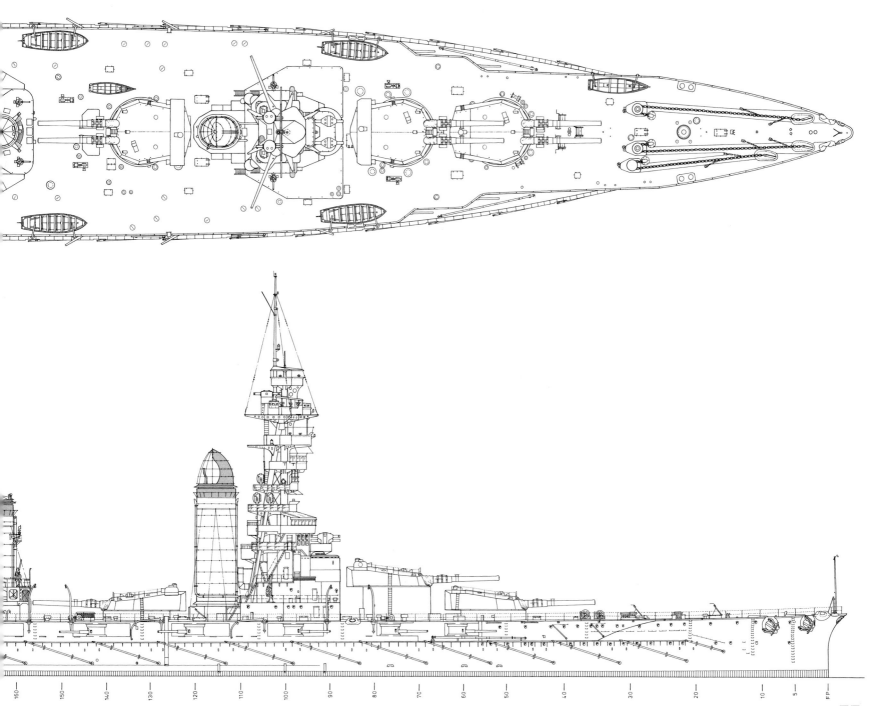

160 150 140 130 120 110 100 90 80 70 60 50 40 30 20 10 5 FP

77

A4/3 – A4/21
(1:400 scale)

1   8cm HA gun post
2   3.5m rangefinder position
3   Signalling post
4   Protected lookout stand
5   110 cm searchlight position

A4/3

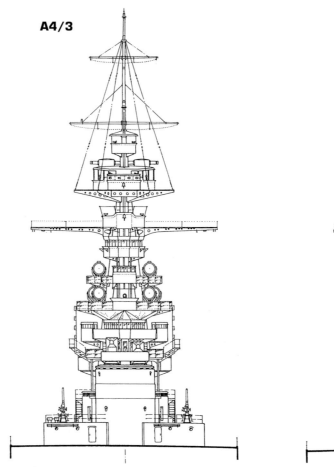

A4/4

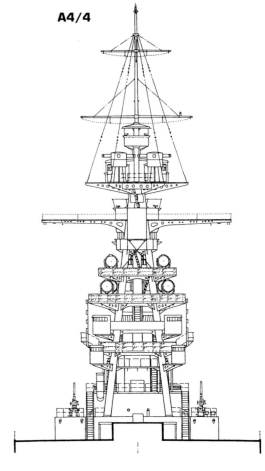

A4/5

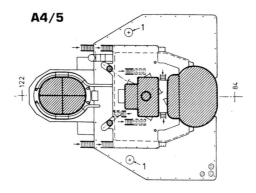

A4/6

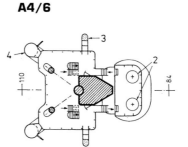

A4/7

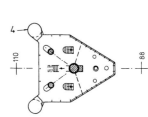

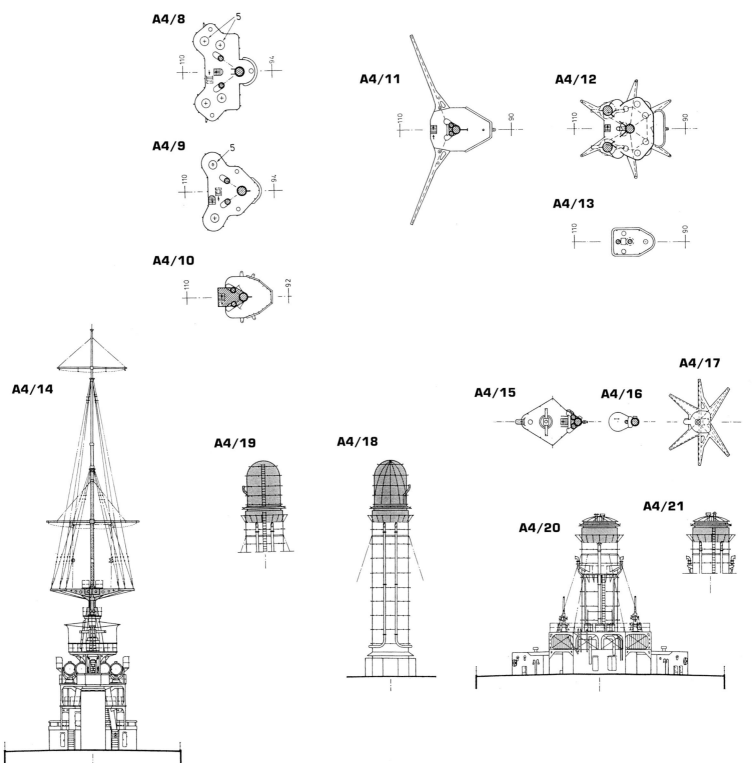

A4/8

A4/9

A4/10

A4/11

A4/12

A4/13

A4/14

A4/15

A4/16

A4/17

A4/18

A4/19

A4/20

A4/21

A5 *Fuso* in May 1933 after main modernisation (1:500 scale)

A5/1 Plan

A5/1

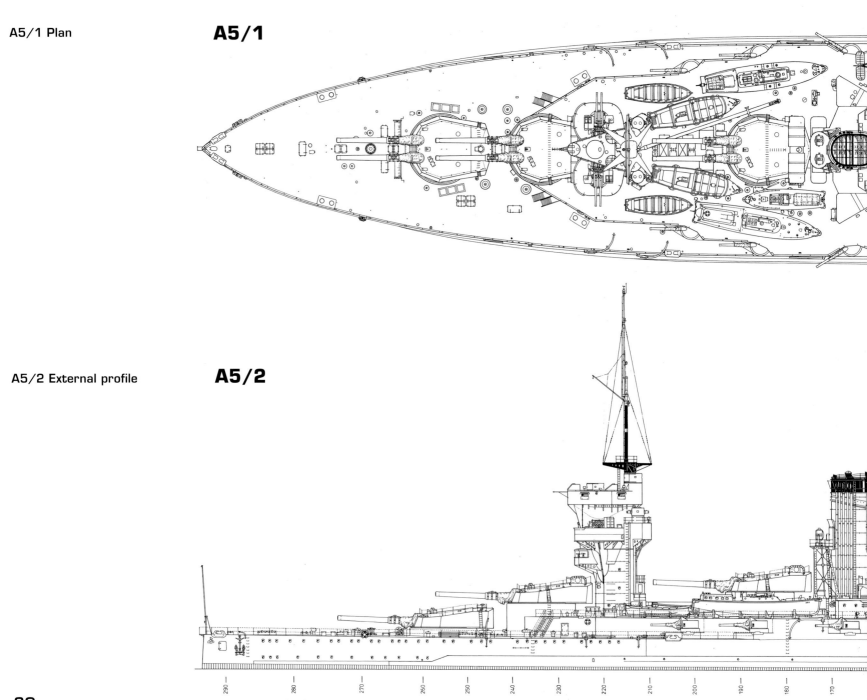

A5/2 External profile

A5/2

290 | 280 | 270 | 260 | 250 | 240 | 230 | 220 | 210 | 200 | 190 | 180 | 170

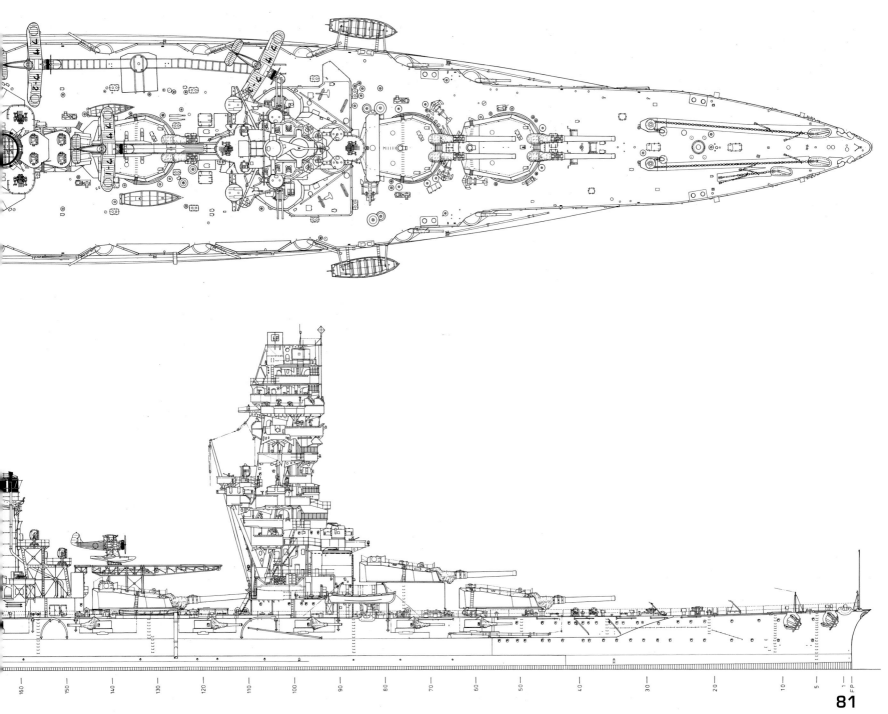

A6 *Fuso* in March 1935 after second phase of main modernisation (1:400 scale)

A6/2

A6/1 External profile

A6/2 Plan

Main changes in comparison with former version:

- elongation of the stern part of hull
- heightening of edge of bulges
- ventilators on both sides of No 2 main gun barbette
- 8m rangefinder fitted on top of pagoda tower
- small changes on pagoda tower platform
- lowering of fore searchlight platform on funnel superstructure
- changes to the outlet of smoke pipe on funnel
- changes to the top of rear superstructure stands
- changes to the arrangement of boats on forecastle deck

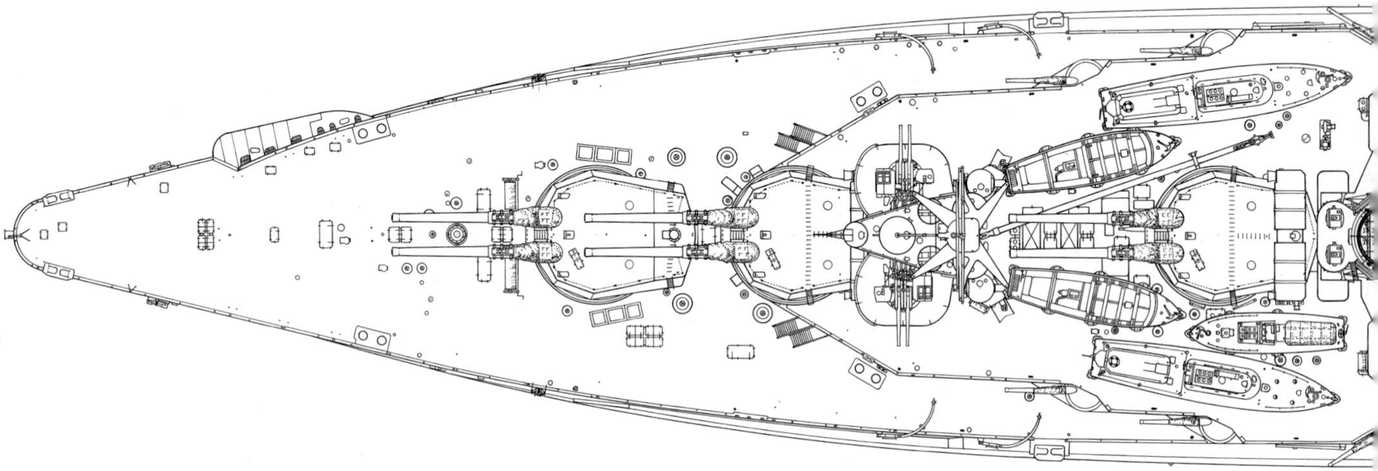

A6/1

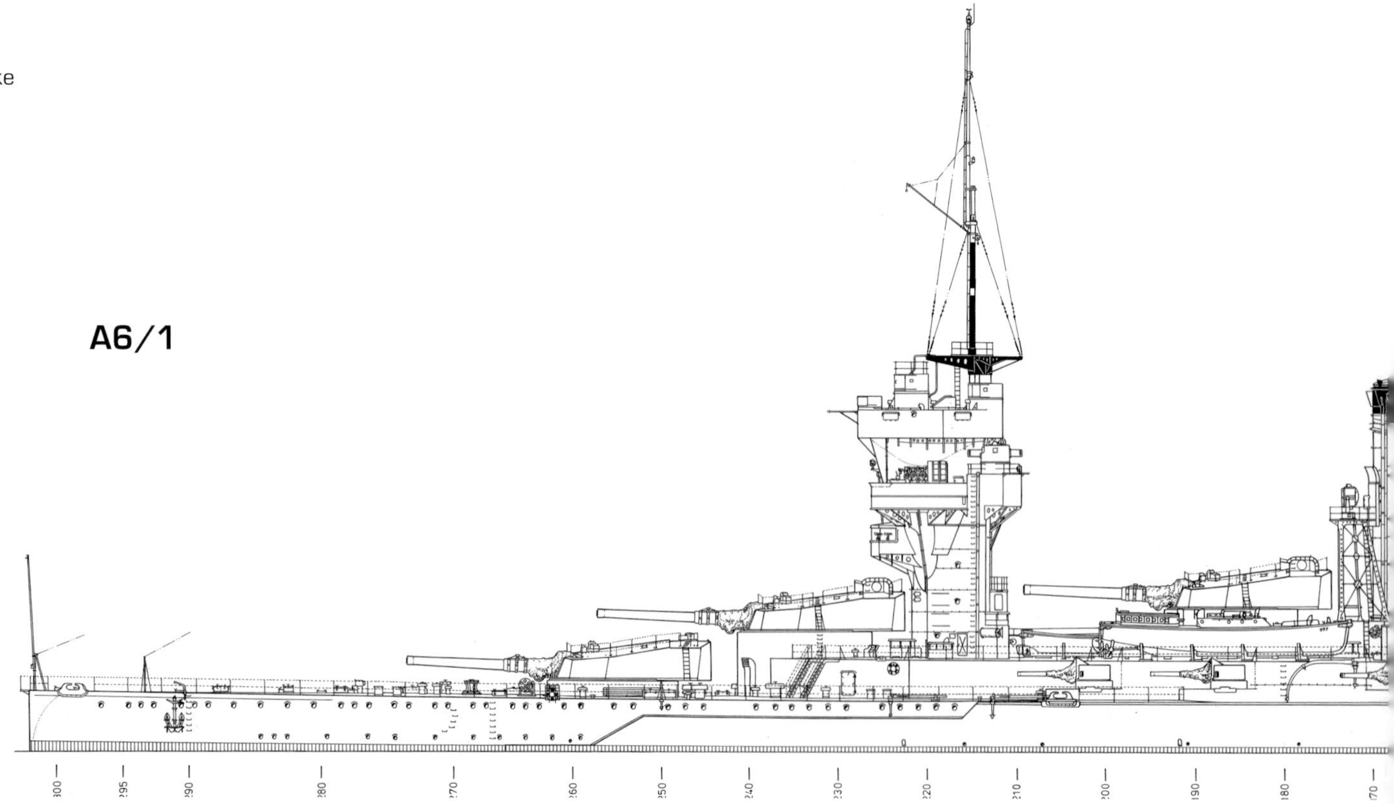

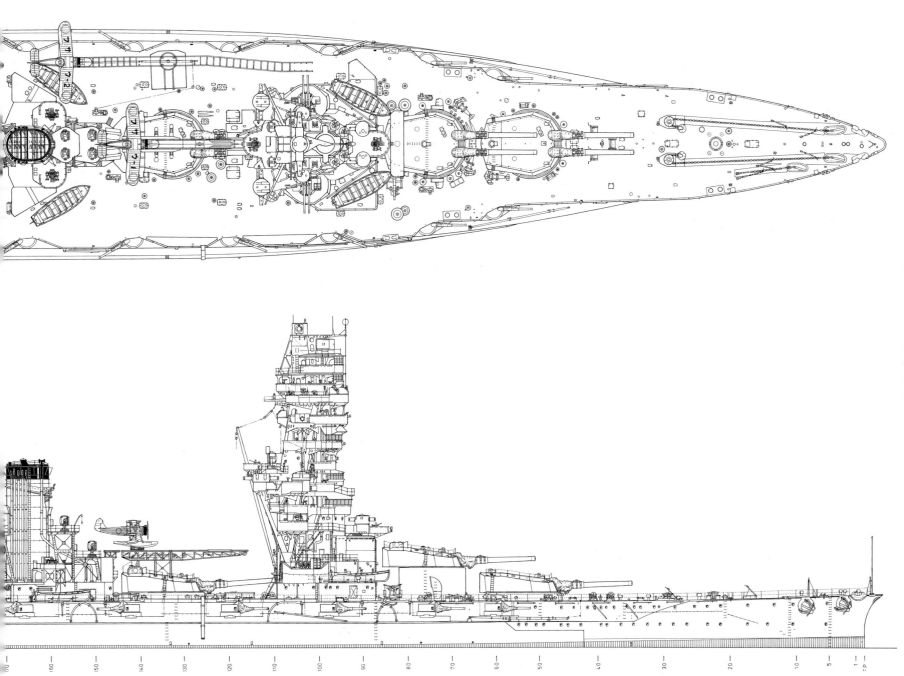

A7 Fuso in April 1938 after first phase of second modernisation (1:500 scale)

A7/1 External profile

A7/2 Arrangement of barge and pontoons for artillery targets

A7/3 Fore view and profile of barge

A7/4 Perspective of barge

1 Target barge

2 Target pontoons

3 White name 'Fuso' 3 (kanji) 40cm-high description

Main changes in comparison with former appearance:

- removal of starboard second anchor
- 10m rangefinder fitted on the top of pagoda tower
- removal of 3.5m rangefinders on level IX (replaced with MG fire directors)
- fore platform of goniometer antenna on upper pagoda tower

- mounting of eight twin 25mm MG on changed platforms of fore and middle superstructures
- E8N2 replaced with E4N7
- Two platforms with MG fire directors and heat protection fitted on both sides of funnel
- lowering of the mast on top of rear superstructure
- 17m pinnaces were not carried after April 1938

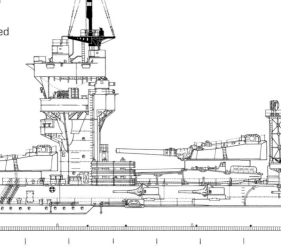

A7/1

A8 Port side elevation with arrangement of side scuttles and scupper pipes and holes (1:500 scale)

A8/1 Hull profile in April 1933

A8/2 Hull profile in March 1935

A8/1

A8/2

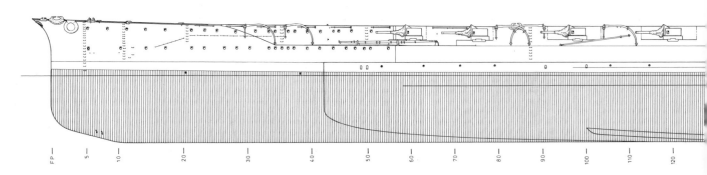

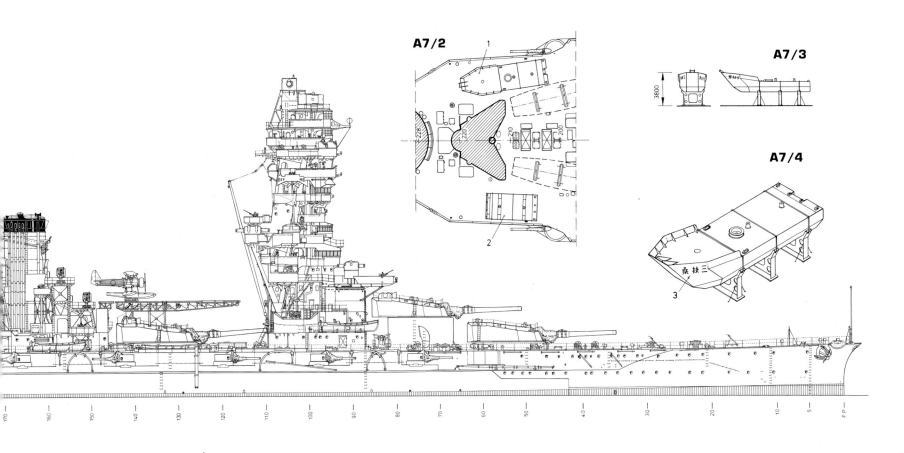

A7/2

1

2

228
220
210
200

A7/3

3600

A7/4

三扶桑

3

170 160 150 140 130 120 110 100 90 80 70 60 50 40 30 20 10 5 FP

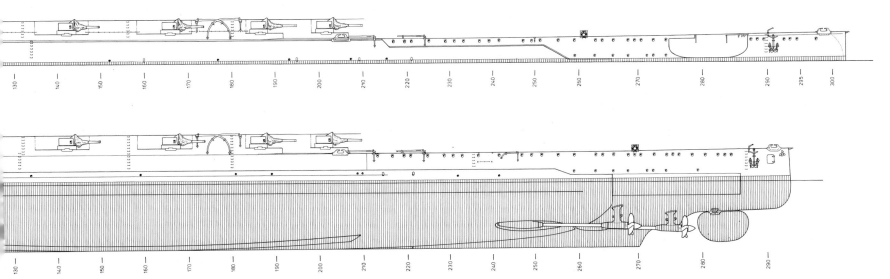

130 140 150 160 170 180 190 200 210 220 230 240 250 260 270 280 290 295 300

130 140 150 160 170 180 190 200 210 220 230 240 250 260 270 280 290

A9 Fuso in April 1941 after second phase of second modernisation (1:500 scale)

A9/1 External profile

A9/2 Plan

Main changes in comparison with former appearance:

- anti-aircraft-defence command platform fitted to the top of pagoda tower, the height of which was lowered about 2m
- two lookout towers were removed from level X
- searching the self-position room and new main gun director fitted on AA-defence command platform level
- 20m derrick on aft pagoda wall removed
- aircraft equipment replaced on stern deck – new 19.5m catapult, derrick, rails, and linoleum covering of deck
- some changes in the funnel structure
- 12m high ensign staff on the stern

A9/1

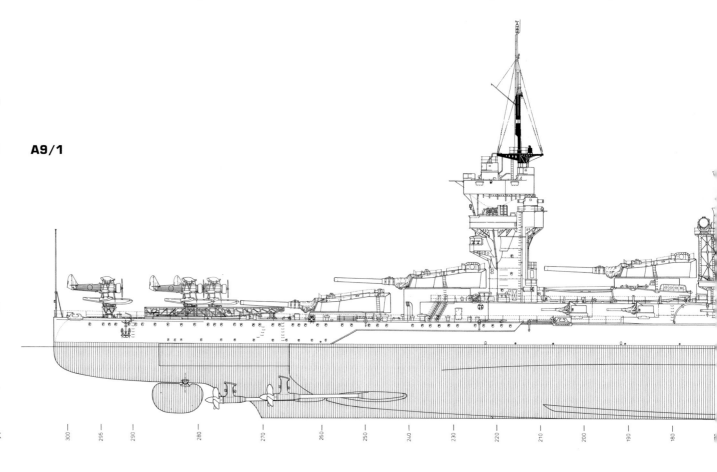

A9/2

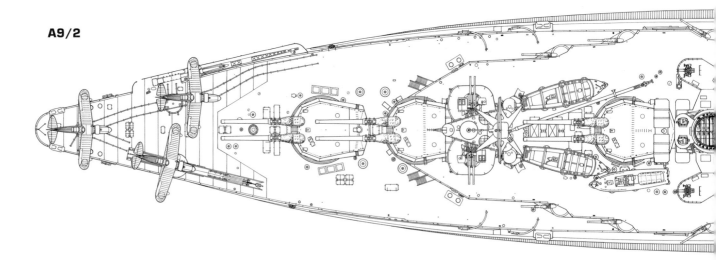

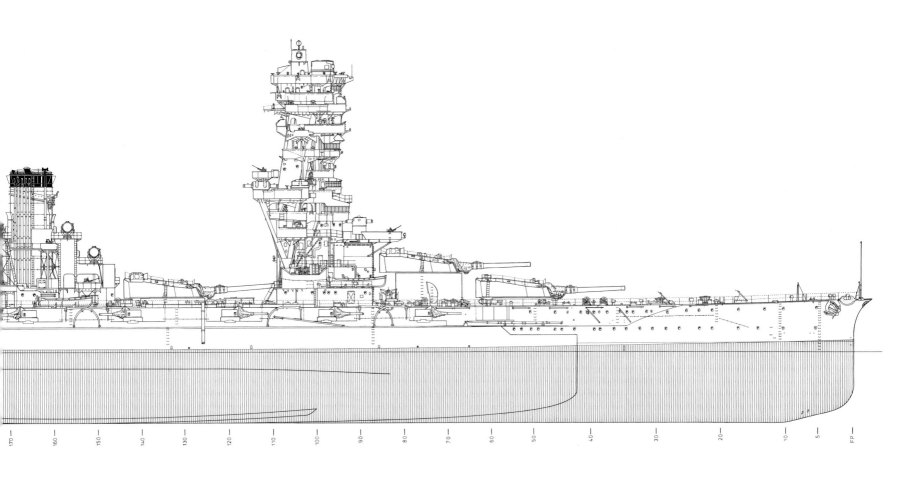

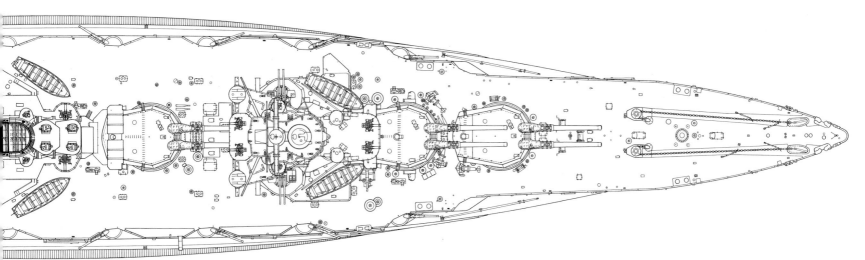

170 160 150 140 130 120 110 100 90 80 70 60 50 40 30 20 10 5 FP

A10 *Fuso* in August 1944 in her last version (1:500 scale)

A10/1 External profile

A10/1

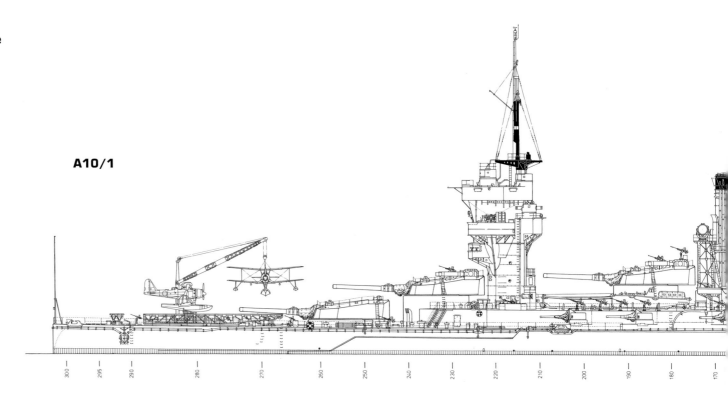

300 295 290 280 270 260 250 240 230 220 210 200 190 180 170

A10/2

A10/2 Plan

Main changes in comparison with former appearance:

- shields from four protected lookout posts level IX and X removed (in 1943)
- total number of 25mm MG reached 95, total number of 13.2mm MG reached 10
- radars Type 13 and Type 22 fitted
- floatplane F1M2 replaced E8N2 (from 1943)
- degaussing cable around hull fitted in 1942

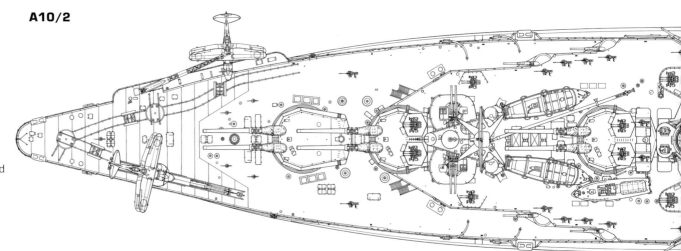

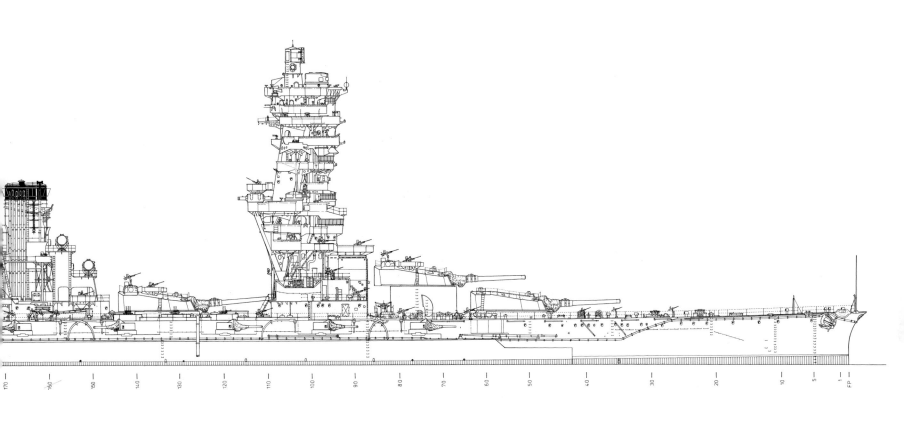

170 160 150 140 130 120 110 100 90 80 70 60 50 40 30 20 10 5 1 FP

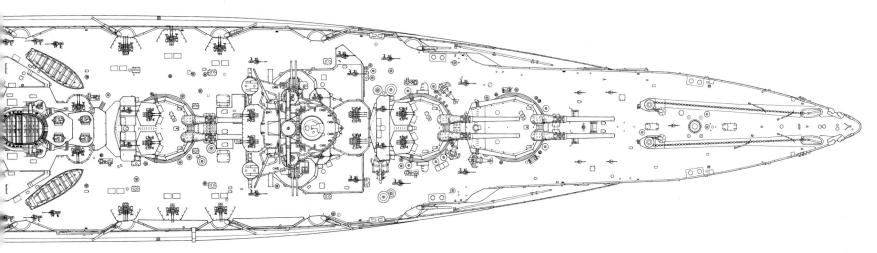

A11/1 View from forward, November 1915 – first version

A11/1

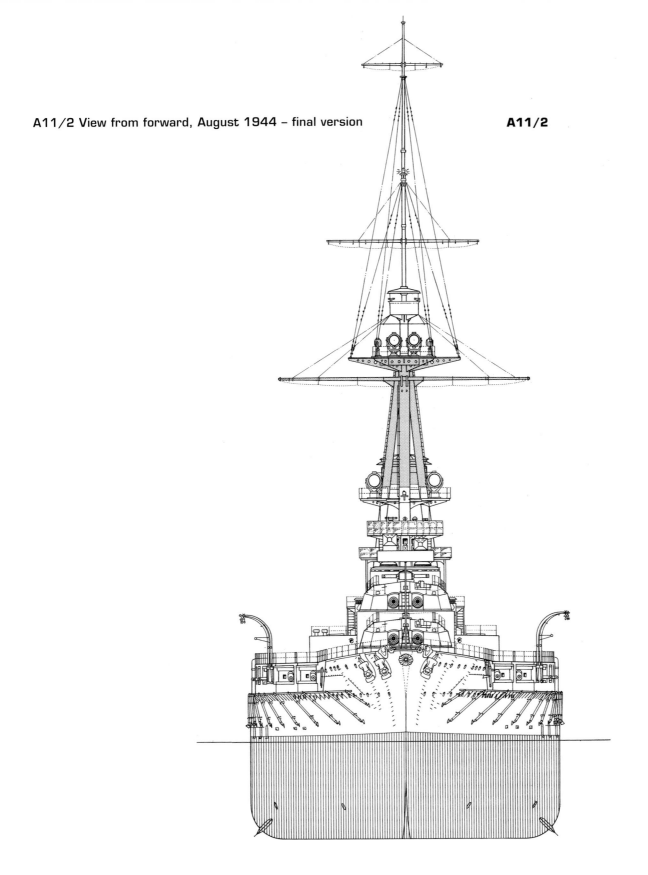

A12 RIG: scheme of rig after 1933 (1:500 scale)

1 Main aerials
2 Dressing line
3 Fore aerials (to forecastle stays: port and starboard)
4 Rear aerials (to stern stays: port and starboard)
5 Aerial wire port (until 1937)
6 Aerial support to starboard edge of signal deck
7 20m derrick (for lifting floatplanes from sea surface to deck)
8 Topping lift

9 Purchase
10 Guy
11 Rear 20m derrick (mainly used for moving boats). When in operation, the gun barrels of No 4 turret were turned towards ship side
12 Topping lift
13 Purchase wire
14 46ft swinging boom
15 24ft boom
16 Funnel stays
17 Awning

18 Awning segments joints
19 Awning stanchion
20 Awning line
21 Accommodation ladder
22 Position of Imperial Japanese Navy ensign on the ensign staff. Dimension of ensign 2700 x 4050mm or 3600 x 5400mm
23 Position of battle ensign – IJN ensign 2700 x 4050mm
24 Position of Admiral's flag
25 Position of jack

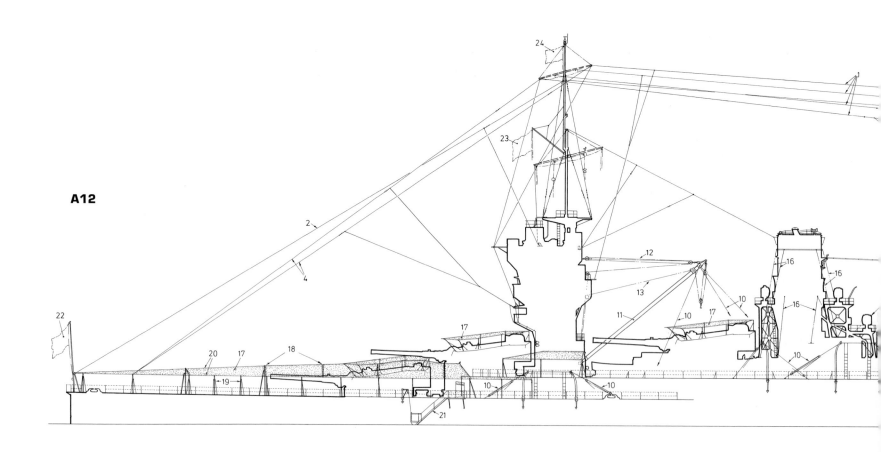

A12

A13 Scheme of awnings 1933–40 (plan, scale 1:1000)

1 Awning surface
2 Awning segments joints
3 Central awning line

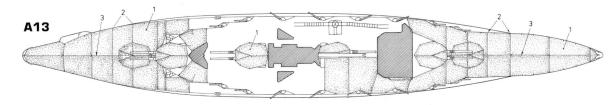

A13

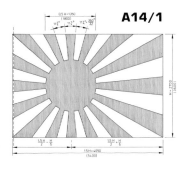

A14/1

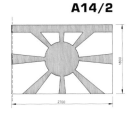

A14/2

A14/3

A14 Flags (scale 1:50)

A14/1 Imperial Japanese Navy Ensign – used on ensign staff
with dimensions 2700mm x 4050mm and 3600mm x
5400mm or as Battle ensign on top of rear mast with
dimensions 2700mm x 4050mm. In this second purchase
there was no flag on the ensign staff

A14/2 Vice Admiral's flag (can be used either as admiral's flag,
with upper and lower red stripes, or rear- admiral's flag,
without upper and lower red stripes)

A14/3 Jack from jack staff

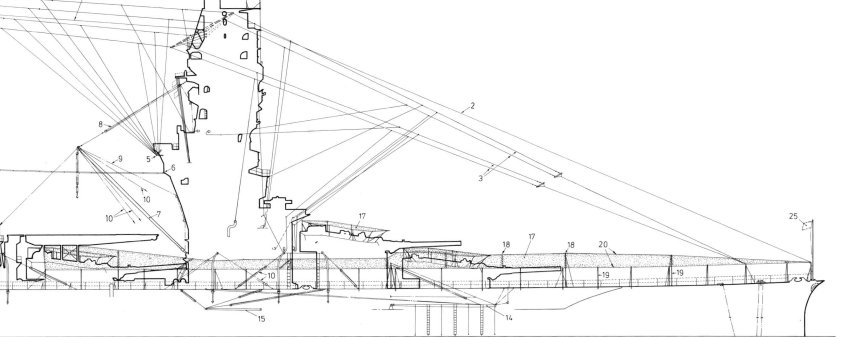

A15 Internal arrangements 1935 (scale 1:500)

A15/1 Profile, arrows indicate view direction for transverse sections

1 Admiral's cabin
2 Officers' saloon
3 Passage
4 Staff office
5 Officers' cabin
6 Steering rudder room
7 Rudder engine room
8 Mess
9 36cm shell room
10 Main guns powder magazine
11 Shell and powder handling room
12 15cm shell supply room

13 Rear lower conning tower room
14 Rear conning tower
15 Engine room ventilating supply
16 Engine room
17 Main engines control room
18 No 1–No 2 boiler rooms
19 No 3–No 4 boiler rooms
20 No 4–No 6 boiler rooms
21 Boiler room ventilation supply
22 Funnel uptake
23 Deck store

24 Rear lookout platform
25 Rear HA gun platform store
26 Rear auxiliary control deck for main and secondary gun
27 Main gun director (Syuho Hoiban Sojun Sochi)
28 12cm spotting sight tower (Kansoku Kyo)
29 Secondary gun director (Fukuho Hoko Shiji Sochi)

30 Smith factory
31 Steriliser room
32 Vegetable store
33 Sea-water tank
34 Radio room
35 Accumulator (battery) room
36 Fore radio room
37 Store
38 Telephone room
39 Store
40 Sea-water/water tanks

A15/1

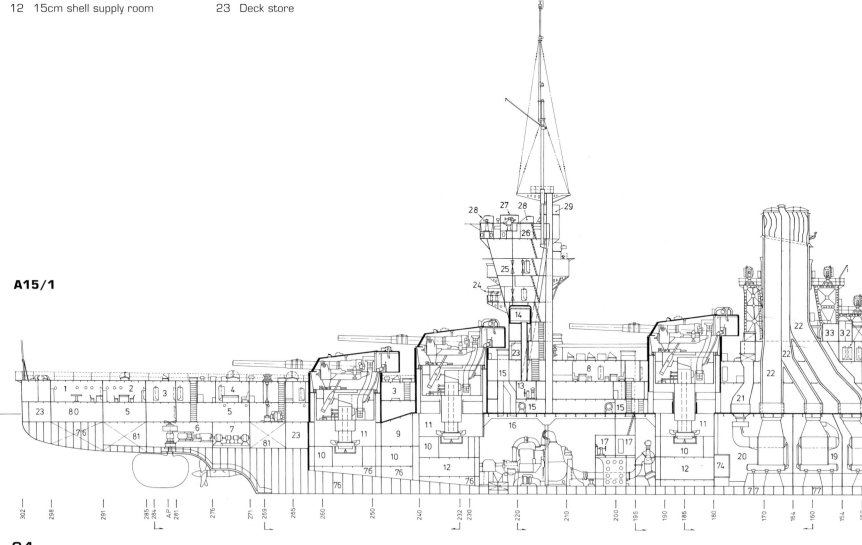

41 Spare main gun command room
42 Conning tower
43 Lower conning tower room
44 Commander's standby room
45 Chart store
46 Chart room
47 Communication command room
48 Electrical-circuit room
49 Compass bridge
50 Telegraph room

51 Transmission room
52 Lower lookout room
53 Operation room
54 Navigation platform
55 Telephone room
56 Battle bridge
57 Upper lookout deck and secondary gun control platform
58 Searching self position room
59 Sokuteki Ban room (target-course-and-speed computer)
60 Fire command platform

(Kansoku)
61 Main gun director
62 8m main rangefinder
63 Rotary goniometer antenna (to search self-position room 58)
64 Galley
65 Crew mess
66 Store
67 Crew living quarters
68 Paint store
69 Paint room
70 Store

71 Anchor cable locker
72 Capstan engine room
73 Trim tank
74 Water supply tank
75 Refrigerated room
76 WTC (watertight compartment)
77 Oil fuel tank
78 Food magazine
79 Fresh water tank
80 Awning canvas store
81 Reserve oil fuel tank

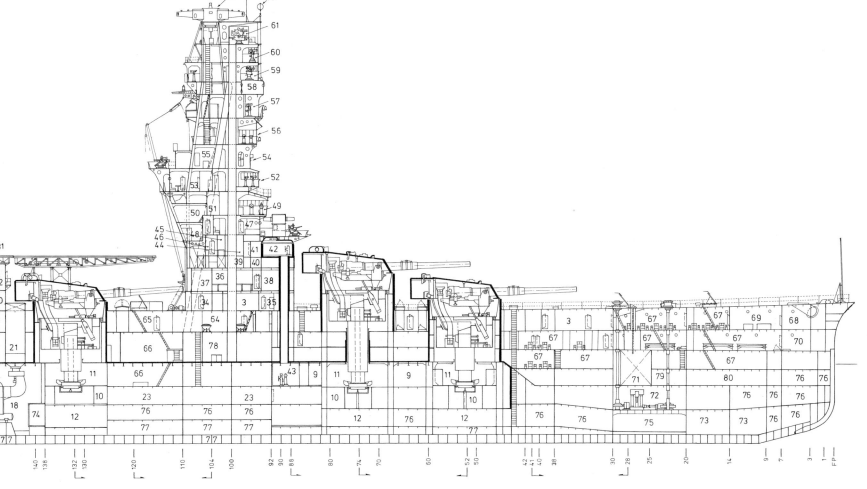

95

A15/2 Upper deck plan (scale 1:500)

1 Paint store	10 Funnel uptake
2 Paint room	11 Ventilation fan for boiler room
3 Crew living quarters	12 Mess
4 Passage	13 Radio room
5 Mess	14 Store
6 Mechanics (ships' engineers) room	15 Ventilator fan
7 Bathroom	16 Galley
8 WC	17 Aircraft elevator movable pillars
9 Crew living space and secondary casemate gun deck	18 Ammunition hoist for 12.7cm HA guns
	19 Radio room

A15/2

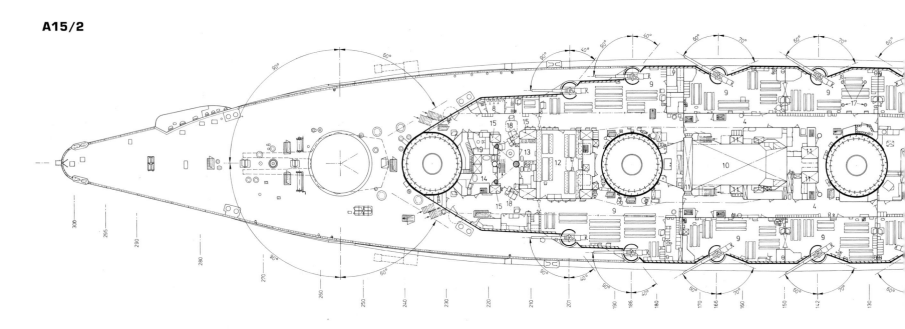

A15/3

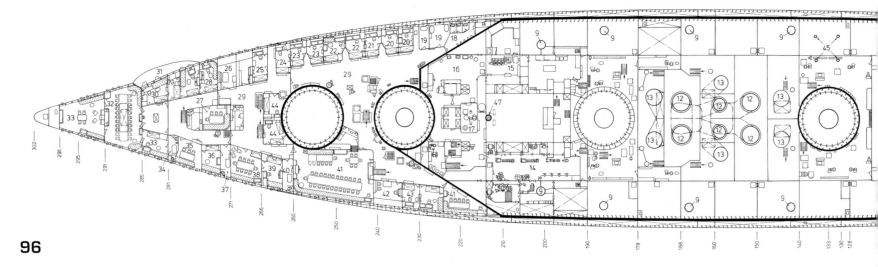

A15/3 Main deck plan (scale 1:500)

1	Store
2	Medicine store
3	Crew living quarters
4	Medicine room
5	Crew infirmary
6	Officers' infirmary
7	Officers' bedroom
8	Generator room
9	15cm gun pillar
10	Petty officers' bathroom
11	Construction hangar
12	Funnel uptake
13	Ventilation fans for boiler room
14	Workshop
15	Generator room
16	Galley
17	Rear lower conning tower room
18	WC
19	Officers' bathroom
20	Naval surgeon's chief room
21	Gunnery chief room
22	Navigator's room
23	Chief engineer's room
24	Staff officer's room
25	Adjutant room
26	Staff officers' office
27	Staff office room
28	Fleet paymaster room
29	Passage
30	Fleet chief engineer's room
31	Further aircraft derrick engine room (from 1940)
32	Officers' saloon
33	Admiral's room
34	Admiral's bathroom
35	Chief of staff's room
36	Chief of staff's bedroom
37	Chief of staff's bathroom
38	Captain's cabin
39	Captain's bedroom
40	Captain's bathroom
41	Officers' mess
42	Paymaster's office
43	Paymaster's cabin
44	Store
45	Aircraft elevator pillars (poles)
46	Base of foremast column
47	Base of after mast column

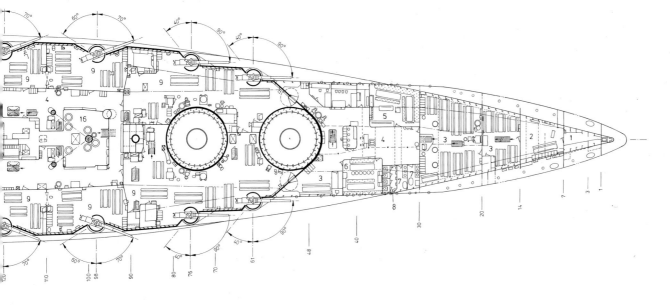

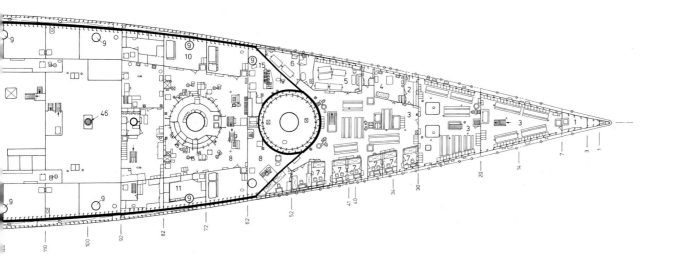

A16 Transverse sections (scale 1:400)

A16/1 Transverse sections 1935

FRAME 28

1 Crew living quarters
2 Sleeping quarters with hammocks
3 Anchor cable locker
4 Capstan machinery (engine) room
5 Refrigerator room
6 Store
7 WTC
8 Passage
9 OFT (oil fuel tank)

FRAME 41

10 Crew infirmary
11 Officers' bedroom
12 Ship engineers' mess
13 Store
14 Office

FRAME 52

15 Officers' infirmary
16 Pump room
17 No 1 turret powder magazine
18 No 1 turret shell-powder handling room
19 15cm secondary gun ammunition magazine

FRAME 74

20 Crew living quarters and secondary gun deck
21 Petty officers' bathroom
22 Construction hangar
23 Ventilator engine
24 Generator room
25 No 2 turret shell-powder handling room
26 No 2 turret powder magazine
27 15cm gun ammunition magazine

FRAME 88

28 Conning tower with two 3.5m rangefinder for secondary guns
29 WC
30 Telephone room
31 Standby room
32 Accumulator (battery) room
33 Lower conning tower room
34 15cm gun ammunition magazine

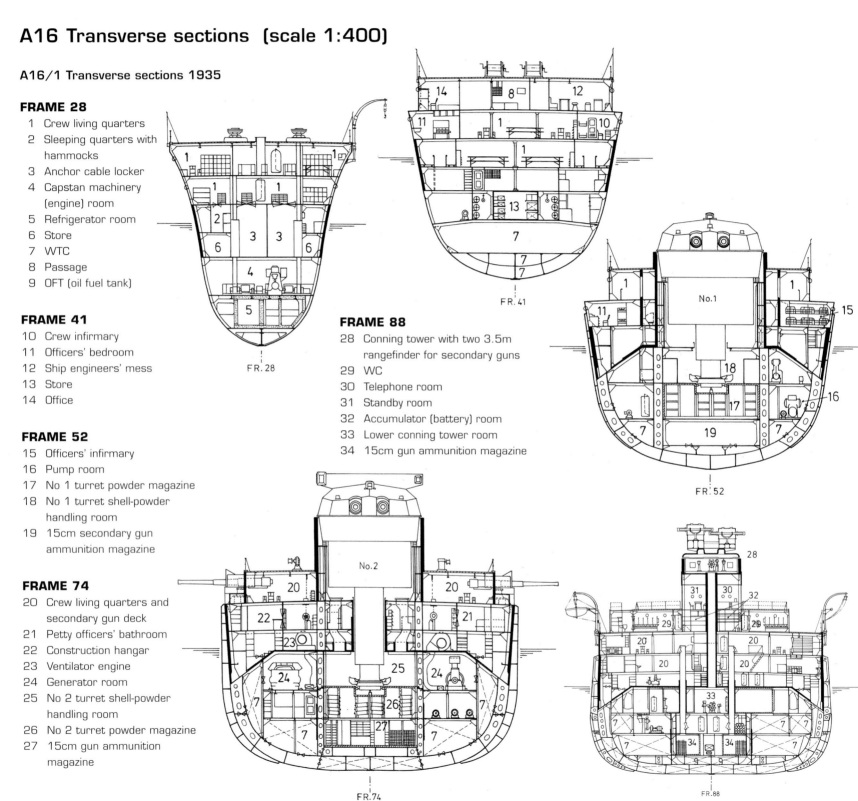

FR. 28

FR. 41

FR. 52

FR. 74

FR. 88

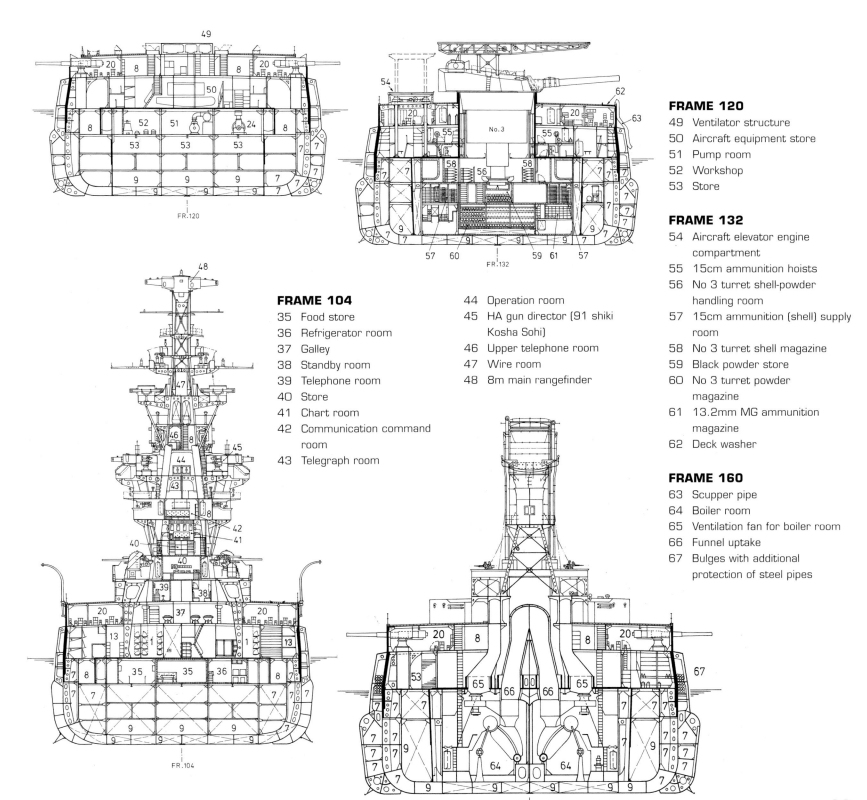

FRAME 120

49 Ventilator structure
50 Aircraft equipment store
51 Pump room
52 Workshop
53 Store

FRAME 132

54 Aircraft elevator engine
   compartment
55 15cm ammunition hoists
56 No 3 turret shell-powder
   handling room
57 15cm ammunition (shell) supply
   room
58 No 3 turret shell magazine
59 Black powder store
60 No 3 turret powder
   magazine
61 13.2mm MG ammunition
   magazine
62 Deck washer

FRAME 104

35 Food store
36 Refrigerator room
37 Galley
38 Standby room
39 Telephone room
40 Store
41 Chart room
42 Communication command
   room
43 Telegraph room

44 Operation room
45 HA gun director (91 shiki
   Kosha Sohi)
46 Upper telephone room
47 Wire room
48 8m main rangefinder

FRAME 160

63 Scupper pipe
64 Boiler room
65 Ventilation fan for boiler room
66 Funnel uptake
67 Bulges with additional
   protection of steel pipes

99

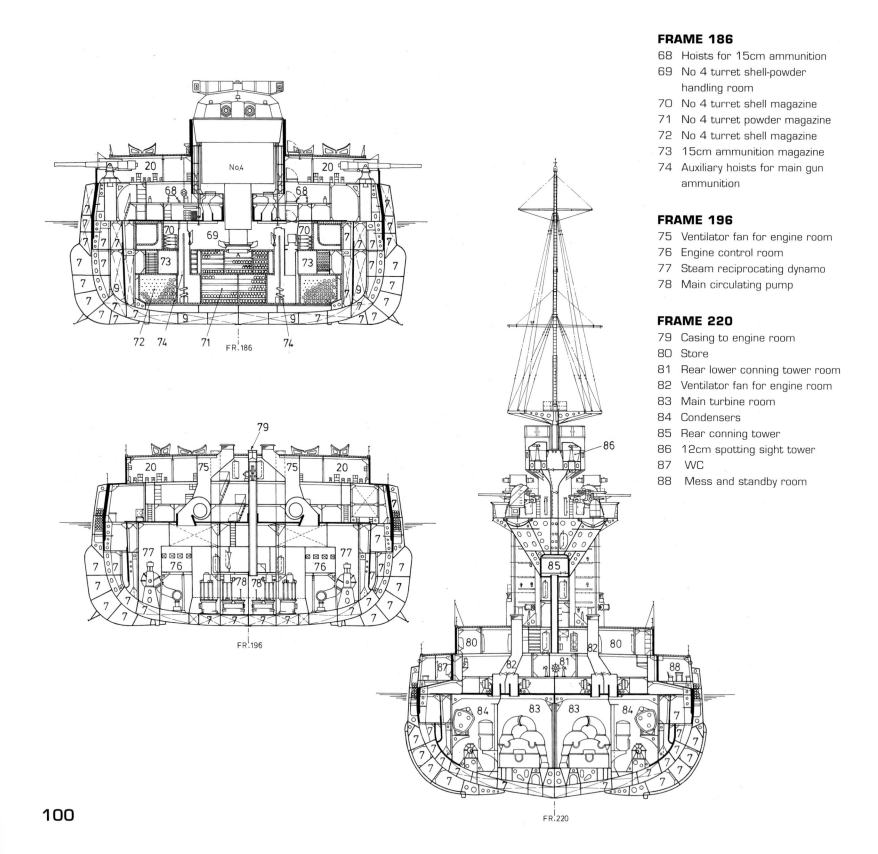

FRAME 186

68 Hoists for 15cm ammunition
69 No 4 turret shell-powder handling room
70 No 4 turret shell magazine
71 No 4 turret powder magazine
72 No 4 turret shell magazine
73 15cm ammunition magazine
74 Auxiliary hoists for main gun ammunition

FRAME 196

75 Ventilator fan for engine room
76 Engine control room
77 Steam reciprocating dynamo
78 Main circulating pump

FRAME 220

79 Casing to engine room
80 Store
81 Rear lower conning tower room
82 Ventilator fan for engine room
83 Main turbine room
84 Condensers
85 Rear conning tower
86 12cm spotting sight tower
87 WC
88 Mess and standby room

FRAME 232

89 Paymaster's room
90 Chief naval surgeon's room
91 No 5 turret shell and powder handling room
92 No 5 turret powder magazine (visible canisters each for two cordite charge bags)
93 Generator room
94 Outer shaft tunnel
95 Inner shaft tunnel

FRAME 269

96 Captain's cabin
97 Staff officers' office
98 Staff office
99 Water tank
100 Rear capstan engine room
101 Store

FRAME 284

102 Admiral's cabin
103 Fleet chief engineer's room
104 Bulge for future (from 1940) aircraft derrick engine room
105 Officers' cabin
106 Steering rudder room

A17 Armour and protective plating after 1933 – sections, (scale 1:100)

A17/1 Transverse hull section frame 74
A17/2 Transverse hull section frame 160 (midship)

(Thickness of armour plates in millimetres)

F.D.	forecastle deck	PL.D.	platform deck
U.D.	upper deck	H.D.	hold deck
MA.D.	main deck	WTC	watertight compartment
MD.D.	middle deck		
L.D.	lower deck	OFT	oil fuel tank

Steel armour plating types

VC	Vickers cemented	HT	High Tensile steel
NVNC	New Vickers – non cemented	NS	Nickel steel

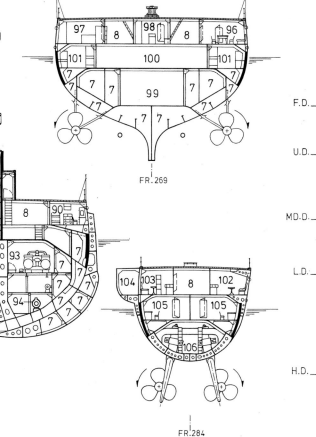

FR.269

FR.232

FR.284

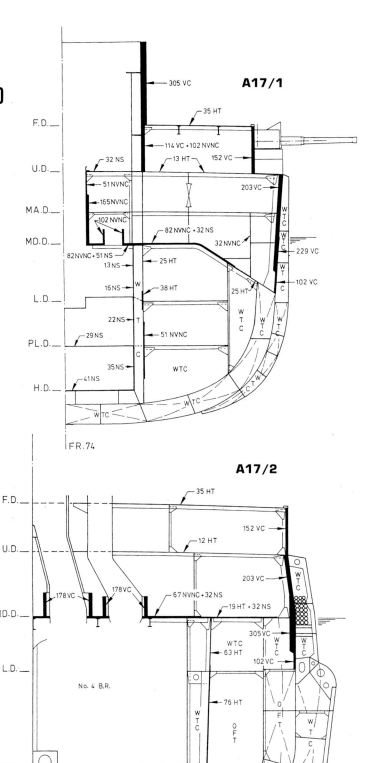

FR.74

FR.160

101

B LINES AND BODY PLANS

DISTANCE BETWEEN FRAMES (FRAME SPACES) – HULL CONSTRUCTION SPACE

B1 Lines in 1915–30 (scale 1:500)

B1/1 Sheer elevation
B1/2 Waterline plan

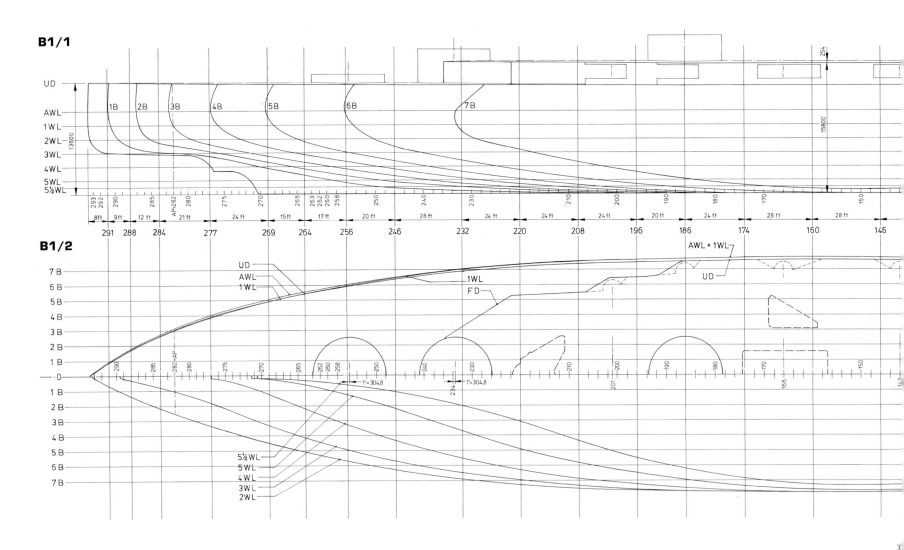

Frame	Distance (ft)	Parts
FP–1	4.0	1
1–46	3.0	45
46–260	4.0	107
260–293 (302)*	3.0	32 (41)*

( )* frames after 1935: 1–46, single numeration; 46–262,
double numeration; 262–302, single numeration

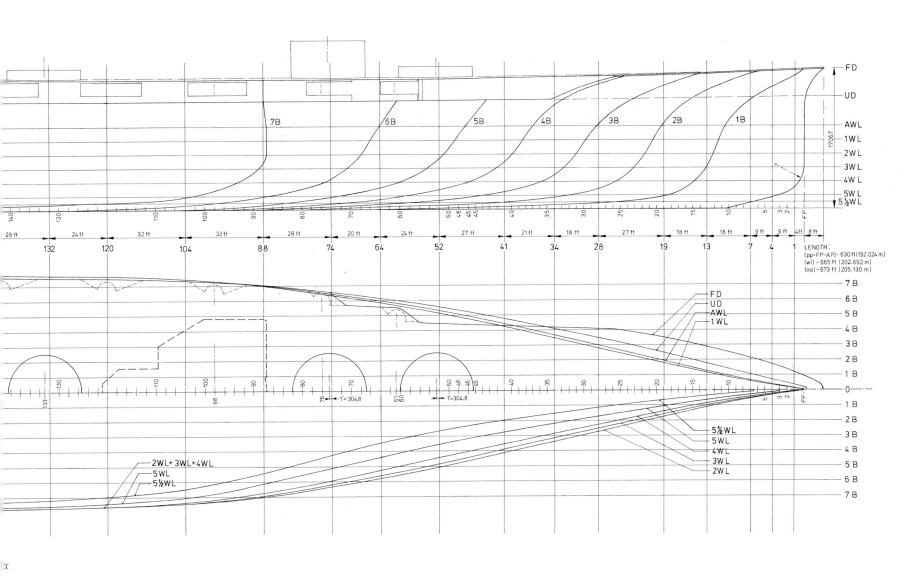

LENGTH:
(pp+FP–AP) – 630 ft (192.024 m)
(wl) – 665 ft (202.692 m)
(oa) – 673 ft (205.130 m)

103

B2 Lines in 1933–35 (scale 1:500)
(bow and stern as on drawings B1)

B2/1 Sheer elevation
B2/2 Waterline plan

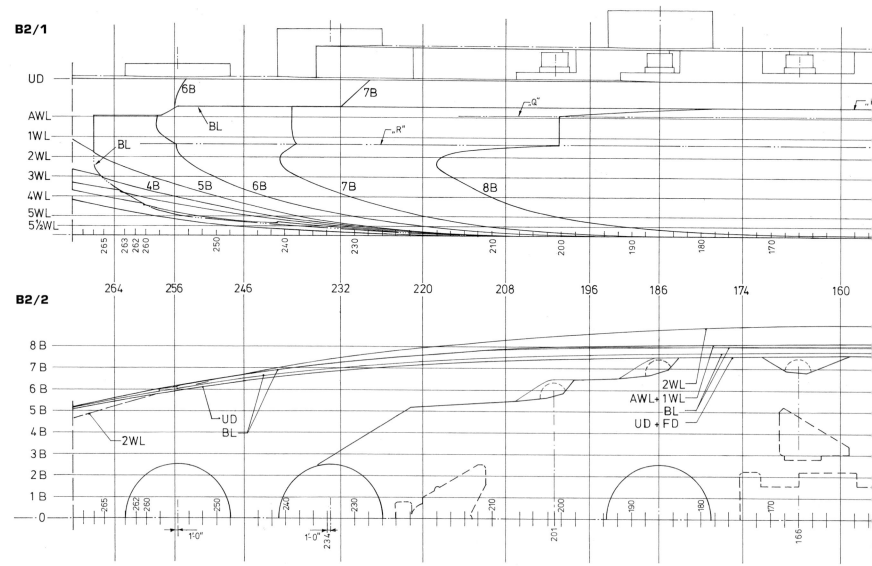

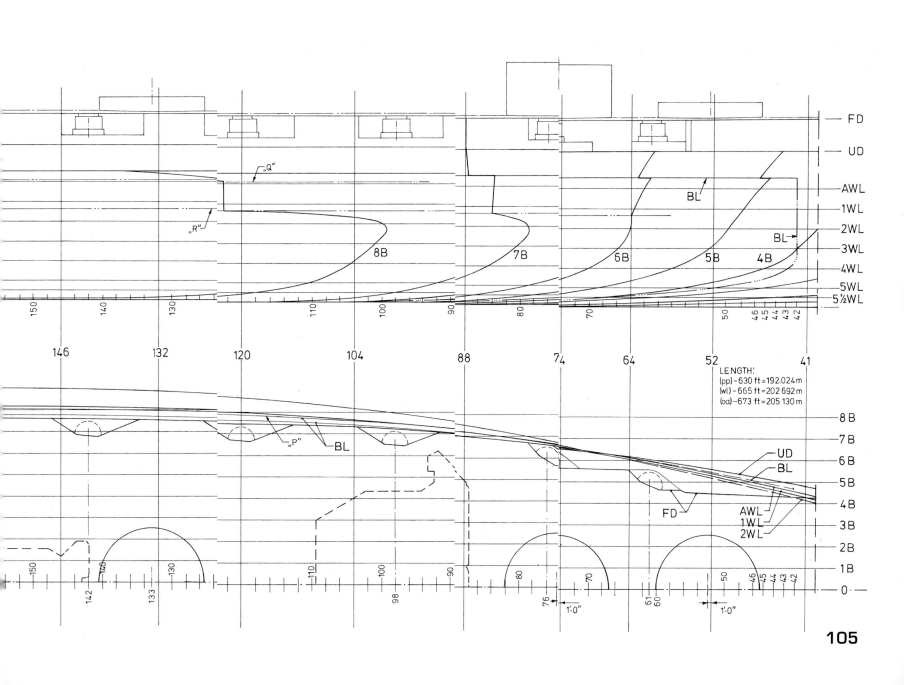

FD
UD
AWL
1WL
2WL
3WL
4WL
5WL
5½WL

„Q"
„R"
8B
7B
6B
5B
4B
BL
BL

150 140 130 110 100 90 80 70 50 46 45 44 43 42

146 132 120 104 88 74 64 52 41

LENGTH:
(pp) – 630 ft = 192.024 m
(wl) – 665 ft = 202.692 m
(oa) – 673 ft = 205.130 m

8 B
7 B
6 B
5 B
4 B
3 B
2 B
1 B
0

„P"
BL
UD
BL
FD
AWL
1WL
2WL

150 140 130 110 100 90 80 70 50 46 45 44 43 42

142 133 98 76 1'-0" 61 60 1'-0"

105

B3 Lines after 1935 (scale 1:500)

B3/1 Sheer elevation
B3/2 Waterline plan

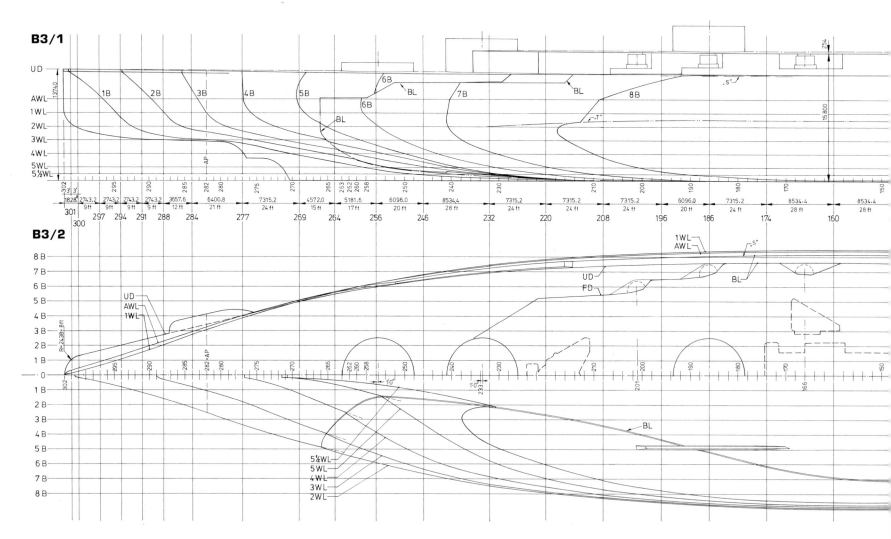

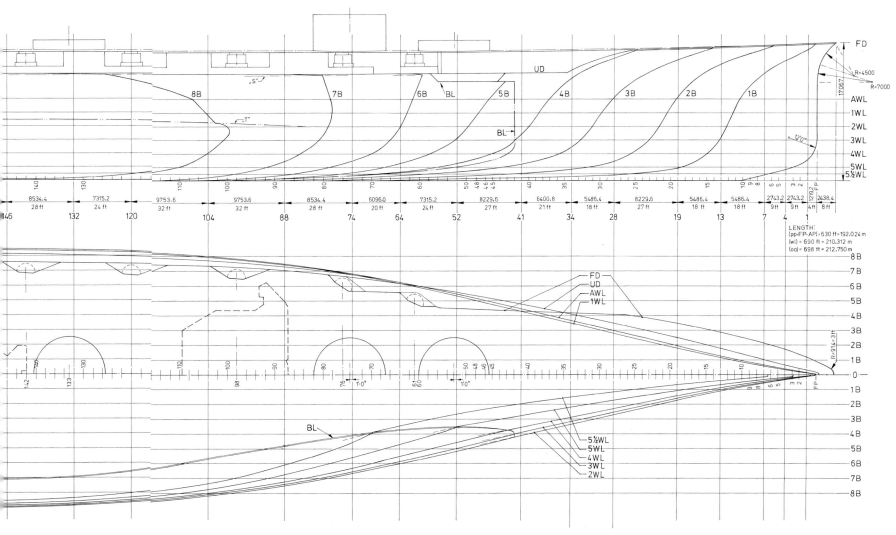

FD

UD

R=4500
R=7000

8B   7B   6B   BL   5B   4B   3B   2B   1B

"S"

17067

AWL

1WL

"T"

2WL

BL

3WL

12'0"

4WL

5WL
5½WL

140		130			110		100		90		80		70		60		50	48	46		40		35		30		25		20		15				10	9	8		6	5	3	2	1	
8534.4		7315.2			9753.6		9753.6		8534.4		6096.0		7315.2		8229.6					6400.8		5486.4		8229.6		5486.4		5486.4							2743.2	2743.2	1219.2		2438.4
28 ft		24 ft			32 ft		32 ft		28 ft		20 ft		24 ft		27 ft					21 ft		18 ft		27 ft		18 ft		18 ft							9 ft	9 ft	4 ft		8 ft

146   132   120   104   88   74   64   52   41   34   28   19   13   7   4   1

LENGTH:
(pp=FP-AP) = 630 ft = 192.024 m
(wl) = 690 ft = 210.312 m
(oa) = 698 ft = 212.750 m

8 B
7 B
FD
6 B
UD
5 B
AWL
4 B
1WL
3 B
R=914-3ft
2 B
1 B

| 142 | 130 | | 110 | 100 | 90 | | 80 | 70 | | | 50 | 46 | 45 | 40 | 35 | 30 | 25 | 20 | 15 | | 10 | | | | | | | | FP |
| 142 | 133 | | 98 | | | | 76 | | 61 | 60 | | | | | | | | | | | 9 | 8 | | 6 | 5 | 3 | 2 | |

0

1'0"   1'0"

1 B

2 B

BL

3 B

4 B

5½WL
5WL
4WL
3WL
2WL

5 B

6 B

7 B

8 B

B4 Body plans (scale 1:200)

B4/1 Body plan 1915–30

B4/1

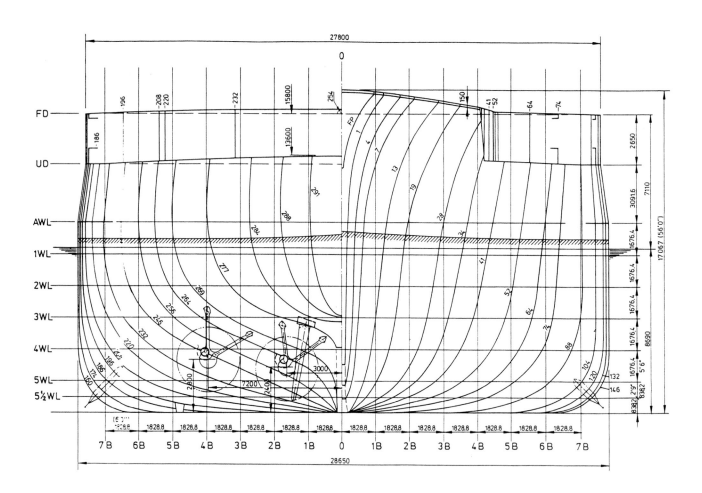

B4 Body plans (scale 1:100)

B4/2 Body plan 1933–35

B4/2

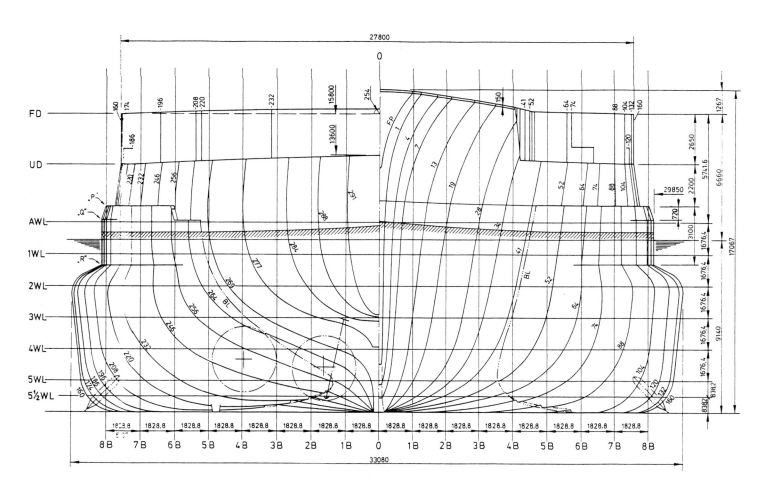

B4 Body plans (scale 1:100)

B4/3 Body plan 1935–44

B4/3

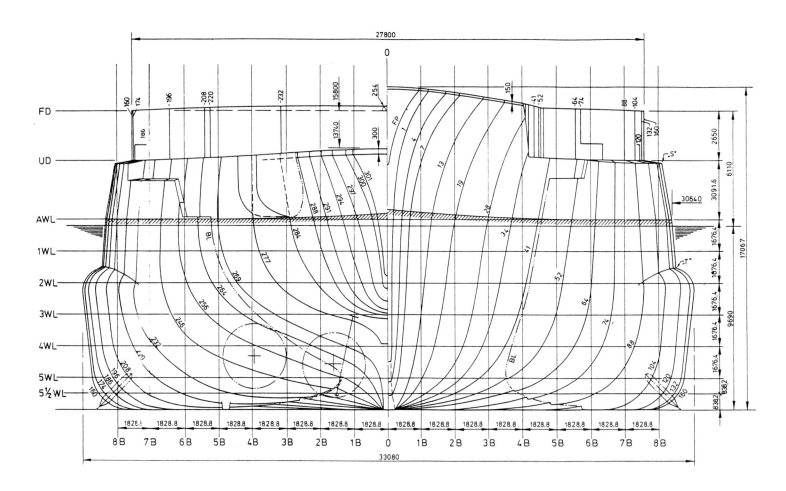

C SUPERSTRUCTURE

C1 Tower bridge superstructure, pagoda tower after main modernisation in May 1933 (scale 1:150)

C1/1   Starboard elevation of the upper part of tower

C1/1A Section of rear part

C1/1A

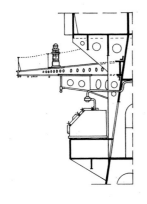

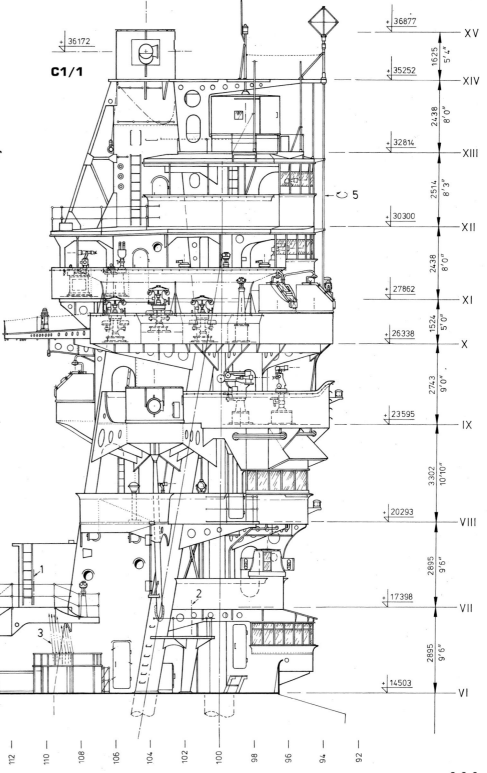

C1/2

C1/2 Front elevation of upper part

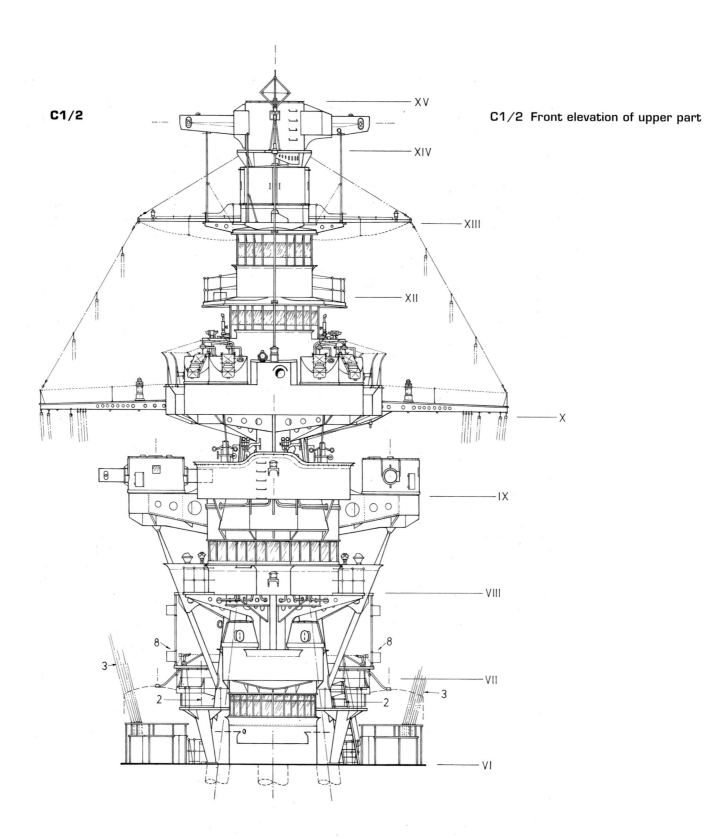

XV

XIV

XIII

XII

X

IX

VIII

8

3

VII

2

3

VI

C1/3 Rear elevation of upper part   **C1/3**

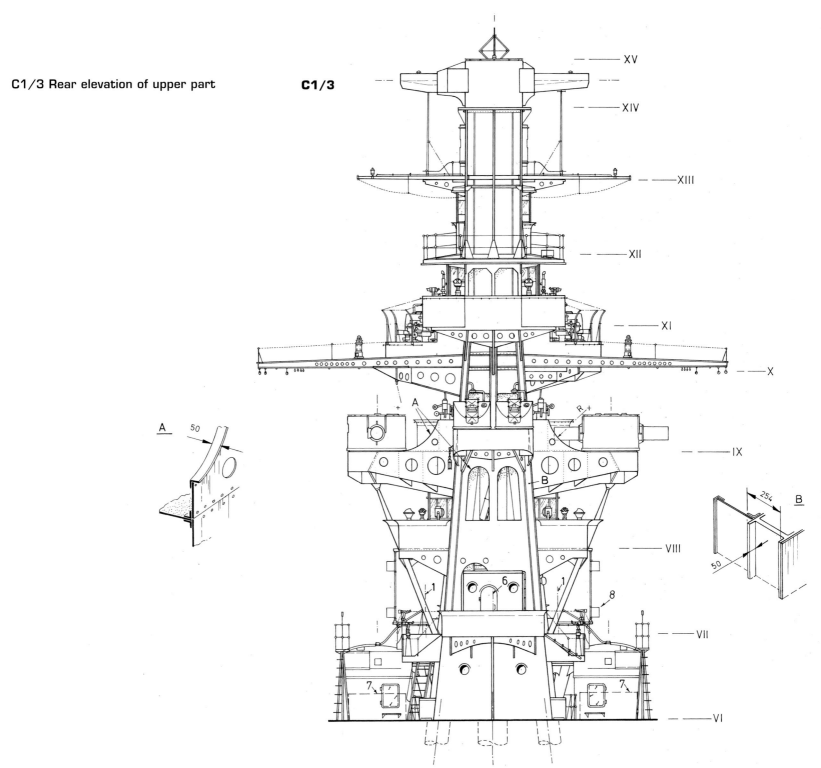

XV

XIV

XIII

XII

XI

X

A

B

R

IX

VIII

VII

VI

A   50

B   254

50

1   6   1   8

7   7

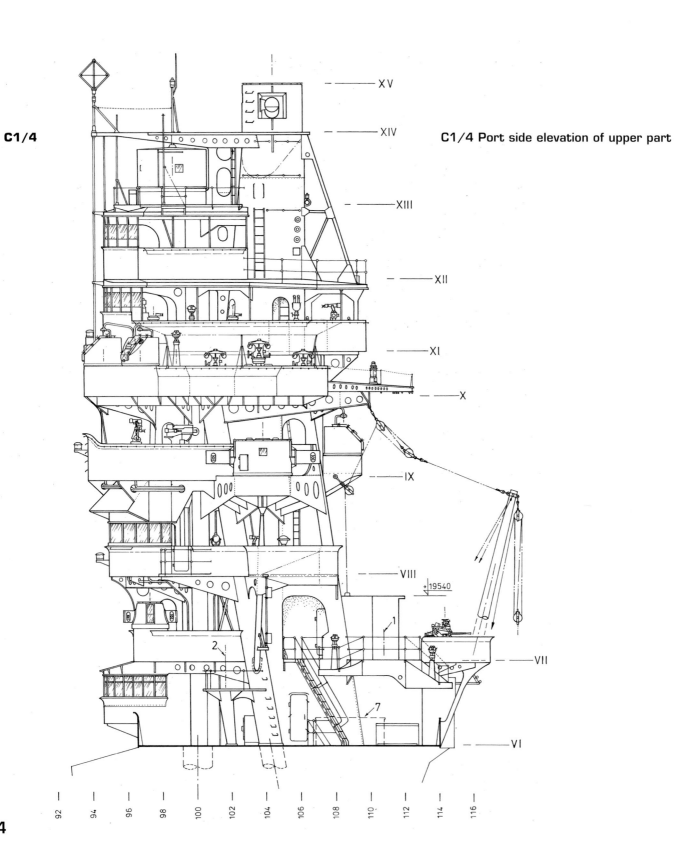

C1/4 Port side elevation of upper part

XV

XIV

XIII

XII

XI

X

IX

VIII

+19540

1

2

VII

7

VI

92 94 96 98 100 102 104 106 108 110 112 114 116

C1/5 Starboard elevation of the lower part of tower
C1/5A Changes shortly after main modernisation

C1/5

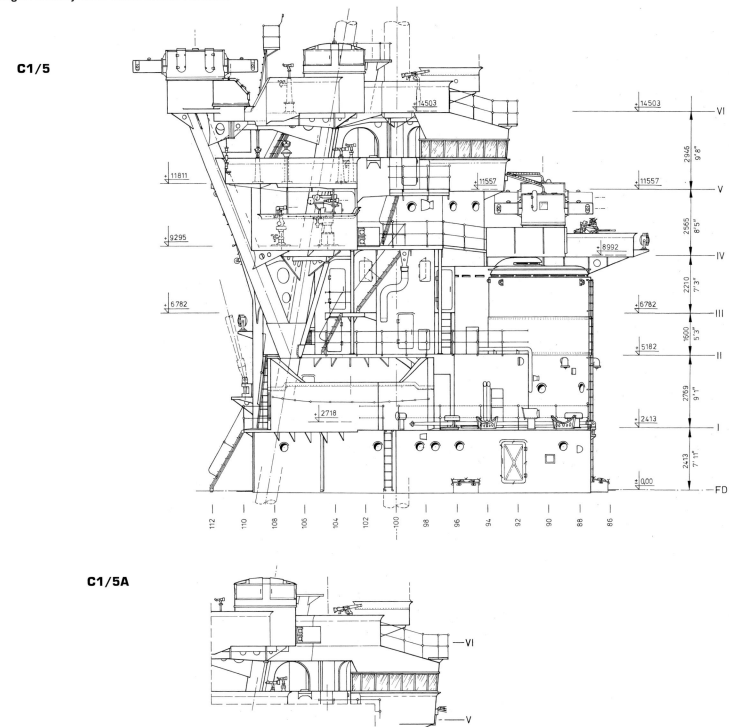

C1/5A

C1/6 Section of rear of lower part
C1/7 Front elevation of lower part

C1/6

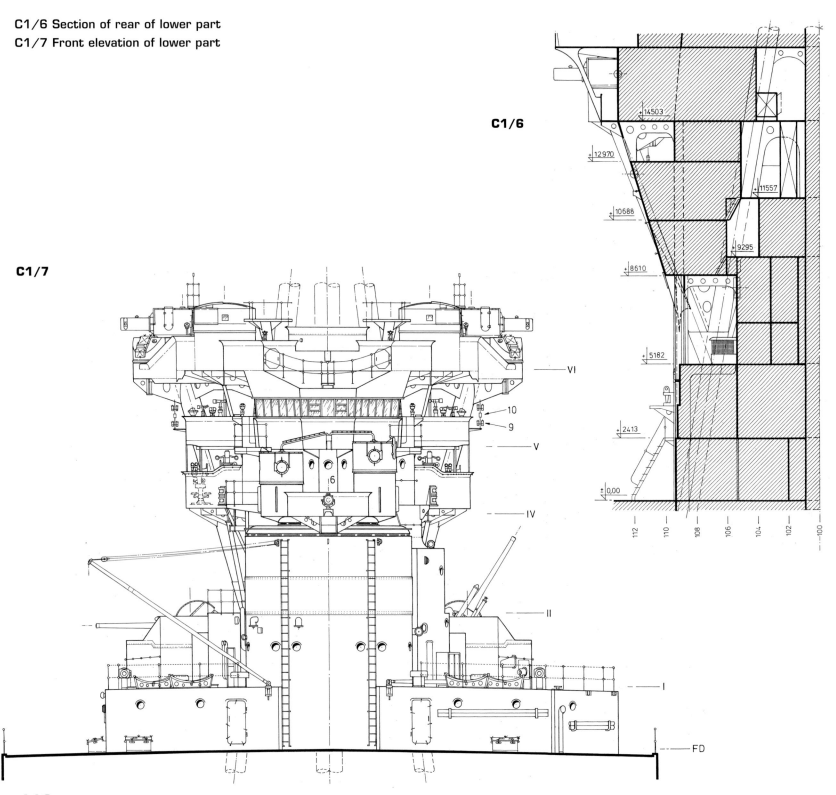

C1/7

C1/8 Port side elevation of the lower part of tower

C1/8

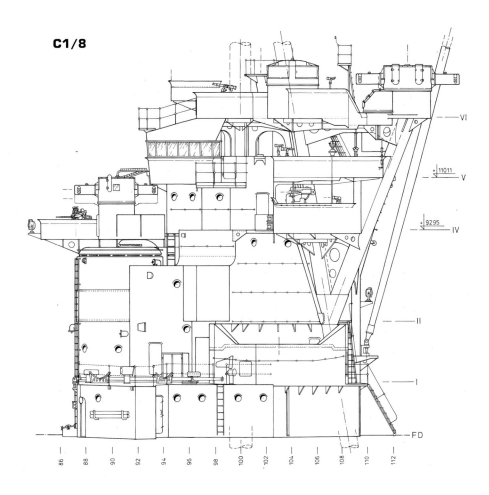

C1/9

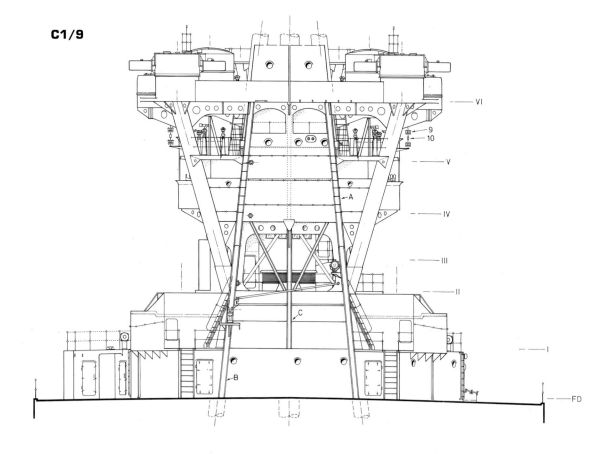

C1/10 Perspective of lower rear part of tower

C1/11 Section of lower part of tower, view towards stern

C1/12 Details of rear wall of tower

   1 Position of 110cm searchlight

   2 Position of 60cm signalling searchlight

   3 Signal wires of signalling flag post

   4 Antenna (aerial) wires

   5 Rotary pillar (steel pipe) for moving goniometer antenna from self-position room (level X)

   6 Position of quadruple 13.2mm MG mount

   7 Signal flag stand

   8 Identity mark signal

   9 Inner (for ship) signal

  10 Reply-answer signal

Levels of the pagoda tower

  FD Forecastle deck

  I   Shelter deck

  II   Lower bridge deck

  III Conning tower platform

  IV Upper bridge deck

  V   Compass bridge

  VI Lower lookout, AA control, signal platforms

  VII Forward searchlight platform

  VIII Battle bridge

  IX Upper lookout platform for secondary gun

  X   Lookout and searchlight control platform

  XI Sokuteki Ban (target-course-and-speed computer platform)

  XII Fire command platform

  XIII Main gun command platform

  XIV Main rangefinder platform

C1/10

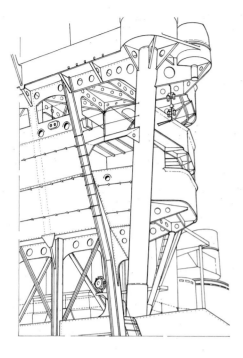

C1/11

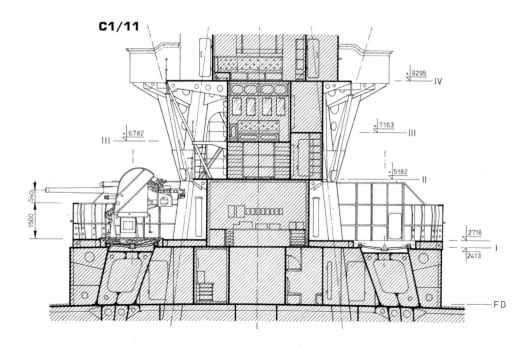

C1/12

C2 Decks of pagoda tower bridge structure 1933–35 (scale 1:150)

C2/1 Forecastle deck level
1 Column of foremast
2 Station of small weapons (personal armament)
3 Standby room
4 No 1 radio-telephone room
5 Pillar
6 Ventilator fan
7 Accumulator (battery) room
8 Passage
9 Fresh water tank
10 Officers' WC
11 Petty officer's WC
12 Crew's WC
13 Pillar of 12.7 cm gun
14 Communication tube
'S' Sofa

C2/2 Shelter deck (Level I)
1 Forward radio room
2 Telephone room (control room)
3 Standby room
4 Passage
5 Communication tube
6 Ventilation fan
7 Military stock room
8 Store
9 Skylight
10 12.7cm HA gun position
11 12.7cm ammunition hoist
12 Derrick for 9m cutter moving
13 9m cutter wartime and underway position
14 Exercise loading machine (used when 9m cutter on davits)
15 Wash-deck locker
16 Ventilation fan
17 Mushroom ventilator
'S' Sofa

C2/1

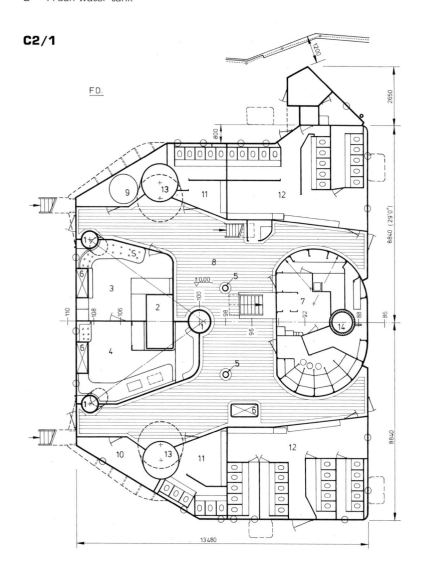

C2/2

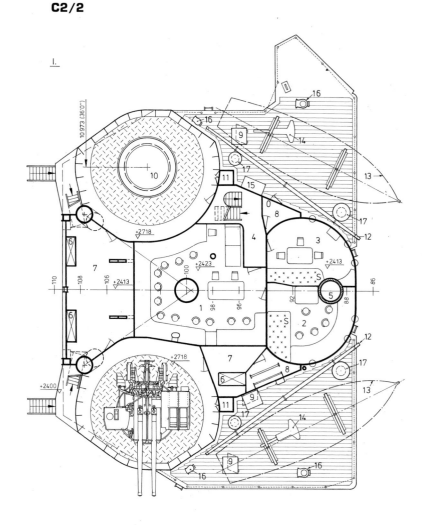

C2/3

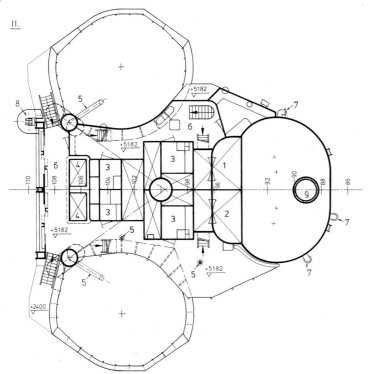

C2/4

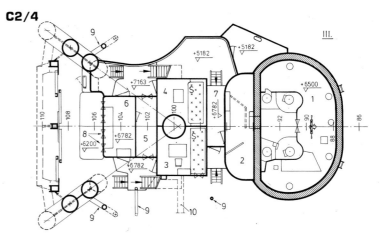

C2/5

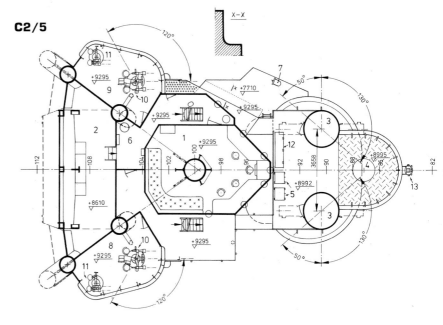

C2/3 Lower bridge deck
(level II)

1 Sea-water tank
2 Freshwater tank
3 Store
4 Ventilator fan
5 Pillar
6 Passage
7 Aerial connecting tube
8 Base of 20m aircraft derrick
9 Communication tube

C2/4 Conning tower platform
(level III)

1 Conning tower
2 Main gun spare command room
3 Commander's standby room
4 Captain's standby room
5 Chart store
6 Chart room
7 Passage
8 Windows on rear wall
9 Pillar
10 Antenna wire connecting tube
   (above position)

C2/5 Upper bridge deck
(level IV)

1 Communication command room
2 Electrical circuit room
3 3.5m rangefinder post (for
   secondary gun)
4 Quadruple 13.2mm MG position
5 13.2mm MG ammunition box
6 Passage
7 Antenna wire connecting tube

8 No 1 starboard secondary gun
  fire commanding room
9 No 2 port secondary gun fire
  commanding room
10 Fuku-ho Hoiban Sojun Sohi
   (secondary gun director)
11 12cm lookout direction panel
12 Wash-deck locker
13 30cm deck lamp

C2/6 Compass bridge (level V)

1 Main compass
2 Gyromagnetic compass
3 Chart table
4 Greeting (750mm x 800mm module)
5 Transmission room
6 Telegraph room
7 Standby room
8 Lookout and direction platform (with compass, 12cm and 8cm binoculars)
9 Cupboard
10 Pillar
11 Ship inner signalling (sound and light)
12 Compass
13 12cm binoculars
14 8cm binoculars

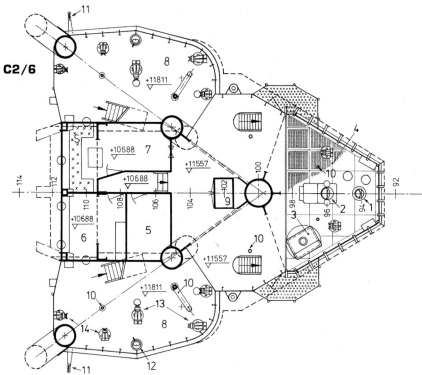

C2/6

C2/7

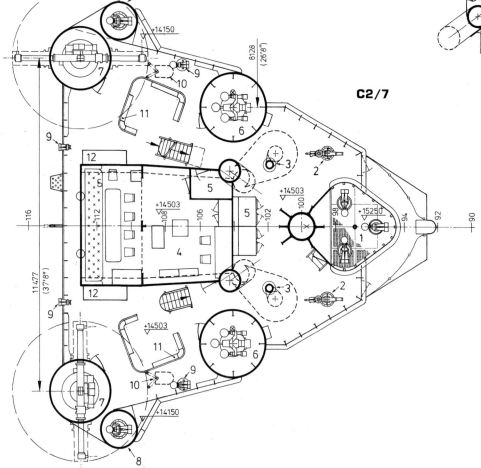

C2/7 Lower lookout platform, anti-aircraft-fire control platform and signalling platform (level VI)

1 Fore lookout cabin with 12cm telescope and two 12cm lookout direction panels
2 7.7mm machine gun (Levis-type)
3 Pillar of 60cm signal searchlight small platform
4 Operation room
5 Store
6 High-angle AA-gun fire director (91 shiki Hoiban Kosha Sochi)
7 4.5m rangefinder HA 91 shiki
8 Protected tower of lookout post
9 8cm binoculars
10 Signalling position (above)
11 Signal flag stand
12 Washdeck locker

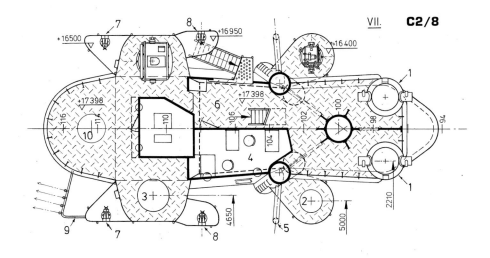

VII. **C2/8**

C2/8 Forward searchlight platform
(level VII)

1 1.5m navigation rangefinder
2 60cm signal searchlight position
3 110cm searchlight position
4 Telephone room
5 Pillar of 3.5 m rangefinder (on level IX)
6 Passage
7 8cm binoculars
8 Vertical deflection measuring stand
9 Antenna wires support
10 Quadruple 13.2mm MG position

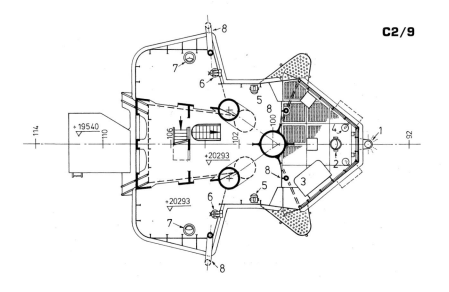

C2/9

C2/9 Battle bridge
(level VIII)

1 Towing light
2 Double magnetic compass
3 Chart table
4 Seat
5 Small signal lamp
6 8cm binoculars
7 Compass
8 Pillar of 3.5m rangefinder (above)

C2/10 Upper lookout platform
for secondary gun
(level IX)

1 Towing light
2 Fuku-ho Hoiban Sojun Sohi
  (secondary gun director)
3 12cm lookout direction panel
4 BU-shiki 3.5m rangefinder for
  secondary gun
5 Wire room
6 Ladder stand
7 Protected tower of lookout post
8 Perforated part of platform deck

C2/11 Lookout and
searchlight control
platform (level X)

1 Searching the self-position room
2 Protected tower of lookout post
3 8cm binoculars
4 Searchlight control panel
5 Awning stanchions and awning
  line
6 2kW daylight signal lantern
7 Small platform for 20m derrick
  topping lift holder
8 Ladder stand
9 Small platform on both sides fitted
  shortly after May 1933

C2/11A Small platform fitted
on both sides of
platform (level X)
shortly after May
1933

C2/10

C2/11

C2/11A

124

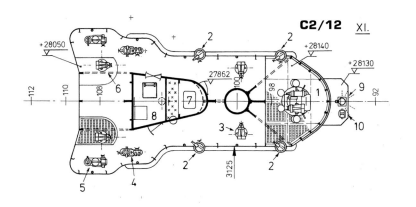

C2/12 XI.

C2/12 Sokuteki Ban platform (level XI)

1 13-Shiki Sokuteki Ban computer for calculation of target course and speed
2 Type-2 direction measurement tabling panel
3 12cm binoculars
4 Target-course-and-speed measurement stand
5 Target tracing stand
6 12cm binoculars
7 Standby room
8 Ladder stand
9 Signal lamp
10 30cm deck lamp

XII. **C2/13**

C2/13 Fire command platform level XII)

1 15cm spotting sight stand
2 Radio equipment box
3 Ladder stand
4 Bar: canvas support

C2/15

XIV.

C2/14 Main gun fire command platform (level XIII)

1 Main gun director tower
2 Ladder stand
3 Small rear platform
4 Dressing line
5 Aerials to rear mast
6 Aerials to bow stays

C2/14

XIII.

C2/16

XV.

C2/15 Main rangefinder platform (level XIV)

1 Goniometer antenna (square form until 1935) – rotary
2 Blink signal light on lighting rod

C2/16 Main rangefinder tower (6m until 1935) (level XV)

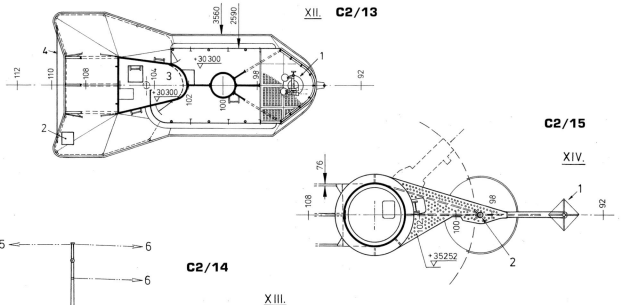

125

C3 Plan of the pagoda tower bridge superstructure, May 1933 (scale 1:150)

C4 Schemes of reinforcing ribs of tower platforms (no scale)

1 Pillars
2 Flat ribs
3 Observation dome of conning tower roof

C4/1 Detail of construction of superstructure platform reinforcement rib

C4/2 Detail of platforms' railing shield

C4/3 Detail of platforms' railing shield with rib

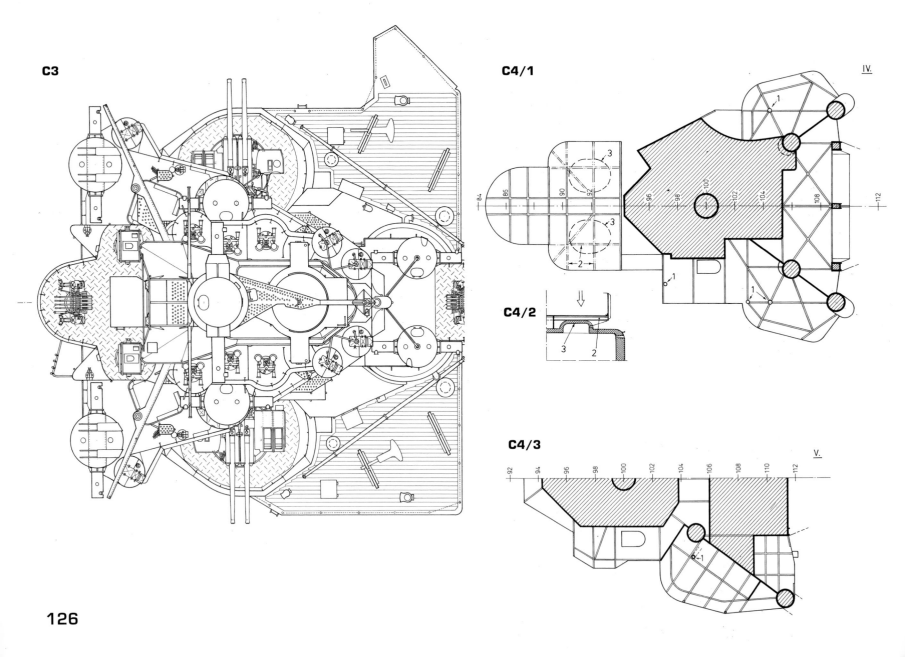

C3

C4/1

C4/2

C4/3

C4/4 Detail of platform opening with lower and upper support
(bar rail) for canvas screen,
fitted on levels IV, IX, X, XI and XII

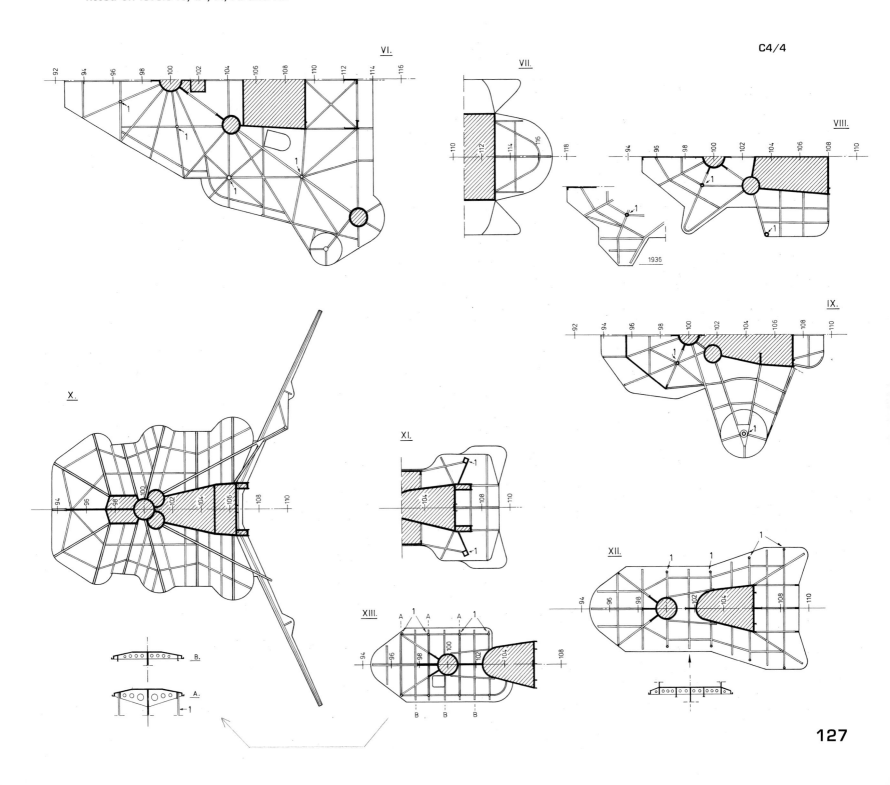

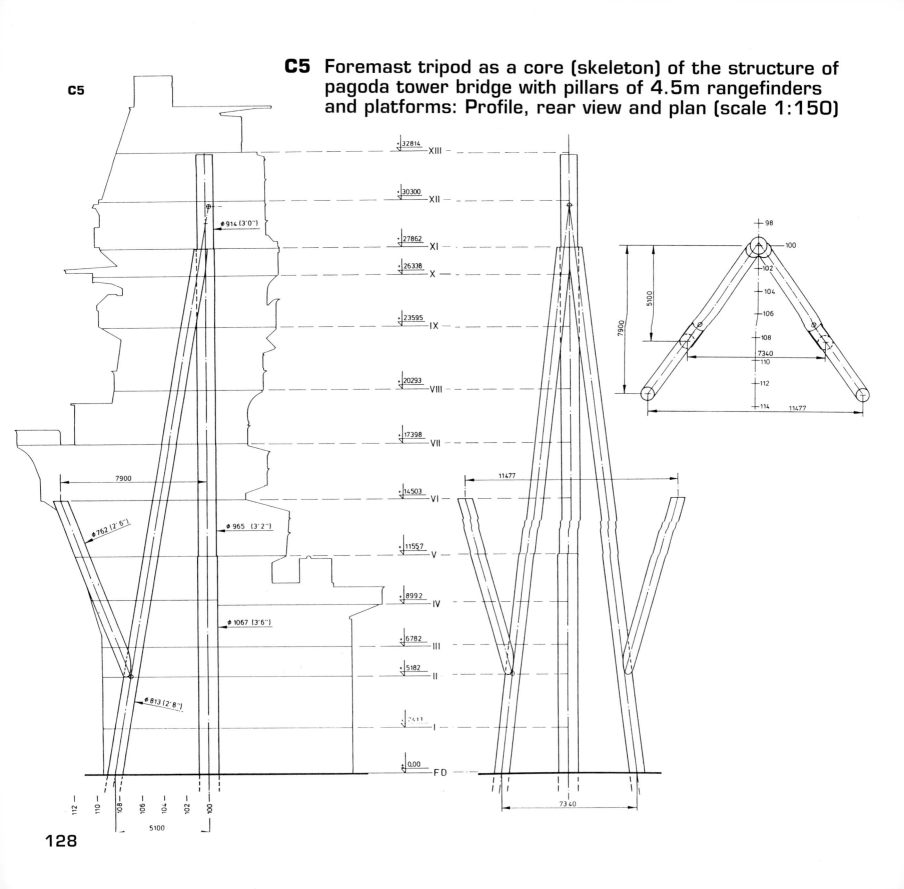

C5

C5 Foremast tripod as a core (skeleton) of the structure of pagoda tower bridge with pillars of 4.5m rangefinders and platforms: Profile, rear view and plan (scale 1:150)

C6 Modernisations of the pagoda tower bridge during second phase of main refit (September 1934 to March 1935)

C6/1 8m main rangefinder, front view

C6/2 8m main rangefinder, plan

C6/3 Profile of the tower top – 8m rangefinder, new circle goniometer antenna etc

C6/4 Rear view of 8m rangefinder tower

C7 Changes of small platforms on both sides of battle bridge (level VIII)

C7/1 Profile

C7/2 Front view

C7/3 Plan

C8 Fitting radio equipment box on rear part of tower (level VII)

C8/1 Profile

C8/2 Plan

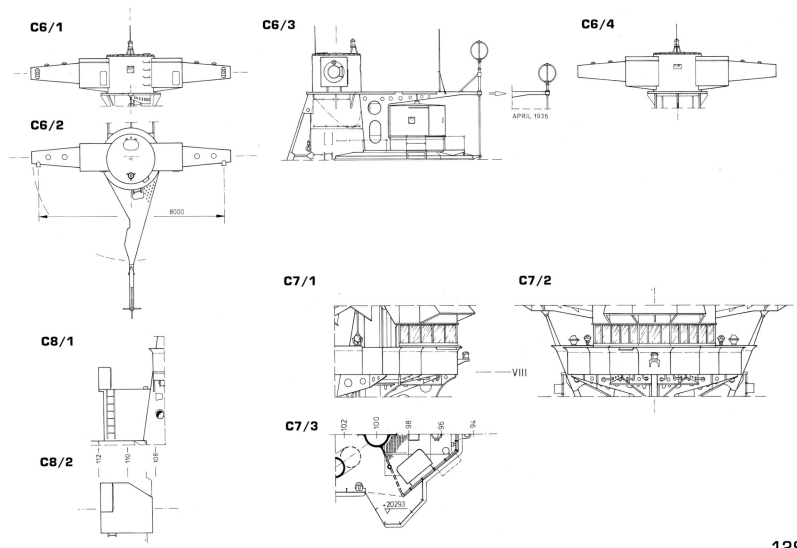

C6/1

C6/2

C6/3

APRIL 1936

C6/4

8000

C7/1

VIII

C7/2

C7/3

102   100   98   96   94

+20293

C8/1

C8/2

112   110   108

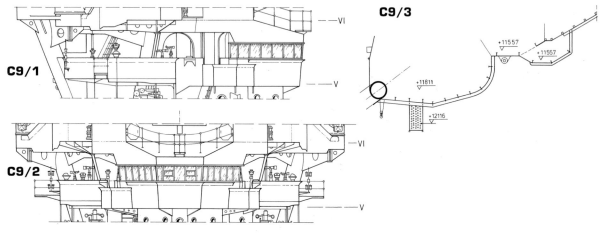

C9/1

C9/2

C9/3

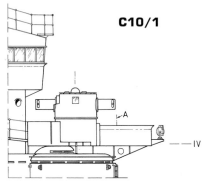

C10/1

C10/2

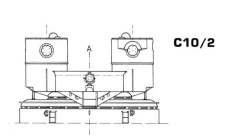

C10/3

C11/2

C11/1

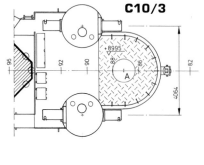

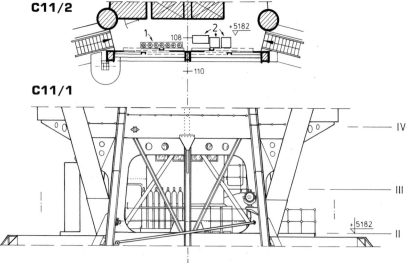

C9 Changes of compass bridge platform (level V)

Small platforms on both sides of platform, with new form, fitting signal platforms (the signal platforms on tripods from signalling platform level VI were removed)

C9/1 Profile
C9/2 Front view
C9/3 Plan

C10 Fitting new type of 3.5m rangefinder tower on platform above conning tower (level IV)

C10/1 Profile
C10/2 Front view
C10/3 Plan A: position of quadruple 13.2mm MG

C11 Fitting of air bottles and equipment boxes on rear part of level II

C11/1 Rear view
C11/2 Plan
   1 Air bottles
   2 Box

C12 Top part of tower bridge with 10m main rangefinder, new mounting of goniometer antenna etc.

C12/1 Profile

C12/2 Front elevation

C12/3 Plan

C12/4 Rear view of 10m rangefinder tower

C12/5 Undersurface of rangefinder arm, black points – ventilation holes

C13 Upper lookout platform (level IX)

Note the replacement of the 3.5m rangefinders with MG fire directors, and the change of support of towing light

C13/1 Profile

C13/2 Front elevation

C13/3 Plan

C13/4 Transverse section

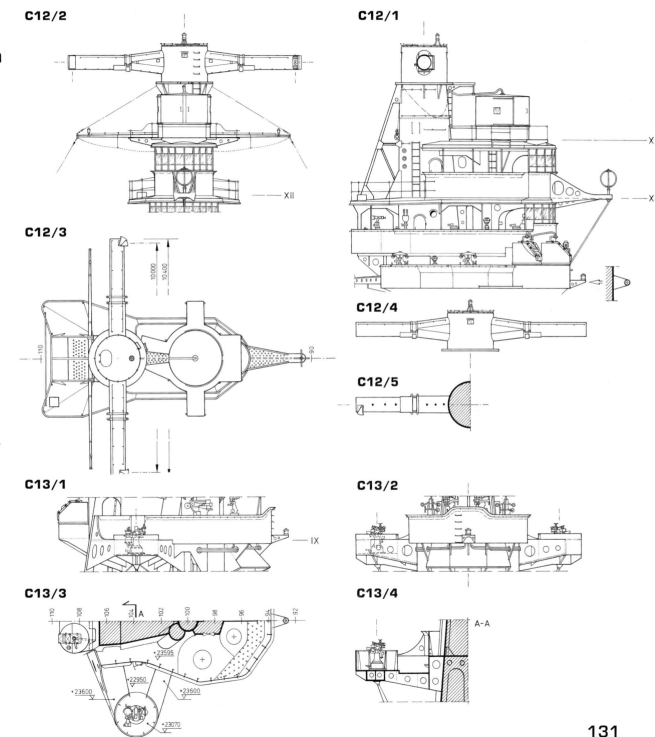

C14 New platform for two twin 25mm MG, fitted on rear part of the tower (level VII) (on sides, two ammunition boxes)

C14/1 Profile

C14/2 Rear elevation

C14/3 Plan

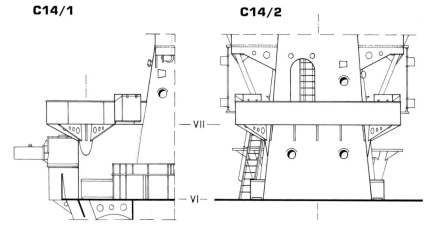

C14/1

C14/2

C15 New bigger platform for two twin 25mm MG mounts, fitted on forward part of the tower bridge (level IV)

C15/1 Profile

C15/2 Front elevation

C15/3 Plan

    1 Position of twin 25mm MG

    2 Ammunition box

Note: Angle view from observation domes on roof of conning tower was limited to ship sides

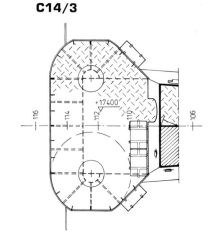

C14/3

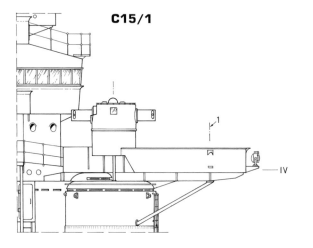

C15/1

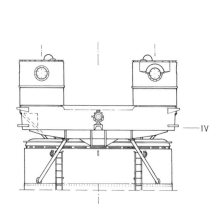

C15/2

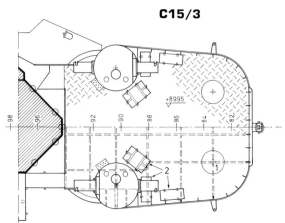

C15/3

C16–21 CHANGES TO PAGODA TOWER BRIDGE DURING SECOND PHASE OF SECOND REFIT, 1940 TO APRIL 1944 (SCALE 1:75)

C16 Top of the tower bridge with new anti-aircraft-defence platform, new main gun fire director tower, new compartment or self-positioning on the back of platform etc

Note removal of two outer towers of protected lookout posts

C16/1 Starboard elevation

C16/2 Front elevation

C16/3 Rear elevation

C16/4 Plan

C17 Level XI (detail)

1 Searching the self-position room (moved from forward part of level X)

2 Yard

3 Antenna support

C18 Detail of level X, plan

C19 Changes on levels V–VII (removal of lookout post towers, new signal stand)

C19/1 Starboard elevation

C19/2 Plan (after removal of lookout tower)

C19/3 New bigger signal stand (view from stern)

C19/4 Plan of signal stand

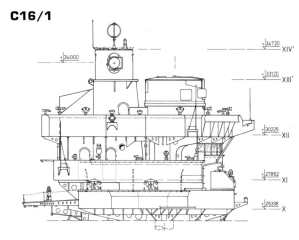

C16/1

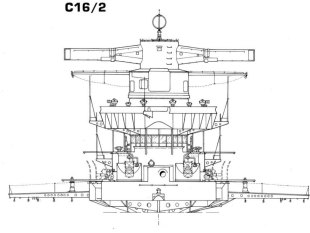

C16/2

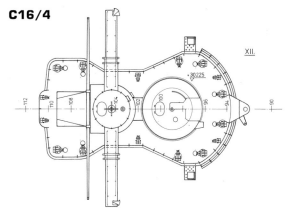

C16/4

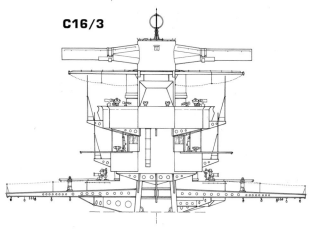

C16/3

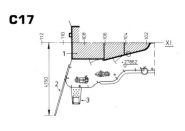

C17

C18

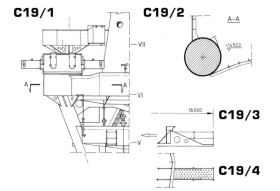

C19/1

C19/2

C19/3

C19/4

C20 Aerials supports on sides of battle bridge platform sides

C20/1 Front view
C20/2 Plan

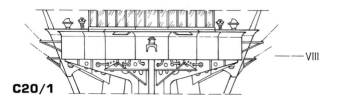

C20/1

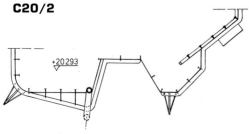

C20/2

+20293

— VIII

C21 Extension of gangway (port side, level IV)

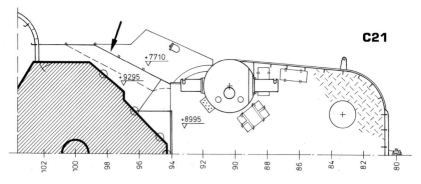

C21

+7710
+9295
+8995

102 100 98 96 94 92 90 88 86 84 82 80

C22 Top of the pagoda tower, August 1944

C22/1 Front elevation
C22/2 Starboard elevation
C22/3 Plan of part of rear
   platform
C22/4 Plan of 10m
   rangefinder with Type-
   21 radar mounting

1 Type-21 radar antenna
   (fitted in July 1943)
2 Type-22 radar antenna
   (fitted in August 1944)
3 Type-21 radar room
4 Searching the self-position
   room

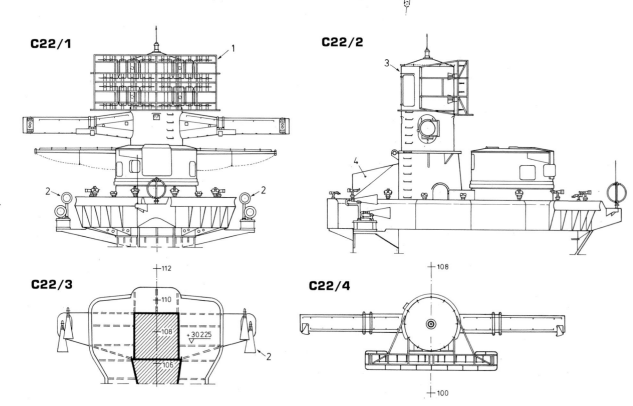

C22/1

1

2   2

C22/2

3

4

C22/3

112
110
108   +30225
106

2

C22/4

108

100

C23 Pagoda tower superstructure after second phase of main modernisation, March 1935 (scale 1:200)

C23/1 Starboard elevation
C23/2 Front elevation
C23/3 Rear elevation

C23/1

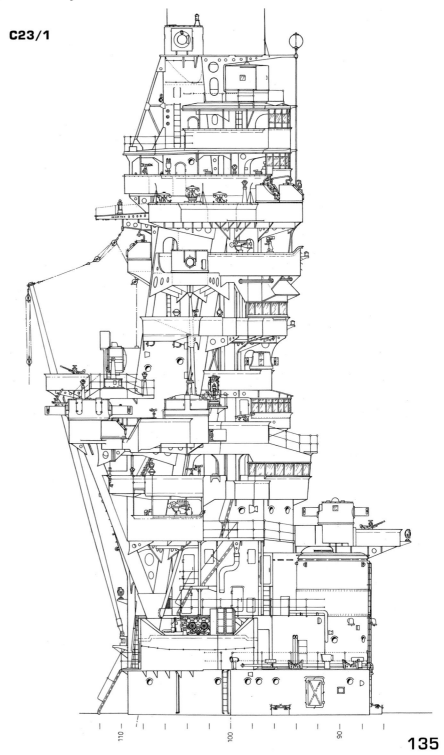

C23/2

C23/3

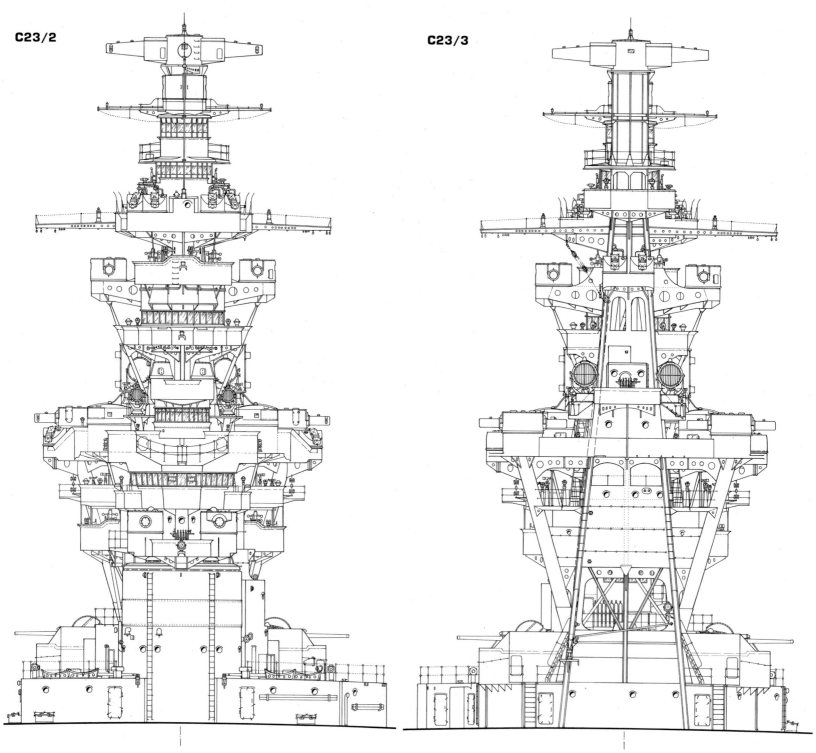

C24 Pagoda tower superstructure after second modernisation, April 1941 (scale 1:200)

C24/1 Starboard elevation

C24/2 Front elevation

C24/3 Rear elevation

C24/1

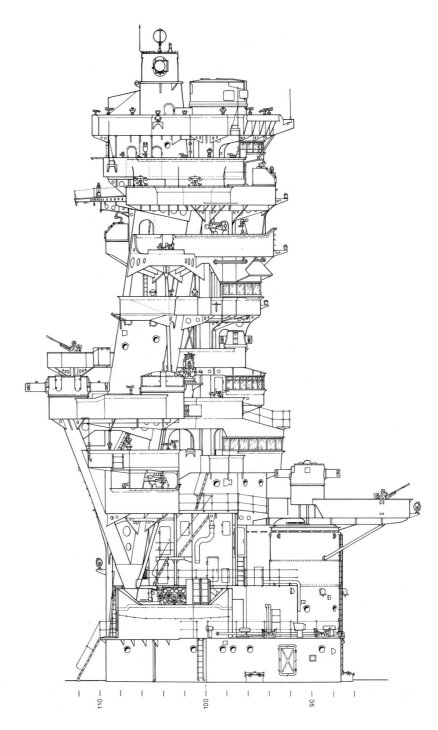

C24/2

C24/3

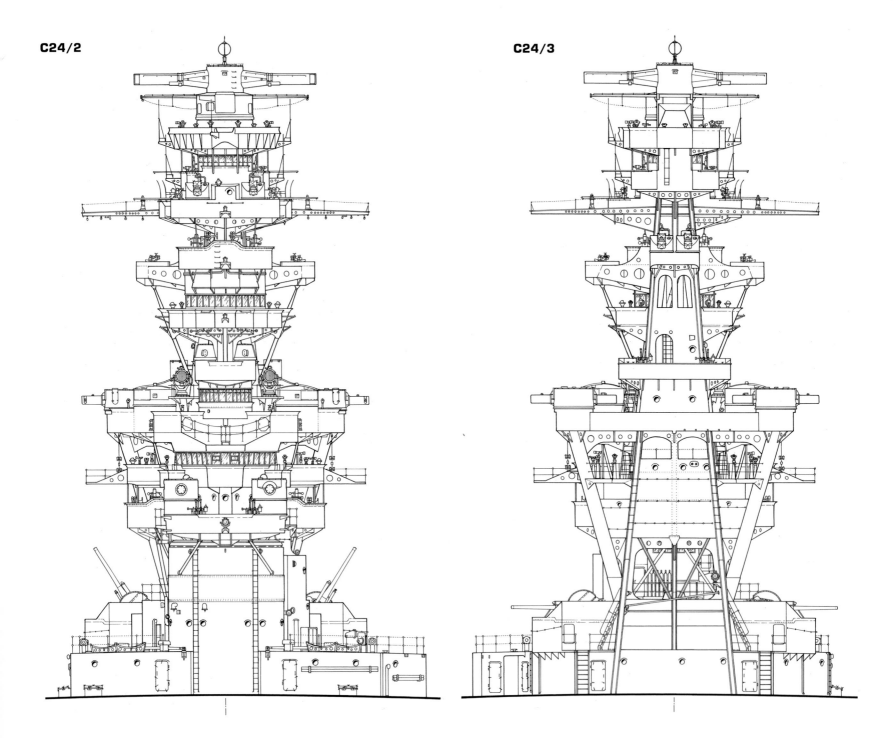

C25 Perspective view of pagoda tower bridge structure, 1934 (no scale)

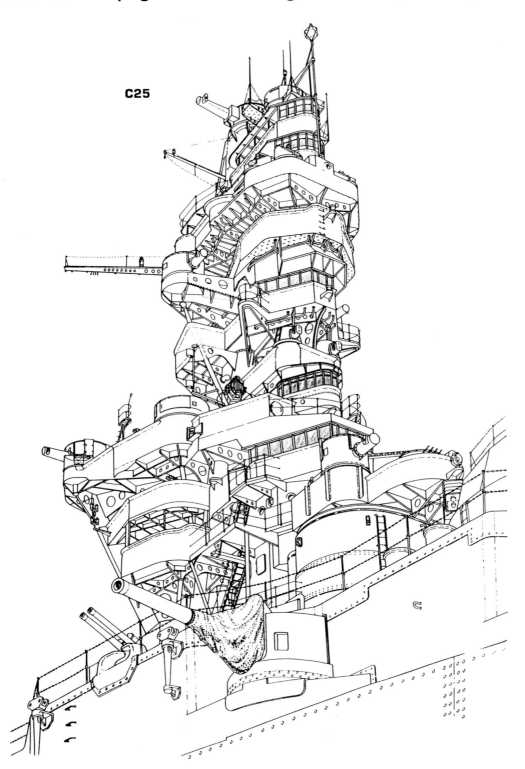

C25

C26 Funnel with midship superstructure after main modernisation, May 1933 (all scales 1:150 except where indicated)

C26/1

C26/2

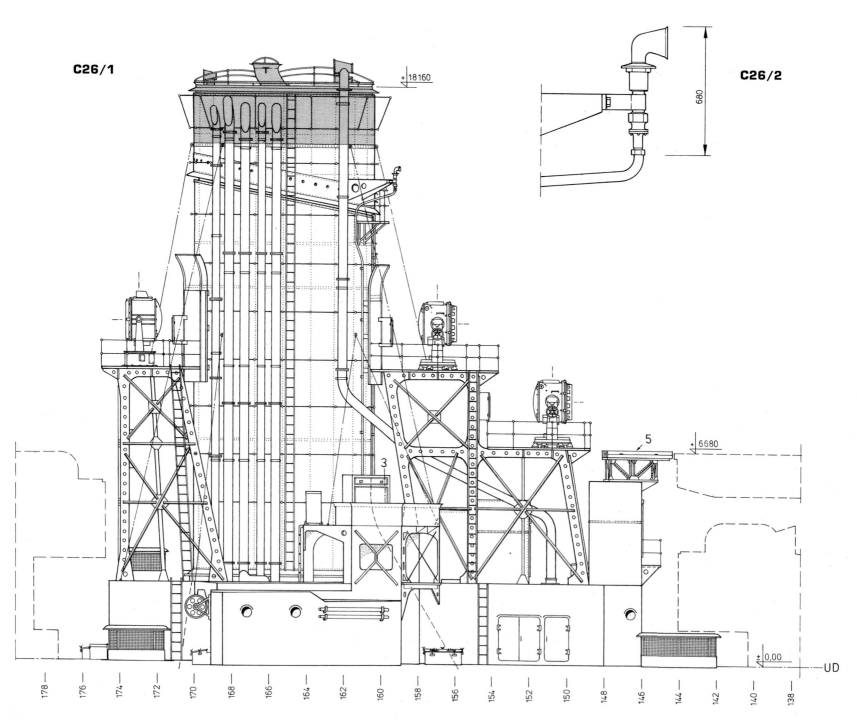

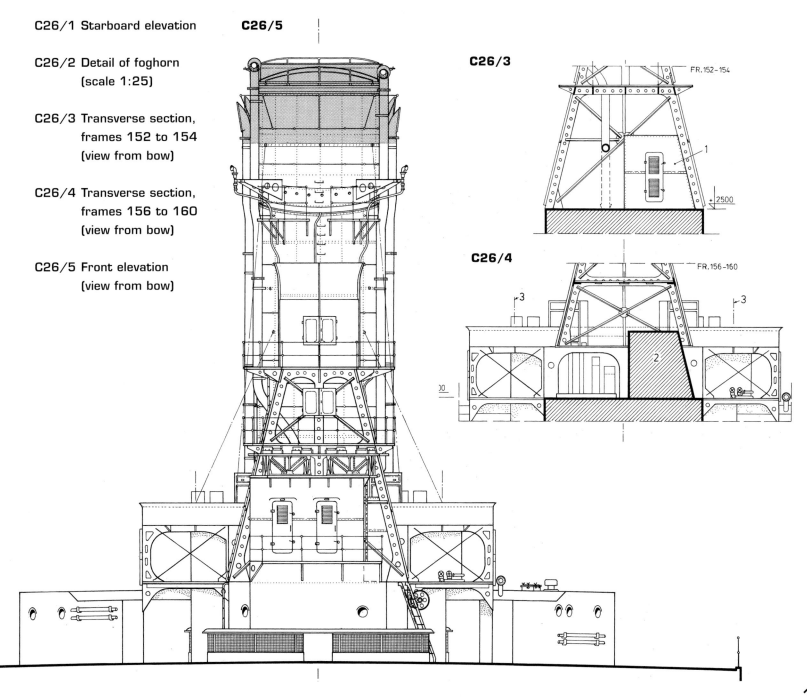

C26/1 Starboard elevation

C26/2 Detail of foghorn
(scale 1:25)

C26/3 Transverse section,
frames 152 to 154
(view from bow)

C26/4 Transverse section,
frames 156 to 160
(view from bow)

C26/5 Front elevation
(view from bow)

C26/5

C26/3

FR.152-154

2500

C26/4

FR.156-160

C26/6 Port side elevation

C26/7 Rear elevation

1 Vegetable store
2 Sea-water tank
3 Position of quadruple 13.2mm
   MG
4 Bamboo storage
5 Catapult cradle stay platform

C26/6

C26/7

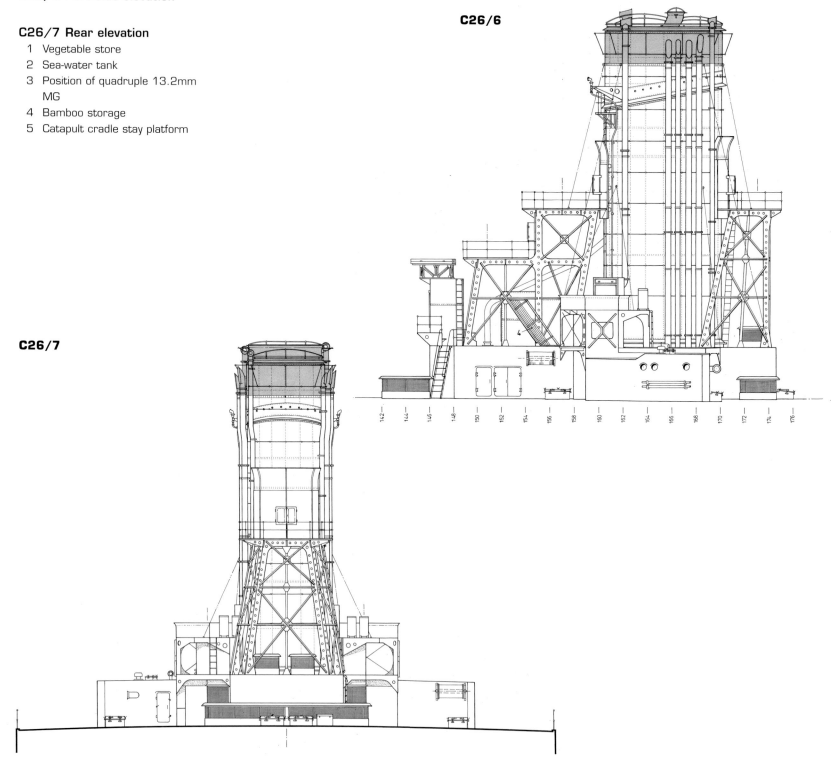

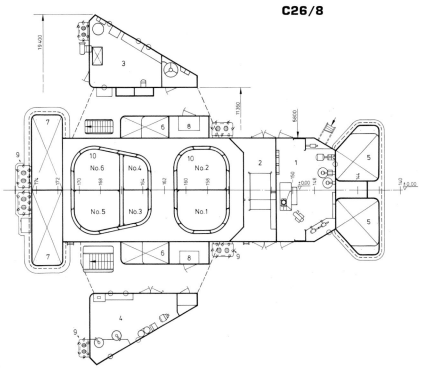

C26/8

C26/8 Plan of forecastle deck level

1 Smith factory
2 Steriliser room
3 Weld factory
4 Casting factory
5 Ventilation fans from No 1 and No 2 boiler rooms
6 Ventilation fans from No 3 and No 4 boiler rooms
7 Ventilation fans from No 5 and No 6 boiler rooms
8 Store
9 Skylight
10 Funnel uptake

C26/9 Plan (level + 2,500)

1 Vegetable store
2 Sea-water tank
3 Store
4 Ventilation fans
5 Hatch
6 Washdeck locker
7 Funnel uptake
8 Rell
9 Steam pipes
10 Smoke pipe (from smith factory)
11 Ventilators
12 Smoke pipe from casting factory

C26/10 Plan (scale 1:150) (without searchlight platform surfaces)

1 Quadruple 13.2mm MG position
2 13.2mm ammunition box
3 Washdeck locker
4 Smoke pipe (from smith factory)
5 Lower structure of catapult cradle platform

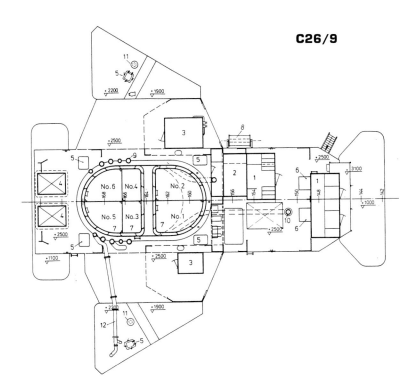

C26/9

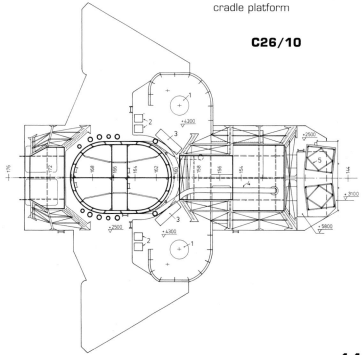

C26/10

C26/11 Plan of 110cm searchlight platforms

1 Small auxiliary crane
2 110cm searchlight post
3 Heat protection (heat resistant steel sheet)
4 Smoke pipe
5 Operating box for searchlights
6 Catapult cradle platform
7 Cradle roller way

C26/12 Plan of upper part of funnel

1 Scupper pipe
2 Steam pipe to foghorn
3 Smoke pipe (from smith factory

C26/13 Horizontal structure of second pair of searchlights

C26/14 Horizontal structure of rear searchlight platform (level + 4,950)

C26/15 Horizontal structure of rear searchlight platform (level + 6,820)

C26/16 Plan of upper part of funnel

1 Foghorn support
2 Gangway
3 Ladder
4 Baffle plates
5 Clamps
6 Casing
7 Uptake
8 Division plate

C26/17 Plan of funnel hood

1 Hood
2 Frame for canvas cover
3 Handrail

C26/18 Longitudinal section of funnel, 1933–44

1 Frame for canvas cover
2 Casing
3 Uptake
4 Division plate
5 Baffle plates
6 Clamp
7 Rain gutter
8 Air space with rain-cover
9 Inner framing
10 Inspection ladder

C26/11

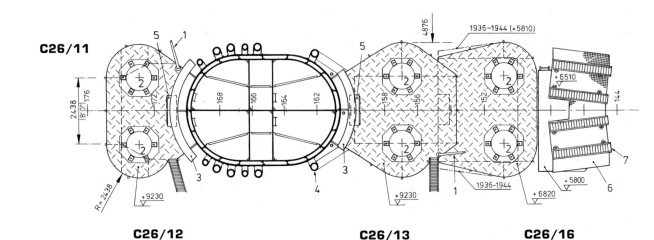

C26/12

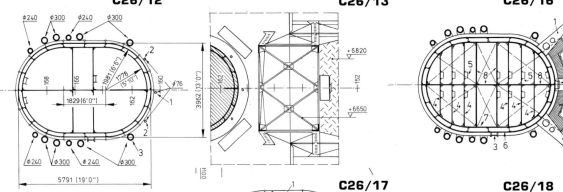

C26/13

C26/16

C26/17

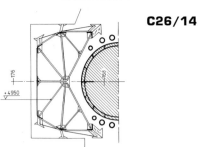

C26/18

C26/14

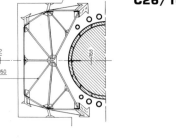

C26/15

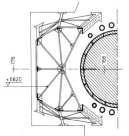

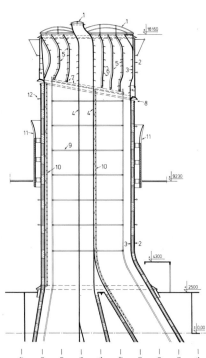

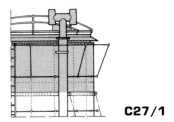

C27/1

C27 Funnel with midship superstructure, March 1935 (scale 1:150)

C27/1 Top of funnel: changing of outlet of smoke pipe

C27/2 Lowering the fore searchlights platform
1 Bamboo storage

C28 Port elevation (detail), April 1938 (scale 1:150)

1 Platform for MG fire director
2 MG fire director position
3 Position of 25mm twin MG mount
4 Fitted heat resistant steel sheet

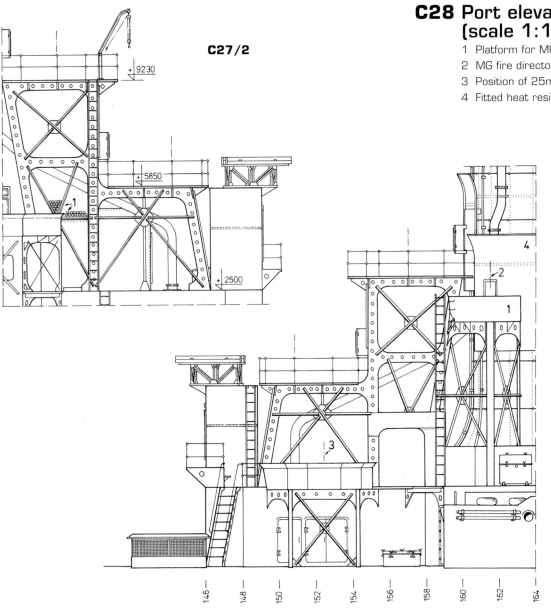

C27/2

C28

C29 Funnel with midship superstructure, April 1941 (scale 1:150)

C29/1 Starboard elevation

C29/2 Front elevation (from bow)

C29/3 Rear view of twin 25mm MG stand on superstructure
1 Twin 25mm MG position
2 MG fire director position
3 110cm searchlight post

C29/4 Plan of funnel structure, April 1941
1 Twin 25mm MG position (fitted 1938)
2 25mm ammunition box
3 Washdeck locker
4 Hatch
5 Platform of MG fire director (fitted 1938)
6 MG fire director
7 Gangway (fitted i 1941
8 Heat protection (fitted 1938)
9 Inner funnel framing (steel pipes)

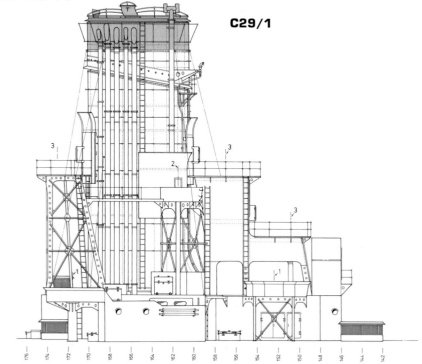

C29/1

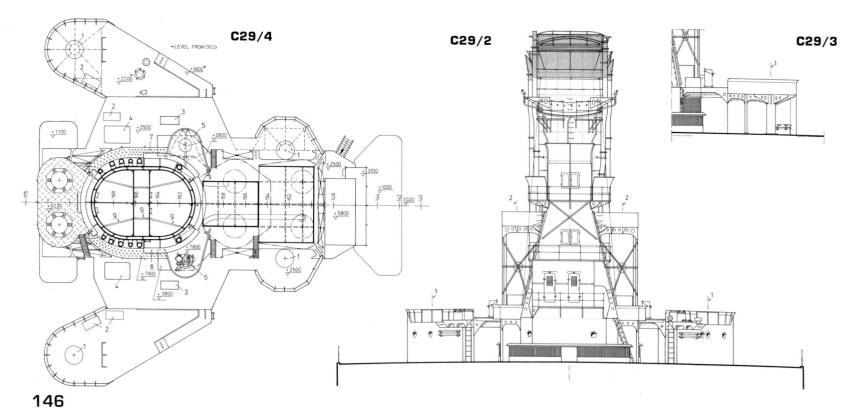

C29/4

C29/2

C29/3

C30 Details of funnel structure, August 1944 (scale 1:150)

C30/1 Funnel with Type-13 radar antennae (profile)

C30/2 Funnel with Type-13 radar antennae (front view)

C30/3 Fore part of superstructure after removing vegetable store

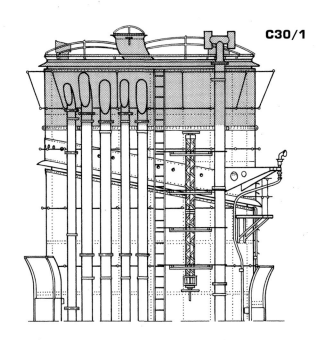

C30/1

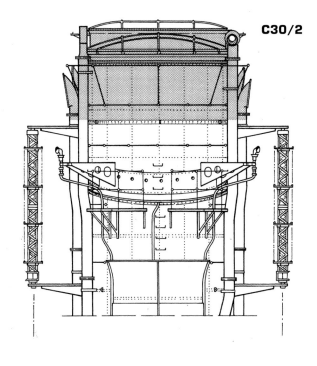

C30/2

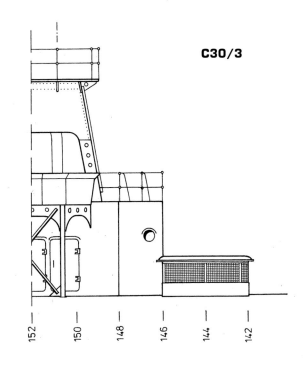

C30/3

C31 Funnel details (scale 1:30)

C31/1 Section of upper fore part

C31/2 Section of 'middle funnel' (for No 3 and No 4 boiler rooms)

C31/3 Detail of air space

C31/4 Detail of heat protection

C31/5 Steam pipe mounting

1   Frame for canvas cover
2   Hood
3   Casing
4   Uptake
5   Baffle plates
6   Clamp
7   Handrail
8   Division plate
9   Air-space cover
10 Ventilation holes
11 Distance bar
12 Air space
13 Rain gutter
14 Steam pipes
15 Heat protection cover
16 Reinforcement rib
17 Thermo-insulation
18 Thin steel plate on thermo-isolation mass

C31/1

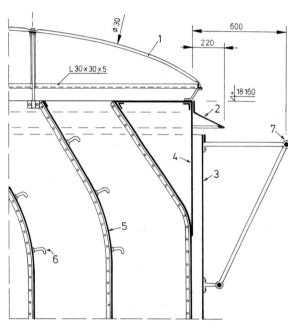

C31/2

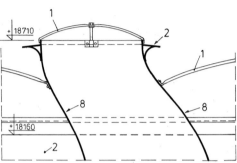

C31/4

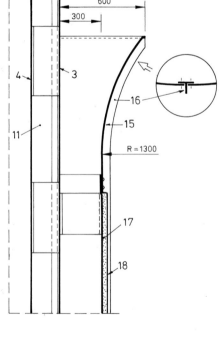

C31/3

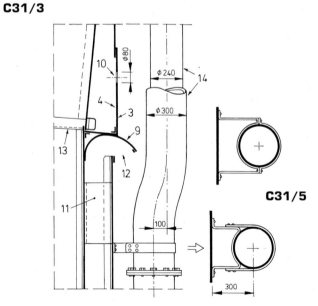

C31/5

148

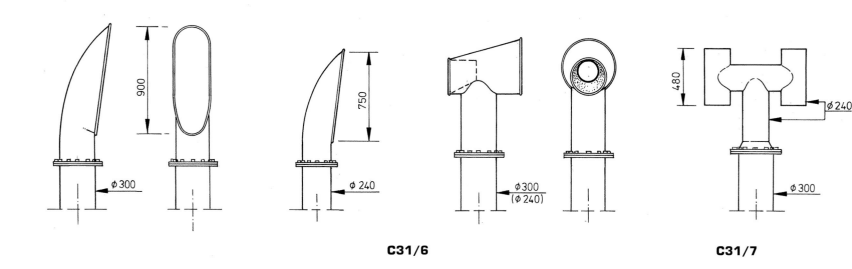

C31/6

C31/7

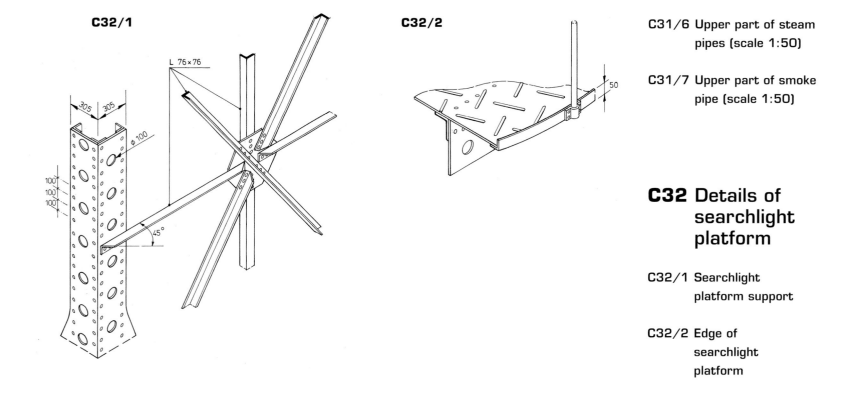

C32/1

C32/2

C31/6 Upper part of steam pipes (scale 1:50)

C31/7 Upper part of smoke pipe (scale 1:50)

C32 Details of searchlight platform

C32/1 Searchlight platform support

C32/2 Edge of searchlight platform

C33 Rear tower superstructure, May 1933 (scale 1:150)

C33/1 Starboard elevation

C33/2 Rear elevation (view from stern)

C33/3 Front elevation (view from bow)

C33/1

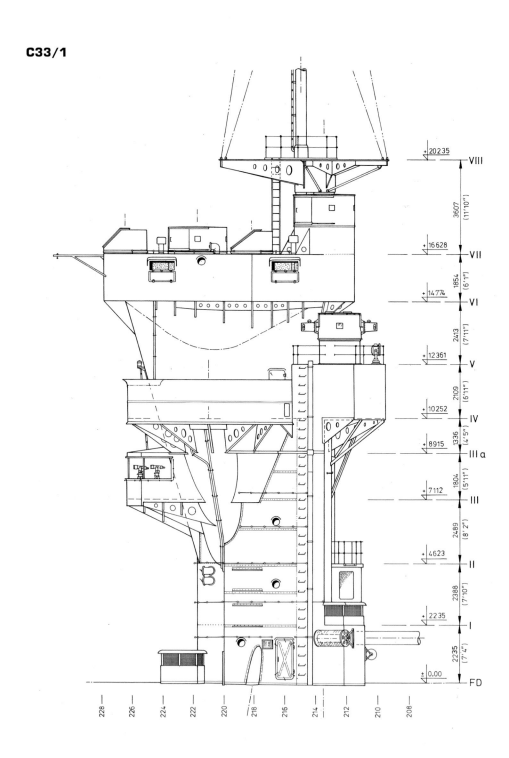

C33/2

C33/3

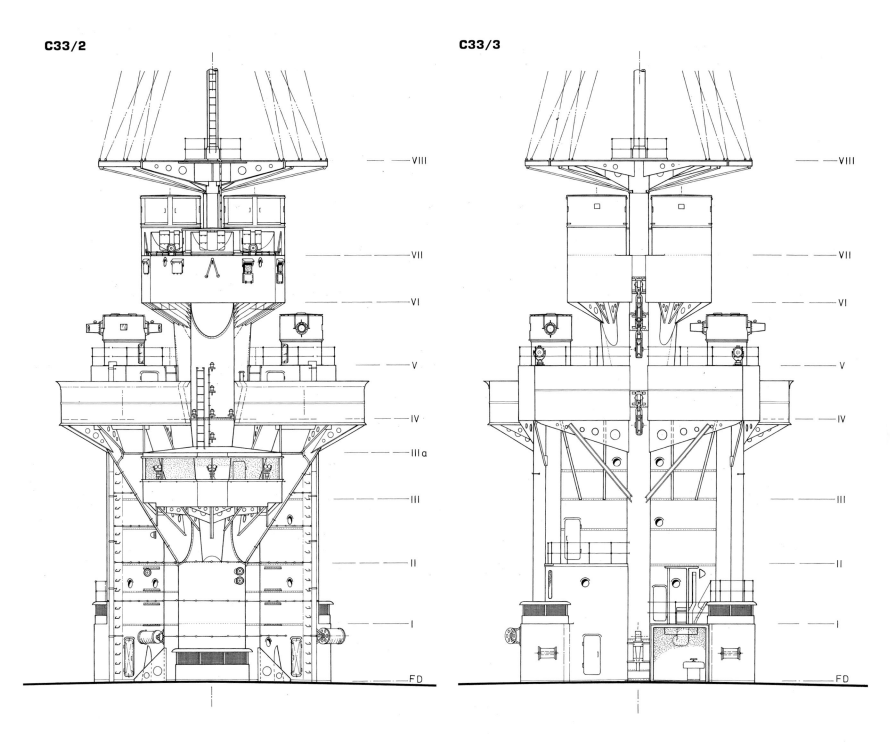

VIII

VII

VI

V

IV

IIIa

III

II

I

FD

C33/4 Plan of rear superstructure (level: forecastle deck)

1 Holes (hatches) for derrick ropes (to motor engine room)
2 Navigation store
3 Column of rear mainmast
4 Antennae connecting tube
5 Deck store
6 Ammunition hoists for 12.7cm HA gun
7 Ventilation fans (from engine room)
8 Mushroom ventilator
9 Pillar
10 Communication tube
11 Passage
12 Clamps
13 Square wire tube

C33/5 After bridge lower deck (level I)

1 20m derrick base support
2 After radio room
3 Communication tube
4 Store
5 Ammunition hoists for 12.7cm HA gun
6 Reels
7 Pillar
8 Antennae connecting tube

C33/6 After conning tower platform (level II)

1 After conning tower
2 Ammunition hoists for 12.7cm HA gun
3 Support (steel bar) of antenna wires
4 Antennae connecting tube

C33/7 After lookout platform (level III)

1 After lookout platform
2 Lookout and direction 12cm binoculars
3 Ammunition hoists for 12.7cm HA gun
4 Support of 12.7cm HA gun mount
5 Pillar

C33/8 Ribbing of lookout platform (level III)

C33/9 Canopy of after lookout platform (level IIIa)

1 Canopy with rain gutter
2 Contour of 12.7cm HA gun deck with ribbing

C33/4

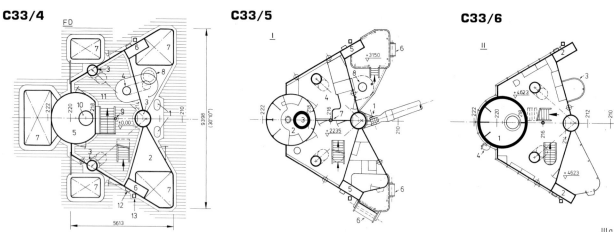

C33/5

C33/6

C33/7

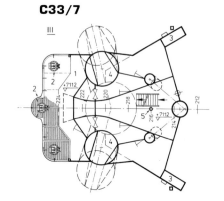

C33/8

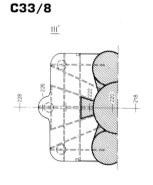

C33/9

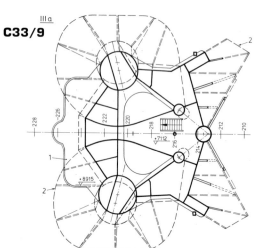

C33/10 Rear 12.7cm high-angle-gun deck (level IV)

1 Twin 12.7cm HA-gun position
2 12.7cm ammunition hoist
3 Wire tube
4 Clamps
5 Escape door

C33/11 2.8m rangefinder for secondary gun post (level V)

1 2.8m rangefinder tower position
2 30cm deck lamp position
3 Wire tube
4 Clamps

C33/12 Roof of level VI with ribbing

1 Contour of wall on level IV
2 Contour of wall on level VI

C33/13 Rear auxiliary control deck for main and secondary gun (level VI)

1 12cm observation panel
2 Main gun fire director (Hoiban Sojun Sochi)
3 12cm lookout direction panel
4 Secondary gun fire director
5 Slit illuminator
6 Mainmast upper column

C33/14 Roof of rear control deck for main and secondary guns (level VII)

1 12cm Observation tower
2 12cm lookout and direction tower
3 Main gun fire director tower
4 Secondary gun fire director tower
5 Hatch
6 Antennae connecting tube
7 Mushroom ventilator
8 Support of derrick block
9 Slit cover
10 Handrail
11 Triangle gird
12 Antennae support

C33/15 Star platform of mainmast (level VIII)

1 Ladder
2 Steel bar
3 Upper mainmast column
4 Hole

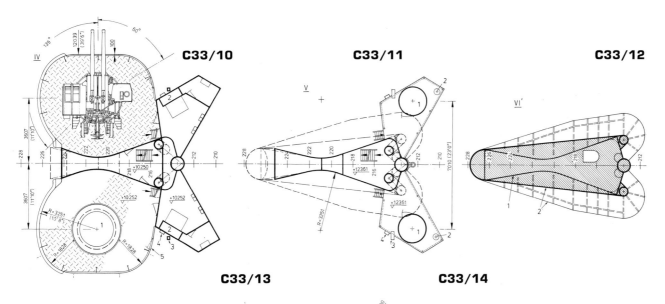

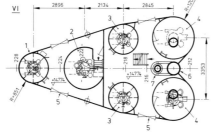

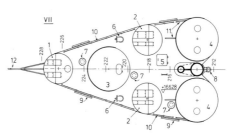

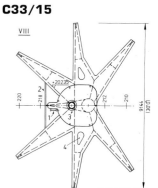

153

C33/16 Profiles of side structure wall in levels (IV–VI)

C33/17 Transverse section of upper part of superstructure with
12.7cm HA gun mounting

C33/18 Axonometric view of after lookout platform (level III)
(no scale)

C33/19 Perspective view of rear part of after superstructure
(no scale)

C33/20 Detail of 12.7cm HA gun platform shield (no scale)

C33/21 Manoeuvring lights (W – white, G – green, R – red)

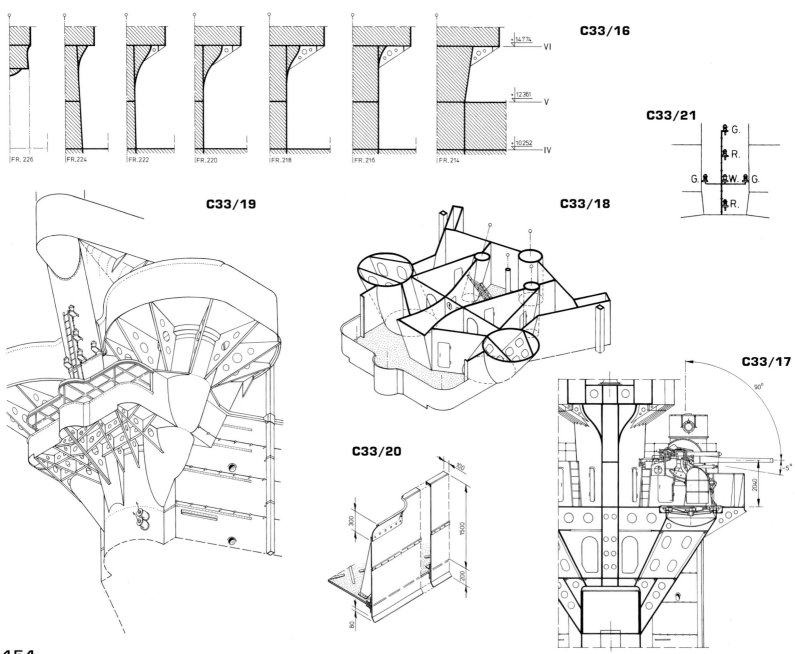

C33/16

C33/21

C33/19

C33/18

C33/20

C33/17

C34 Rear mast tripod as a core of the superstructure (scale 1:150)

C34/1 Port side view of mast tripod and 20 m derrick

C34/2 View on mast tripod from stern direction

C34/3 Plan

C34/4 Plan of derrick edge (1933)

C34/5 Undersurface of derrick edge (1933)

C34/6 Plan of derrick edge after 1935

1 Topping lift
2 Purchase wire
3 20m derrick: working position
4 20m derrick: stay position
5 No 4 36cm turret barbette

C34/7 Profile of Derrick edge after 1935

6 Derrick support
7 All derrick wires attached to derrick in stay position
8 Support of secondary gun director tower

C34/4

C34/5

C34/6

L = 21000

C34/7

C34/3

212
8   8
216
9
218
220
5004
222
2770

C34/1

914
∅ 762 (2'6")   ∅ 406 (1'4")
9
1
2
∅500
20000
3
∅914 (3'0")   ∅610 (2'0")
5
4
6
7
1750
305(1')

VIII
VII
VI
V
IV
IIIa
III
II
I
FD

186 — 188 — 190 — 192 — 194 — 196 — 198 — 200 — 202 — 204 — 206 — 208 — 210 — 212 — 214 — 216 — 218

C34/2

8

155

C35 Upper part of rear superstructure after second phase of main modernisation, March 1935 (scale 1:150)

C35/1 Starboard profile

C35/2 Plan

  1 Voice tube

  2 Antenna support

  3 30cm deck lamp

     Note: heightening of main gun director tower; lowering of secondary gun director towers

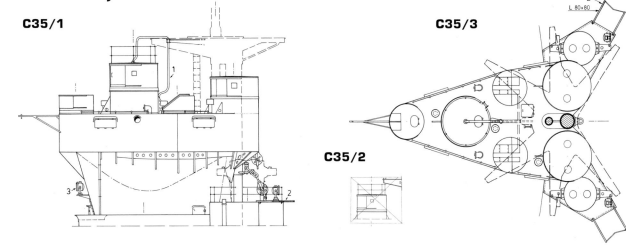

C35/1

C35/3

C35/2

C36 3.5m rangefinder in place of original 2.8m rangefinder, shortly after second phase of main refit in 1935 (these types of turrets were also fitted above conning tower of fore superstructure) (scale 1:150)

C36/1 Astern view

C36/2 Starboard profile

C36/3 Plan

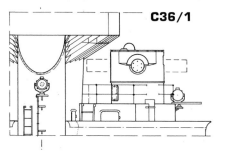

C36/1

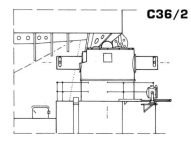

C36/2

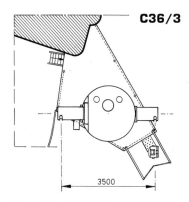

C36/3

3500

C37 New Small periscope tower on roof of main gun director tower, April 1938 (scale 1:150)

C37/1 Starboard profile

C37/2 Plan

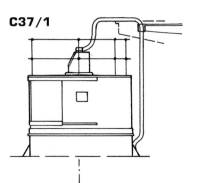

C37/1

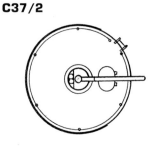

C37/2

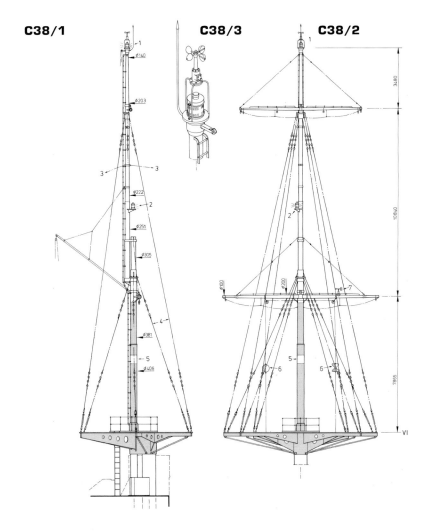

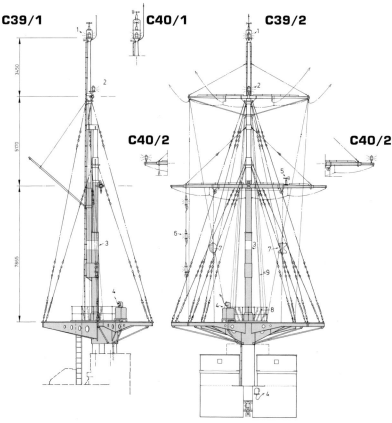

C38 Mainmast on top of rear super-structure, May 1933 (scale 1:150)

C38/1 Starboard profile

C38/2 View from bow

C38/3 Perspective view of mainmast top: masthead light, wind strength transmitter, reel of flag rope, lighting arrester (no scale)

1 Top of mast with masthead light and wind strength transmitter
2 Navigation light
3 Dressing line
4 Topmast stay
5 White stripe
6 Helm signals: green ball to starboard and red cones to port; grey colour indicates part of mast painted black

C39 Mainmast after modernisation, April 1938 (scale 1:150)

C39/1 Starboard profile

C39/2 View from bow

1 Head light with wind strength transmitter and lighting arrester
2 Navigation light
3 White stripe
4 Antenna connecting tube with radio equipment box
5 Wind direction indicator
6 Signal lamp
7 Helm signals
8 Signal flags
9 Wires for signal flags

C40 Details of mainmast changes after April 1941 (scale 1:150)

C40/1 Top of mast: head light, wind strength transmitter, wind direction indicator, and lighting arrester

C40/2 Navigation lights fitted on both edges of yard; grey colour indicates part of mast painted black

D ARMAMENT

D1 '41-shiki' 36cm 45cal main gun turrets: all general views and plans, except details of turret No 1 and No 2 (scale 1:100)

D1/1 Profile elevation

D1/2 Plan

D1/3 Front elevation

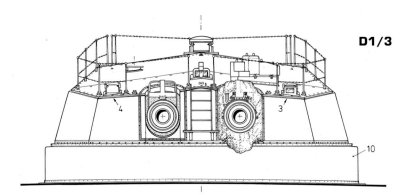

D1/3

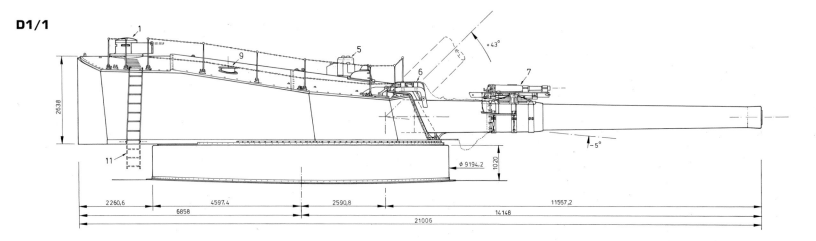

D1/1

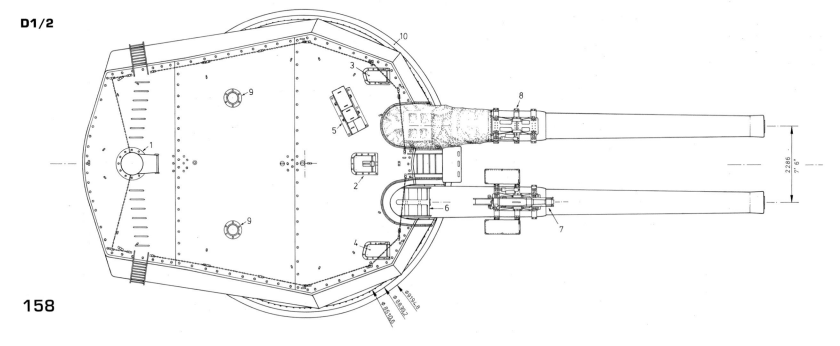

D1/2

D1/4 Rear elevation

1 Turret captain's sighting tower
2 Central sighting hood with support of derrick for moving 8cm exercise guns (fitted temporarily on gun barrels)
3 Left gun-sighting hood (for periscope): open
4 Right gun-sighting hood (for periscope): closed
5 Exercise aiming device (winch for derrick for moving 8cm guns)
6 Upper support for canvas blast cover
7 8cm (7.62cm) exercise gun with two operating platforms
8 Clamping with support of 8cm exercise gun
9 Lower support (base) of rotary turret intake ventilator (fitted sporadically)
10 Barbette (only for No 1 and No 6 turrets)
11 Folding part of turret ladder: right, closed; left, open

D2 Gunhouse of turret No 2 of 36cm main gun (scale 1:100)

D2/1 Profile elevation

D2/2 Plan

D2/3 Front elevation

1 Turret captain's sighting tower
2 8m turret rangefinder (only on turret No 2, without heat protection)
3 Left gun-sighting hood (for periscope)
4 Right gun-sighting hood (for periscope)
5 Position of third sighting hood
6 Rotary intake ventilator
7 Lower support for canvas blast cover
8 Fore platform
9 Handrail of turret ladder

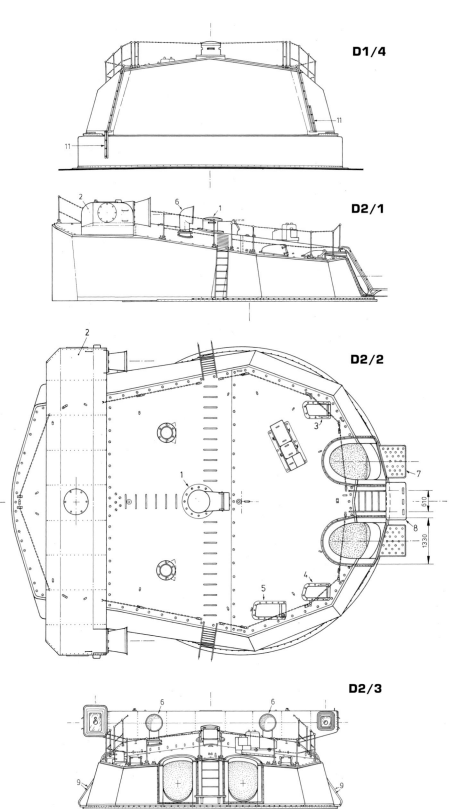

D3 Rear part of gunhouse of turrets No 4 and No 5 (fore part arrangement as on turret No 1 and No 2) (scale 1:100)

D3/1 Profile elevation: 8m rangefinder shield with heat protection (heat resistant sheet lagging)
D3/2 Plan
D3/3 Fore view of 8m turret rangefinder
D3/4 Rear elevation
D3/5 Rangefinder objective lens hood (no scale)
1 Turret captain's periscope
2 Heat shield (heat resistant sheet lagging)

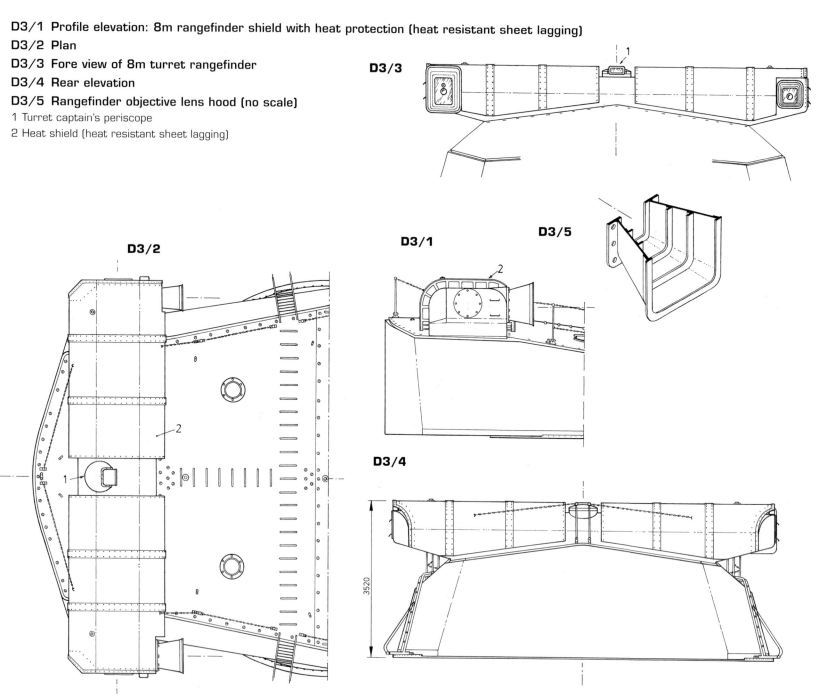

D4 36cm main gun turret No 3 (with 16.53m aircraft catapult type 'Kure Shiki 2 Go 5 Gata'; stay position of barrel +4°)

D4/1 Profile elevation

D4/2 Plan

D4/3 Front view on catapult and catapult support

D4/4 Rear view of upper part of turret with catapult

D4/5 Pillar of catapult support (no scale)

1 Main catapult support
2 Rear catapult support
3 Hatch
4 Lower catapult gangway
5 Upper catapult platform

D5 Catapult cradle platform: left half of platform and support construc- tion (fitted on roof of vegetable magazine compart- ment of midship superstructure)

1 Ship forward direction
2 Roller way for catapult cradle
3 Eyes for cradle fixing

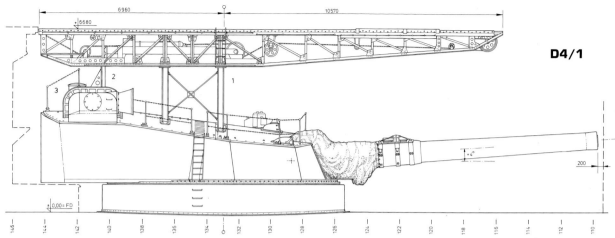

D4/1

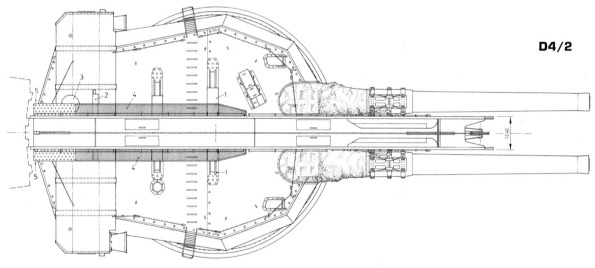

D4/2

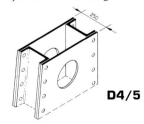

D4/5

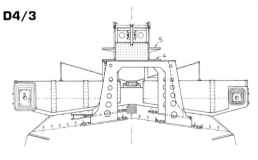

D4/3

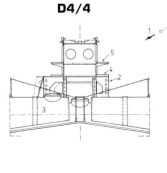

D4/4

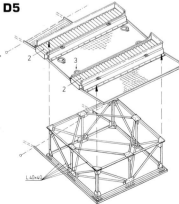

D5

161

D6 36cm turret gunhouse armour, after 1933

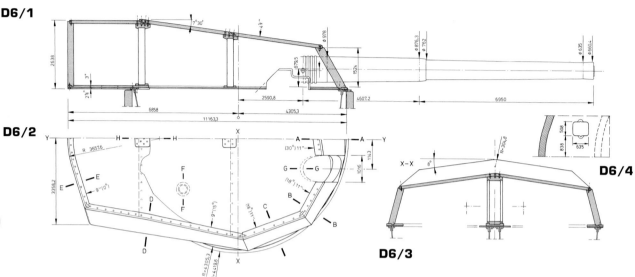

D6/1

D6/2

D6/4

D6/3

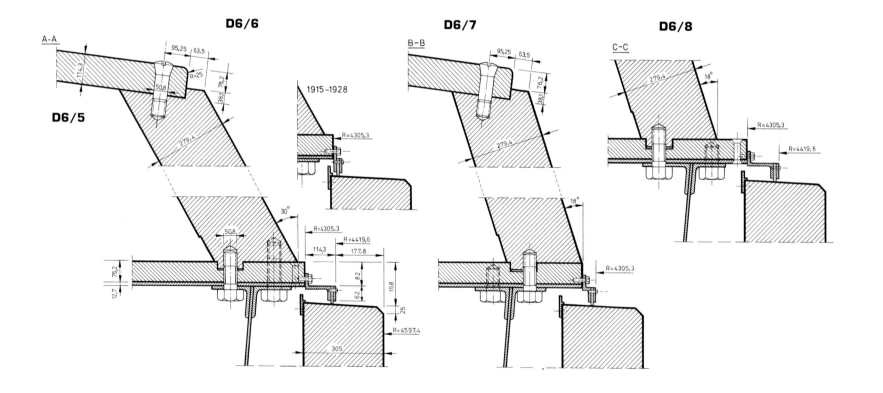

D6/6

D6/7

D6/8

A-A

B-B

C-C

1915–1928

D6/5

D6/9 Section D-D, rear side
(scale 1:12.5)

D6/10 Section E-E, rear part
(scale 1:12.5)

D6/11 Section F-F: hole of roof for intake
ventilator, in battle condition
covered by 114.3mm thick disc
armour (scale 1:25)

D6/12 Barrel hole of roof with canvas
blast cover support (scale 1:25)

D6/13 Central support of gunhouse roof
(scale 1:12.5)

D6/14 Joining wedge of side armour walls
(scale 1:12.5)

D6/15 Screw of gunhouse roof mounting
(scale 1:6.25)

D7 Armour block of (lower)
barrel opening part of right
gunhouse (scale 1:25)

D7/1 Forward view

D7/2 Plan

D7/3 Profile view

D8 Details of 36cm gun
barrel muzzle

D8/1 Profile section (scale 1:25)

D8/2 Front view (scale 1:25)

D8/3 Detail of barrel rifling (scale 1:1)

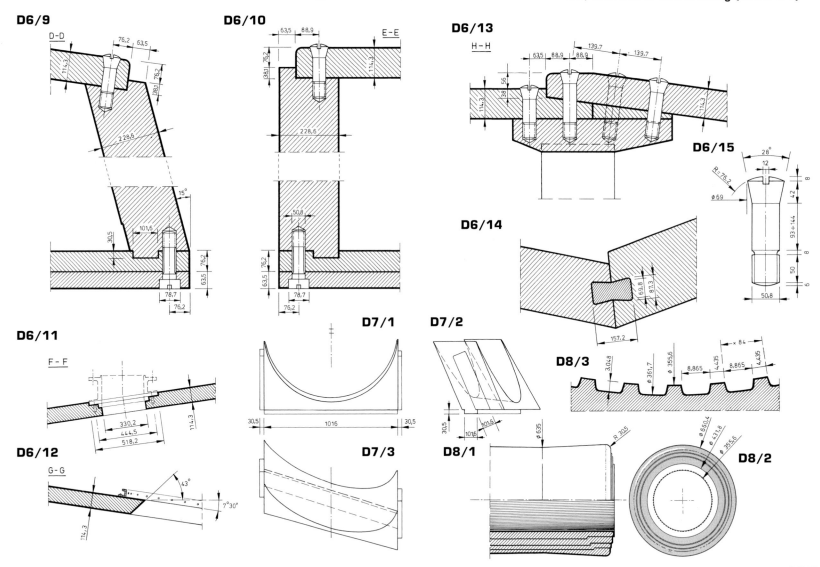

163

D9 '41-shiki' (type-41) 36cm gun mounting of turret No 1, after 1933: internal section (scheme) (scale 1:100)

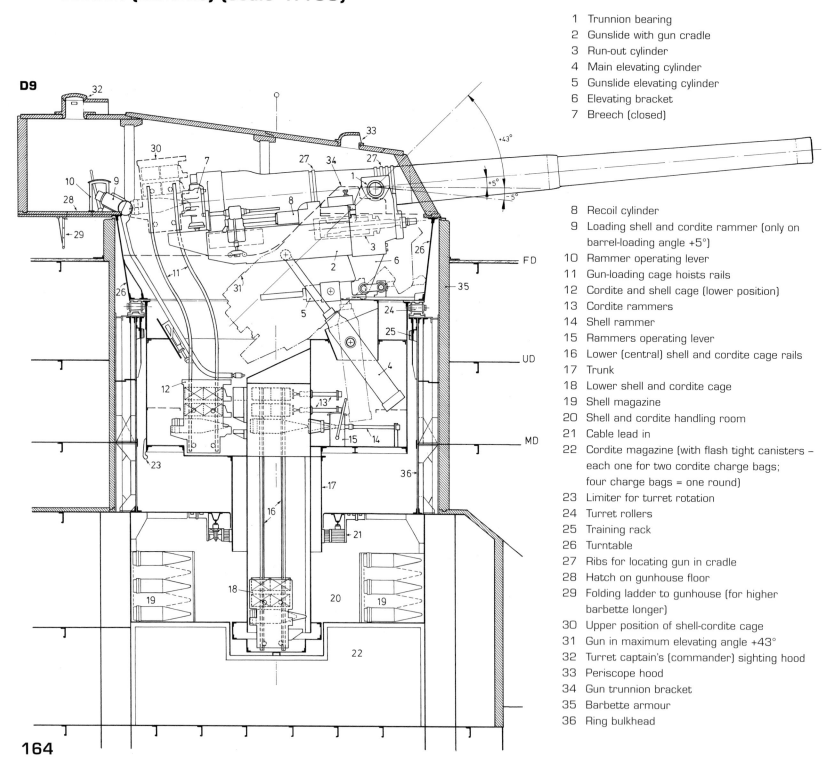

D9

1 Trunnion bearing
2 Gunslide with gun cradle
3 Run-out cylinder
4 Main elevating cylinder
5 Gunslide elevating cylinder
6 Elevating bracket
7 Breech (closed)

8 Recoil cylinder
9 Loading shell and cordite rammer (only on barrel-loading angle +5°)
10 Rammer operating lever
11 Gun-loading cage hoists rails
12 Cordite and shell cage (lower position)
13 Cordite rammers
14 Shell rammer
15 Rammers operating lever
16 Lower (central) shell and cordite cage rails
17 Trunk
18 Lower shell and cordite cage
19 Shell magazine
20 Shell and cordite handling room
21 Cable lead in
22 Cordite magazine (with flash tight canisters – each one for two cordite charge bags; four charge bags = one round)
23 Limiter for turret rotation
24 Turret rollers
25 Training rack
26 Turntable
27 Ribs for locating gun in cradle
28 Hatch on gunhouse floor
29 Folding ladder to gunhouse (for higher barbette longer)
30 Upper position of shell-cordite cage
31 Gun in maximum elevating angle +43°
32 Turret captain's (commander) sighting hood
33 Periscope hood
34 Gun trunnion bracket
35 Barbette armour
36 Ring bulkhead

D10 Detail of canvas blast cover frame (no scale)

D11 8cm exercise gun support on 36cm gun barrel in 1917–30 (scale 1:50)

D11/1 Profile view (right barrel)

D11/2 Plan of testing instruments table

D11/3 Front view of instrument-testing table (right barrel)

 1 Exercise gun support
 2 Clamping rings
 3 Holders for operating platform
 4 Instrument-testing table

D12 8cm (7.62cm = 3in) exercise gun mounting, after 1933 (scale 1:25)

Gun with operating platforms was mounted only for time of firing exercises. It was fitted and refitted with a folding crane mounted on the roof of the gunhouse and moved with exercise aiming device (winch). The gun support on clamping rings was not removed.

D12/1 Profile of right mounting

D12/2 Fore view of right mounting

D12/3 Rear view of 8cm gun breech mechanism

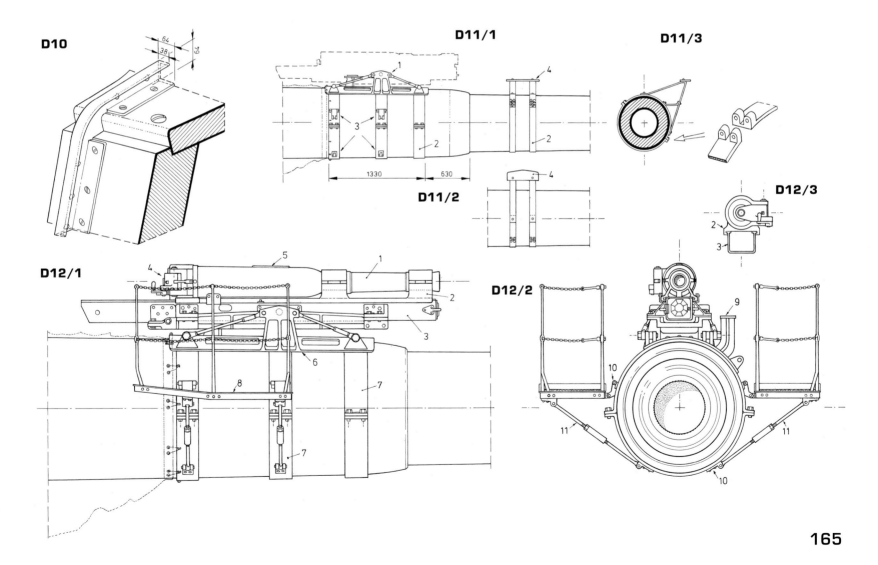

D12/4 Plan of right mounting

D12/5 View from gun turret axis (detail, from inner side)

D12/6 Eyes on ring (inner side only, no scale)

D12/7 Upper holder of operating platform (no scale)

D12/8 Exercise gun support in normal ship service
　　　(not exercise time); right, 36cm barrel

D12/9 Plan of gun support
  1 Gun barrel
  2 Gun cradle
  3 Gun slide
  4 Breech mechanism
  5 Measuring surface
  6 Gun support
  7 Clamping rings
  8 Operating platforms
  9 Instrument-testing table (on inner side of 36cm barrels)
 10 Holders
 11 Platform fixing support: thimble

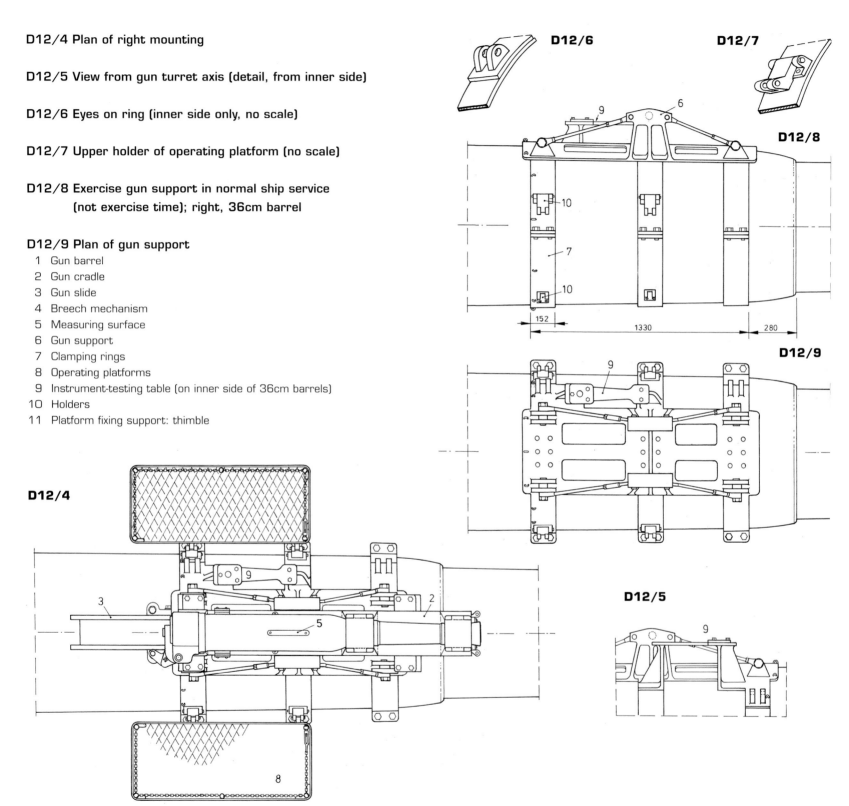

D12/6

D12/7

D12/8

D12/9

D12/4

D12/5

D13 Awning stanchions on 36cm guns gunhouse roof (scale 1:100)

D13/1 Profile of turrets No 1 and No 6

D13/2 Plan of turrets No 1 and No 6

D13/3 Front view of turrets No 1 and No 6

D13/4 Profile view of turrets No 2 to No 5

D13/5 Plan of turrets No 2 to No 5

D13/6 Fore view of turrets No 2 to No 5

1 Side awning stanchions
2 Centre awning stanchions
3 Awning ropes
4 Rear awning stanchion of turret No 2
5 Awning stanchion of turrets No 3, No 4 and No 5

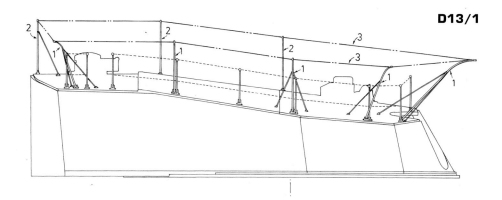

D13/1

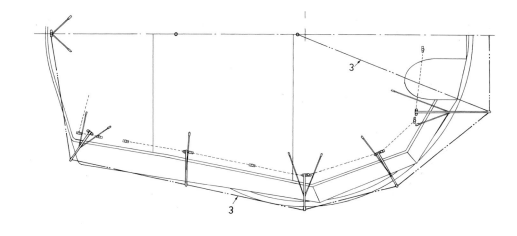

D13/2

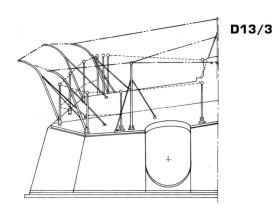

D13/3

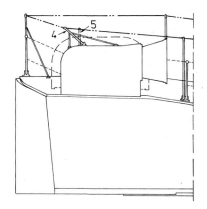

D13/4

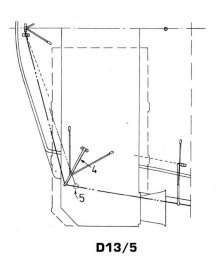

D13/5

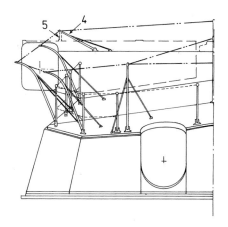

D13/6

D14 Perspective view of No 2 36cm main gun turret, in 1935 (no scale)

For clear view the canvas blast cover of right gun was omitted.

D15 Rear view of heat-resistant protection of steel-sheet lagging (solar heat radiation) on No 3, No 4 and No 5 turrets' rangefinders (no scale)

D16 Main gun turrets barbettes height above deck surface (wood planking, scale 1:600)

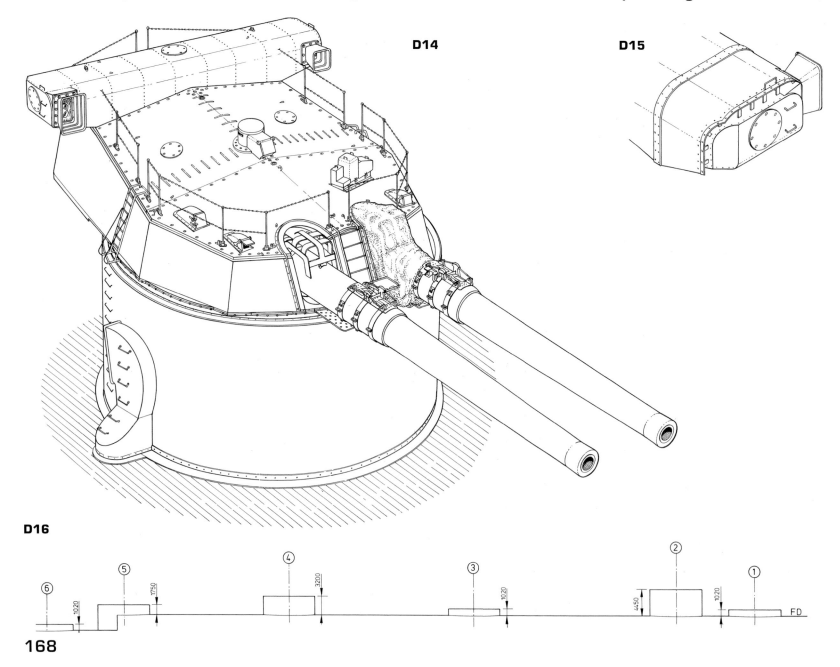

D14

D15

D16

D17 36cm ammunition

D17/1 356mm (14in) '3-shiki' 'Sankaidan' anti-aircraft projectile (section, scale 1:12.5)

No of fragments 672 (480 rubber thermite and 192 stays); weight 625kg

1. Time fuse
2. Projectile head
3. Speed fuse rod
4. Filler lining
5. Projectile head set screw
6. Rotating attachment rivet
7. Incendiary fragment rubber thermite
8. Quick match on fuse plate
9. Shell body
10. Base block
11. Ejecting charge and black powder
12. Copper rotating bands
13. Adaptor (wood)
14. Delayed action charge

D17/2 Transverse sections of projectile '3-shiki' 'Sankaidan' cluster braces (scale 1:12.5)

1. Rotating attachment rivet
2. Rotating attachment notch
3. Shell case
4. Stay – grey circle – 192 fragments
5. Rubber thermite (incendiary fragments) – white circle – 480 fragments

D17/3 Incendiary fragment – rubber thermite (scale 1:2)

1. Steel pipe
2. Incendiary composition
3. Hole

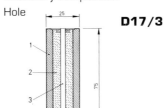

D17/3

D17/4 '91-shiki 'Hibo Tetsukodan' 356mm (14in) AP (armour piercing) shell (section, scale 1:12.5)

Weight 673.5 kg

1. Hood (special wind/water shield)
2. Cap head
3. Cap
4. Body
5. Wool wrap around filler
6. Tri-nitro-anisol filler
7. Type-13 Mark 5 short delay base fuse
8. Copper rotating bands
9. Base
10. Fuse adaptor
11. Copper gas-check rings

D17/5 Type-13 Mark 5 short delay base fuse (profile, scale 1:2)

Weight 1,289g; delay time 0.4 seconds

D17/6 Type-13 Mark 5 short delay base fuse (section, scale 1:1)

1. Body
2. Gaine – shimose 21g
3. Auxiliary booster (1g tetryl)
4. No 2 primer
5. Delay train
6. Delay filling plug
7. No 1 primer
8. Primer holder
9. Copper cup
10. Interlocking arming delay pawls
11. Interlocking pawl pin
12. Interlocking pawl seat ring
13. Striker
14. Ignition chamber
15. Setback pin
16. Setback pin spring
17. Plug
18. Detent
19. Striker seat ring
20. Set plug
21. Base plug
22. Base plug stop screw

D17/1

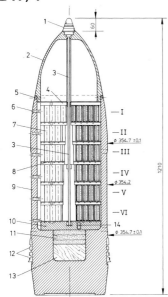

D17/2

D17/5

D17/6

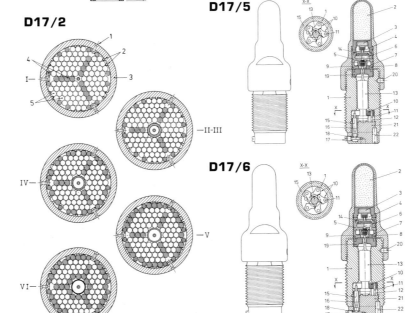

D17/4

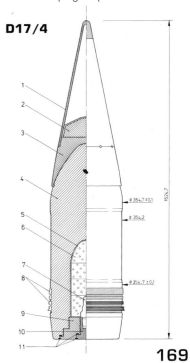

D18 '41-shiki' 15cm (6in) 50-calibre secondary gun in casemate mounting, after 1933

D18/1 Side elevation of gun
casemate turret No 3
(starboard second
pair) (scale 1:50)

D18/2 Plan of No 3 turret
(Scale 1:50)

D18/5 Plan (inner view) of
turret casemates No 5
to No 12 (scale 1:50)

1 Maximum elevation
2 Maximum depression
3 Working recoil

D18/6 Principles of deck (FD)
edge form for guns No
1–No 4 and No 13–No
16 (scale 1:100)

D18/7 Principles of deck (FD)
edge form for guns No
5 to No 12
(scale 1:100)

1 Deck (forecastle deck) edge
2 Axis parallel to ship axis

D18/8 152mm HE type
projectile (section,
scale 1:6.25)

1 Body
2 Wool wrap around filler
3 Tri-nitro-anisol filler
4 Short delay base fuse
5 Adaptor (wood)
6 Copper rotating bands
7 Base
8 Fuse adaptor
9 Fuse gas-check rings

D18/3 Side elevation of gun
turret No 5 to No 12
(scale 1:50)

D18/4 Section of turret
(scale 1:50)

D18/3

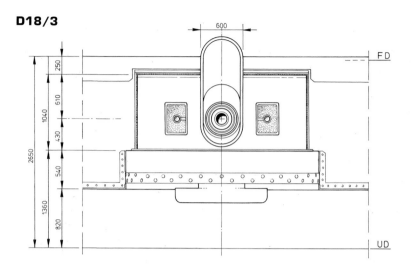

D18/1

D18/2

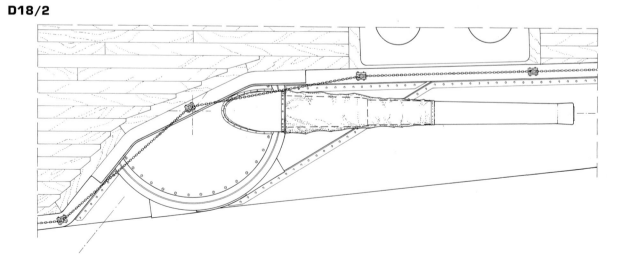

170

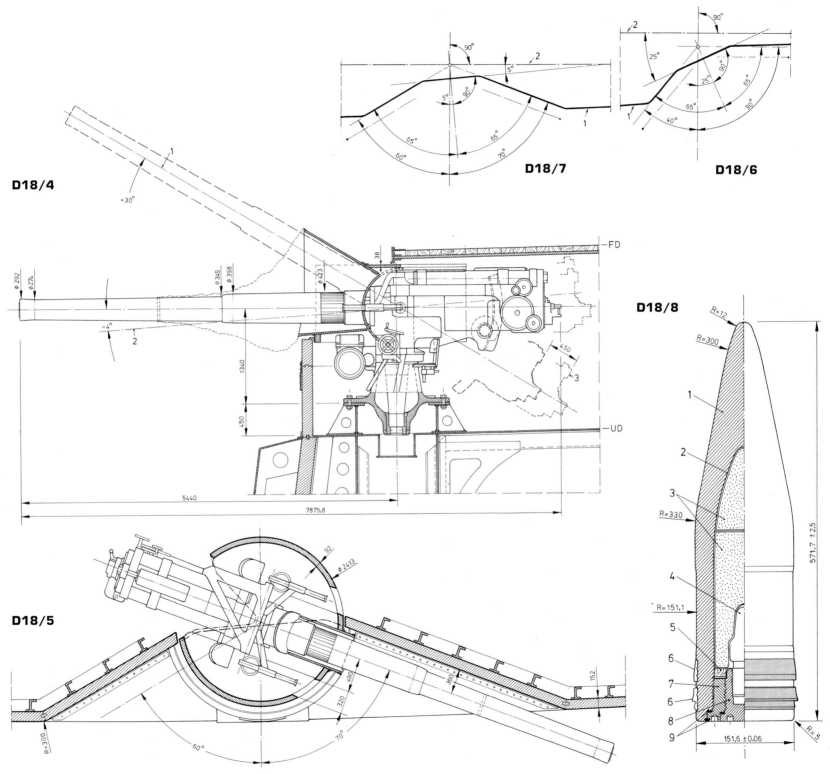

D18/4

D18/7

D18/6

D18/8

D18/5

D18/9 Elevation of 15cm
secondary gun
casemate, 1915–30
(scale 1:25)

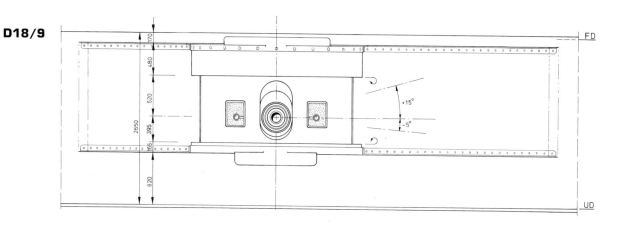

D18/9

D19 Type-89 12.7cm 40-calibre anti-aircraft gun, twin turret Model A-1 (scale 1:50)

Gun fitted during main modernisation,
1930–33

D19/1 Right profile
D19/2 Front elevation with
section of base and
rollers
D19/3 Plan
D19/4 Rear elevation

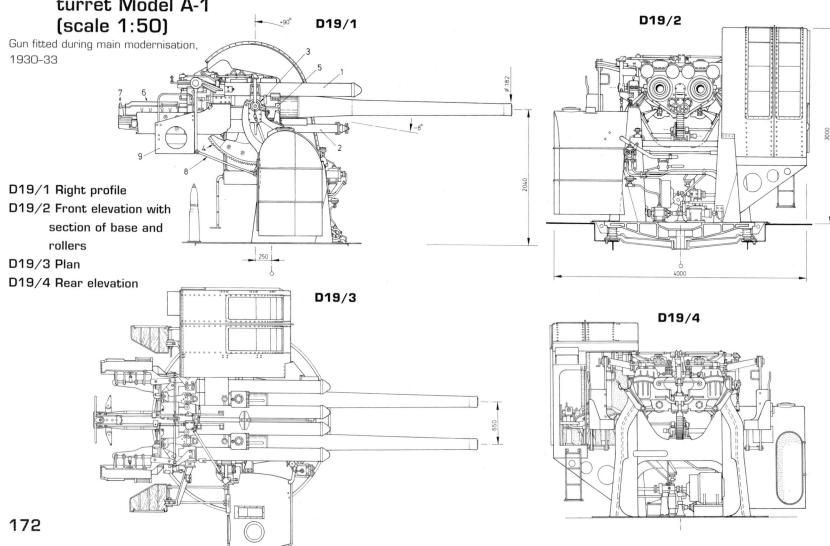

D19/6

D19/5

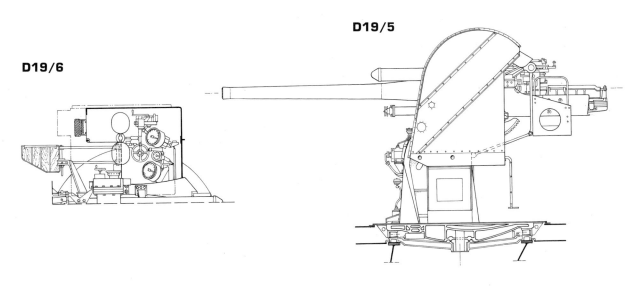

D19/5 Left profile with gun
base

D19/6 Plan of gun direction
platform

D19/7 Perspective view of
mount (view from
forward, no scale)

D19/8 Perspective view of
mount (rear view,
no scale)
1 Recoil cylinders
2 Recuperators
3 Trunnion
4 Elevating arc (toothed quadrant)
5 Support
6 Shell waiting tray
7 Shell rammer
8 Pantograph
9 Charger platform

D19/7   **D19/8**

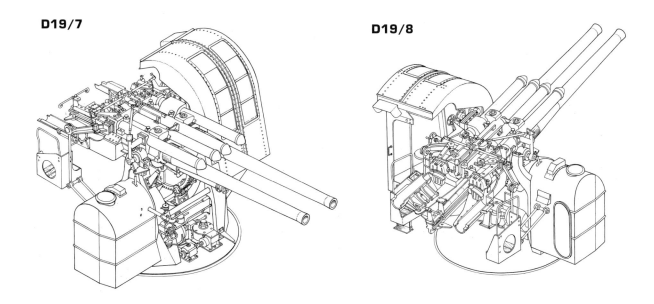

173

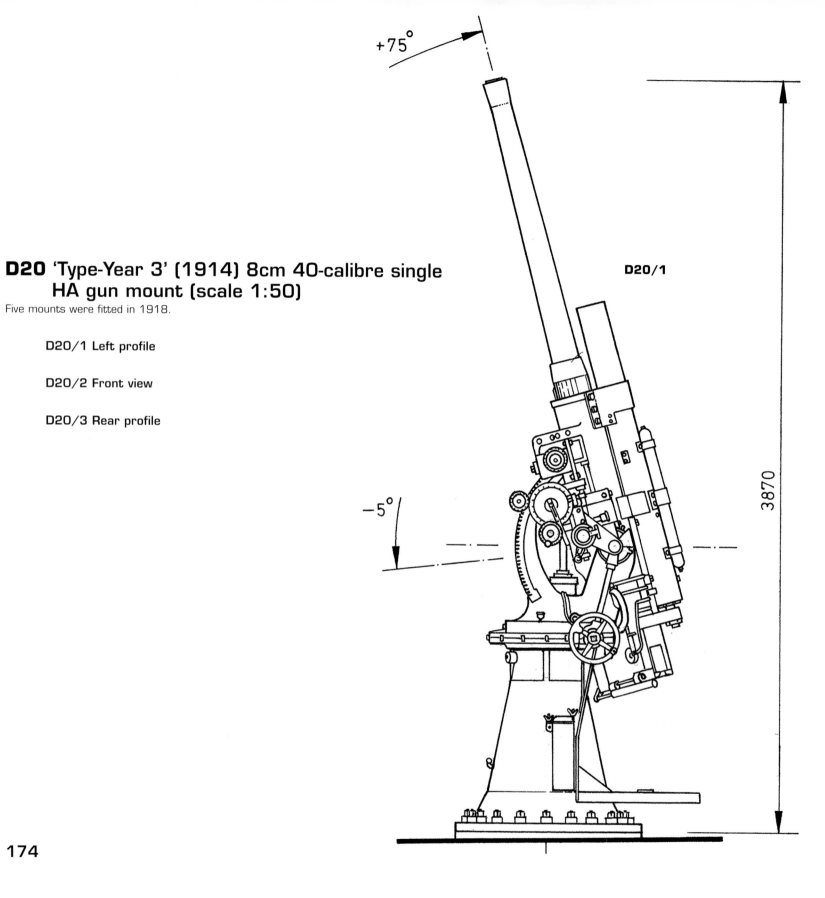

D20 'Type-Year 3' (1914) 8cm 40-calibre single
   HA gun mount (scale 1:50)

Five mounts were fitted in 1918.

D20/1 Left profile

D20/2 Front view

D20/3 Rear profile

+75°

D20/1

−5°

3870

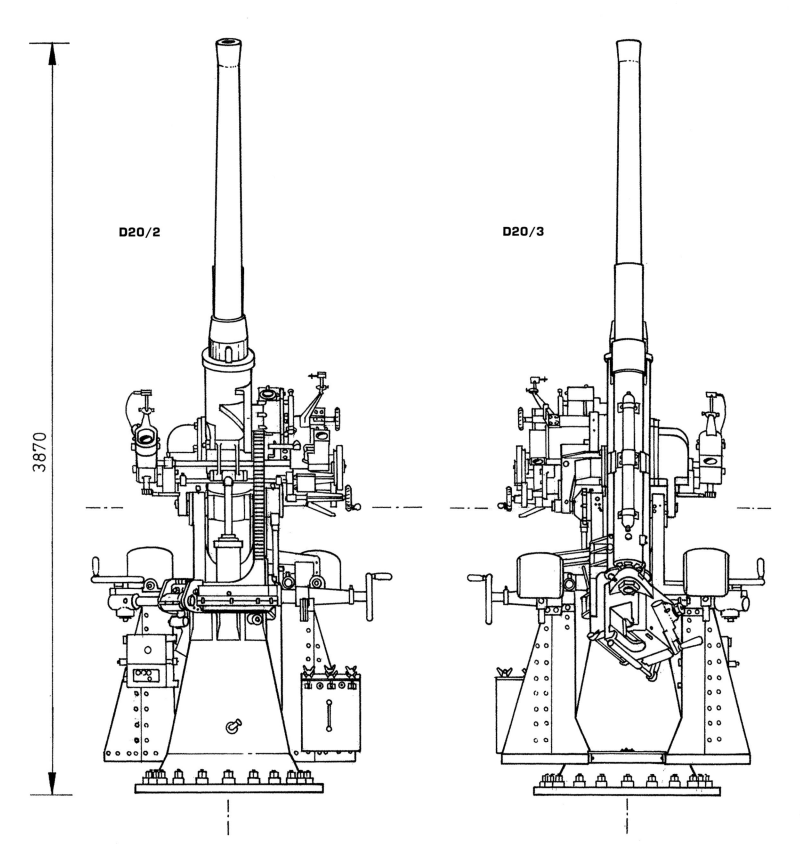

D20/2

D20/3

3870

175

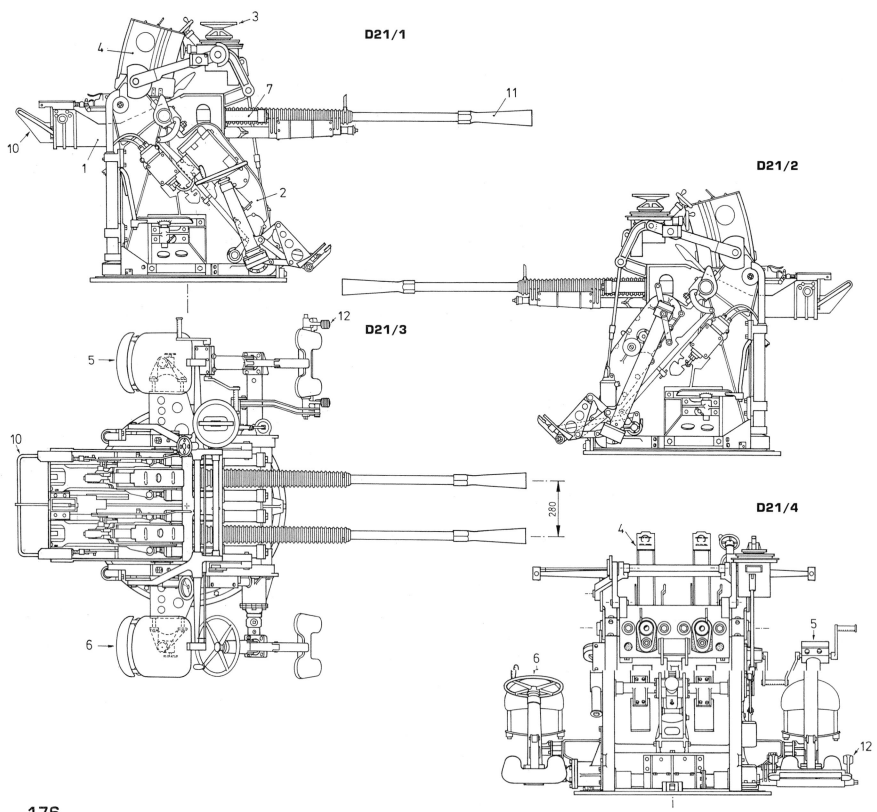

D21/1

D21/2

D21/3

D21/4

176

D21 Type-96 25mm twin machine gun mounting (scale 1:25)

First eight mounts fitted during 1937–38 modernisation.

D21/1 Right profile

D21/2 Left profile

D21/3 Plan

D21/4 Front elevation

D21/5 Cross section of
trunnion bracket

D21/6 Perspective of fore
part of trunnion
bracket (no scale)

D21/7 Perspective of lower
part of gun mounting –
support of pointer seat
(no scale)

 1 Top carriage
 2 Trunnion bracket
 3 Range dial
 4 Magazine with fifteen rounds
 5 Trainer
 6 Pointer
 7 Recoil cylinder
 8 Toothed elevating quadrant
 9 Cartridge case ejector: shield
10 Recoil guard
11 Old type muzzle flash eliminator
12 Firing pedal

D21/5

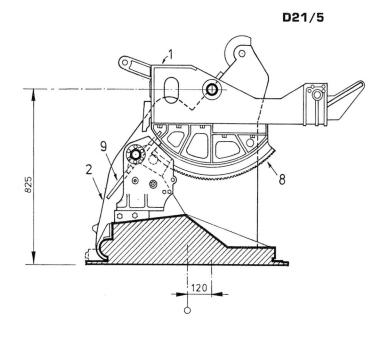

D21/6

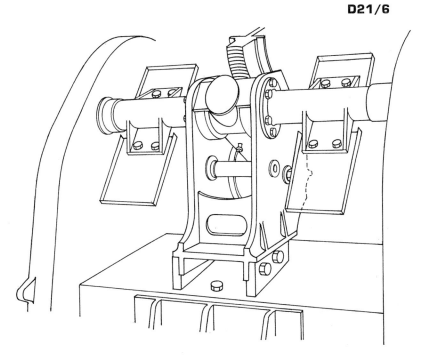

D21/7

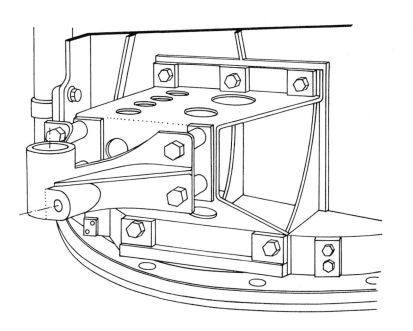

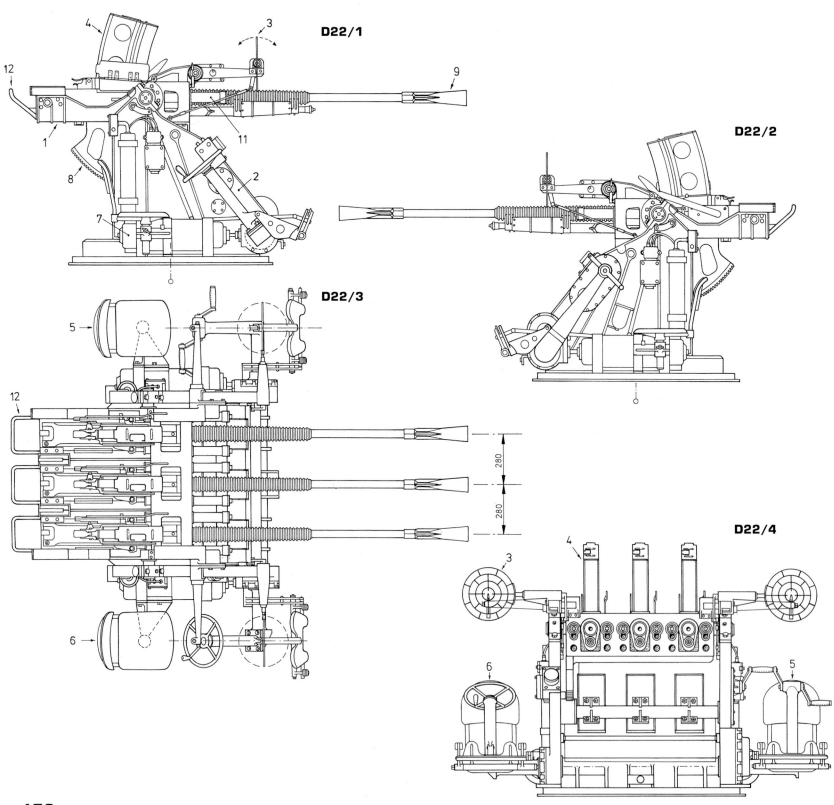

D22/1

D22/2

D22/3

D22/4

D22 Type-96 25mm triple machine gun mounting (scale 1:25)

Eight triple MG mounts were fitted in August 1944.

D22/1 Right profile

D22/2 Left profile

D22/3 Plan

D22/4 Front elevation

D22/5 Cross section of trunnion bracket

D22/6 Perspective view of gun sight and barrel (no scale)

1 Top carriage
2 Trunnion bracket
3 Gun sight
4 Magazine with fifteen rounds
5 Trainer
6 Pointer
7 1hp electric motor
8 Toothed elevating quadrant
9 New-type muzzle flash eliminator
10 Pusher of cartridge case
11 Recoil cylinder
12 Recoil guard
13 Pantograph
14 Rotation axis of top carriage

D22/6

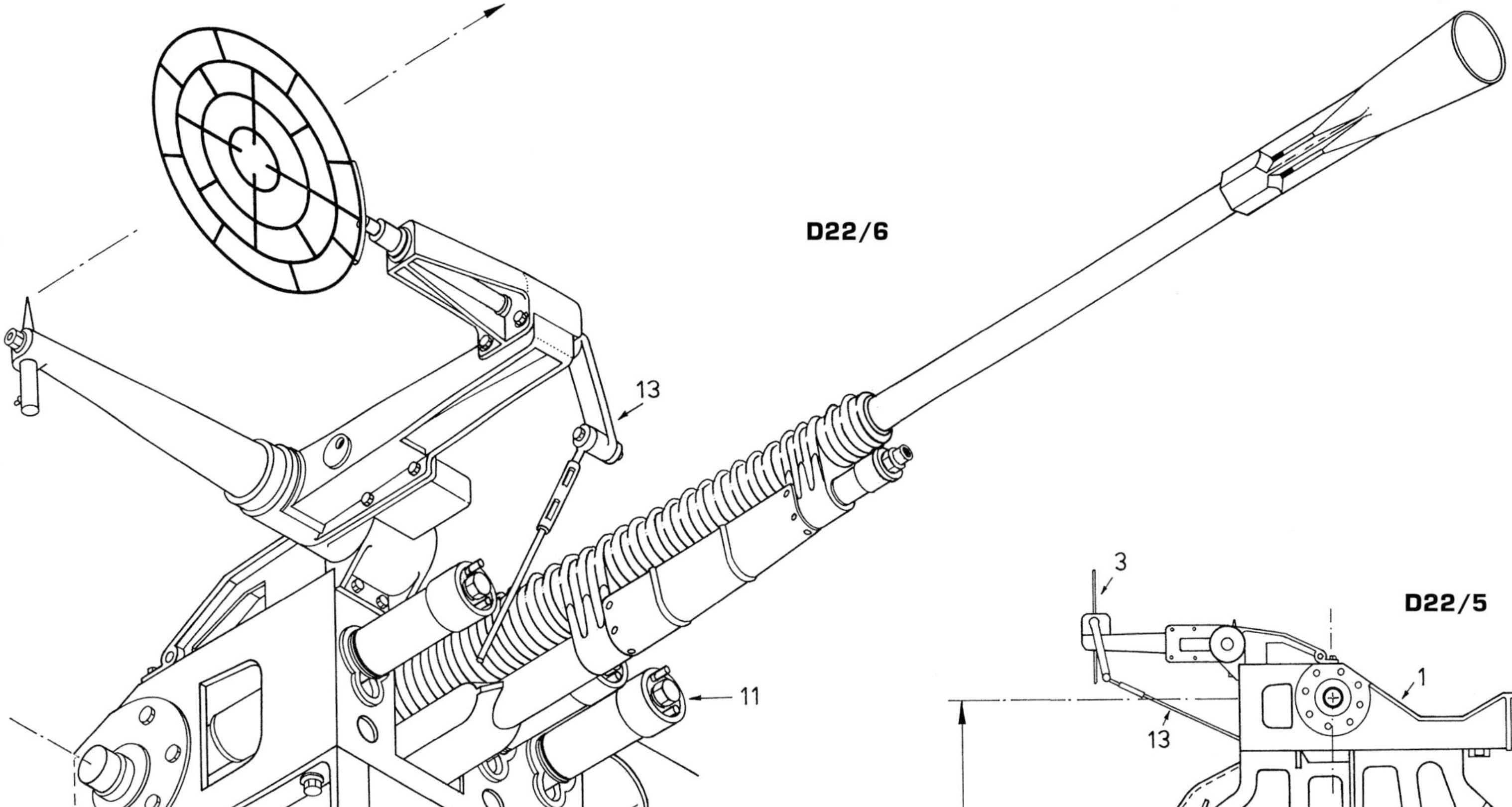

D22/5

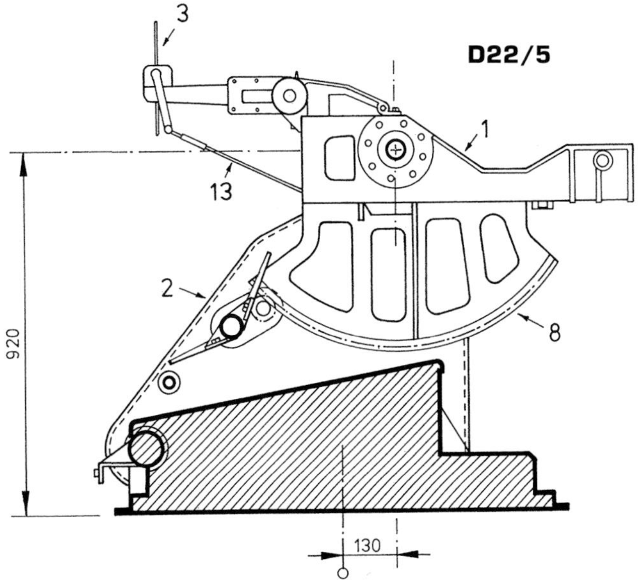

130

920

179

D23 Type-96 25mm single MG mounting (scale 1:25)

Seventeen mounts fitted in July 1943, 22 mounts in August 1944 – five of these were on a moveable pedestal

D23/1 Right profile

D23/2 Left profile

D23/3 Plan

D23/4 Front elevation

D23/5 Profile of moveable
      pedestal

D23/6 Plan of moveable
      pedestal

D23/1

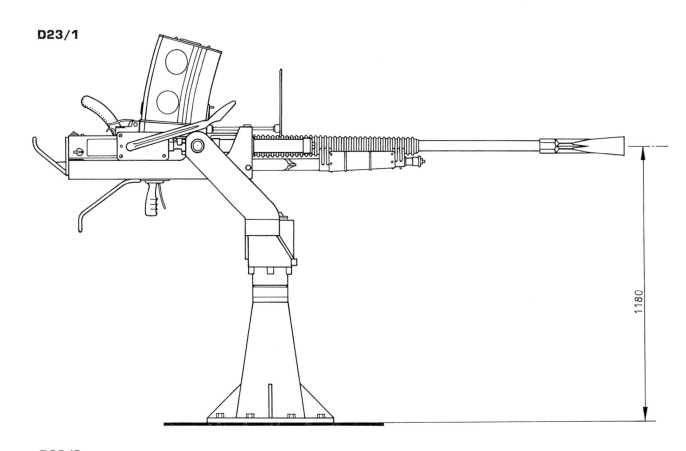

1180

D23/3

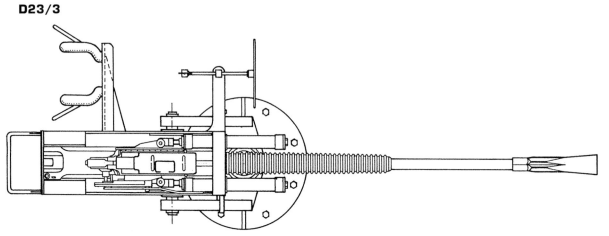

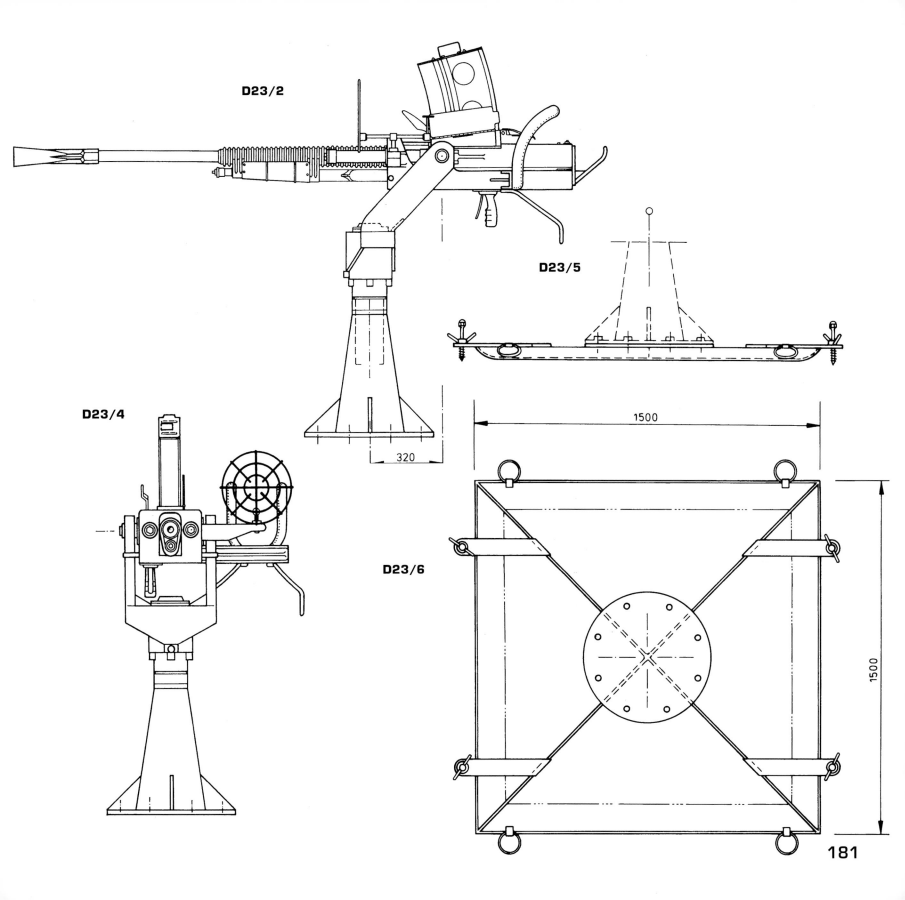

D23/2

D23/5

D23/4

D23/6

320

1500

1500

181

D24 Type-96 25mm gun barrel with breech block

D24/1 Profile (scale 1:12.5)

D24/2 Plan (scale 1:12.5)

D24/3 Sections (scale 1:12.5)

1 Old-type muzzle flash eliminator
2 Radiator
3 Breech block reloading gas cylinder
4 Pressure regulator for gas cylinder (gas plug)
5 Gas pipe (in shield)
6 Breech block housing
7 Grip: manual operating lever
8 Counter-recoil piston rod lug
9 Slide rail
10 Magazine insert

D24/4 Detail of barrel cooling fins (scale 1:2.5)

1 Cooling fins
2 Barrel
3 Gas pipe for gas cylinder
4 Gas pressure regulator (gas plug)
5 Shield

D24/1

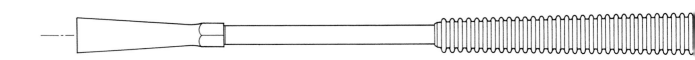

D24/2

D24/4

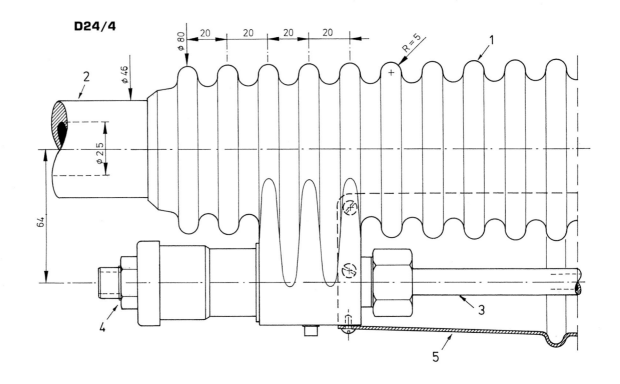

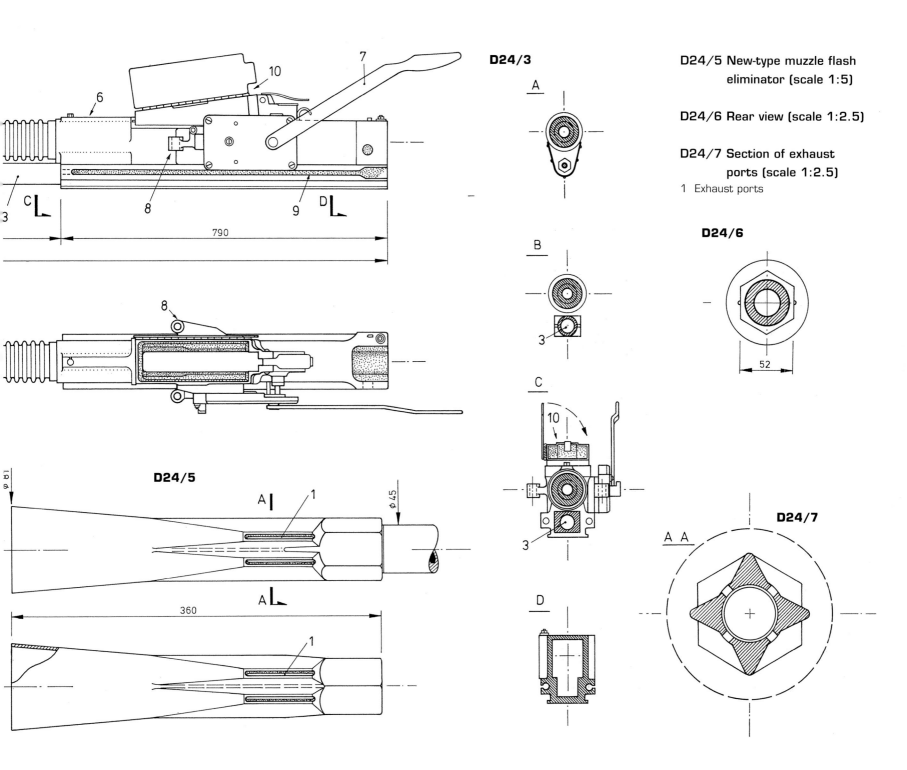

D24/3

A

B

3

C

10

3

D

D24/5 New-type muzzle flash
eliminator (scale 1:5)

D24/6 Rear view (scale 1:2.5)

D24/7 Section of exhaust
ports (scale 1:2.5)

1 Exhaust ports

D24/6

52

D24/5

A

1

∅ 45

∅ 81

A

360

1

A A

D24/7

D25 '93-shiki' 13.2mm (0.52in) 76-calibre quadruple machine gun mount
(scale 1:25)

Four mounts were fitted during main modernisation 1930–33.

D25/1 Right profile   D25/2 Left profile   D25/3 Front elevation   D25/4 Plan

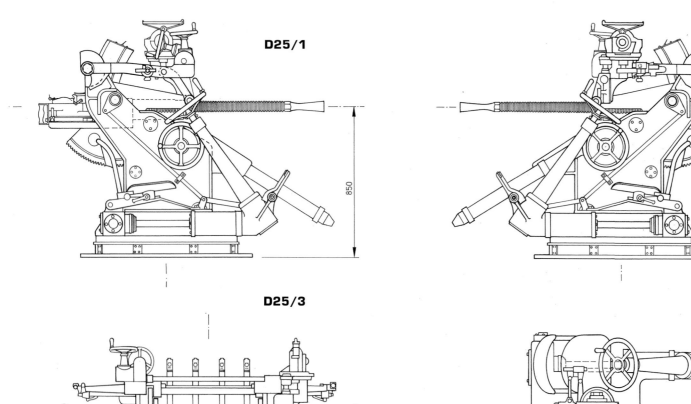

D25/1   D25/2

850

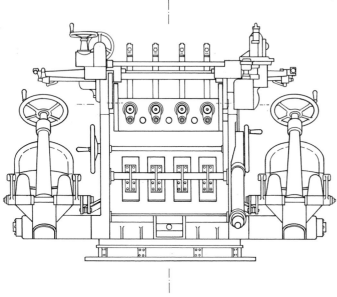

D25/3

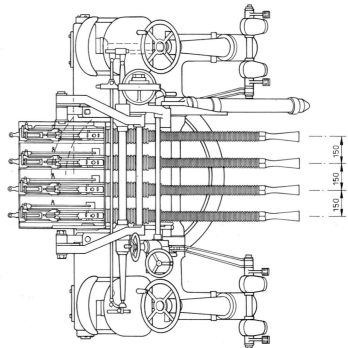

D25/4

150 150 150 150

D26 Type-93 13.2mm MG barrel with breech block (scale 1:10)

D26/1 Profile

D26/2 Plan

D26/3 Sections

1. Muzzle flash eliminator
2. Muzzle sight (foresight)
3. Radiator
4. Gas cylinder (chamber)
5. Pressure regulator (gas plug)
6. Barrel catch
7. Breech block
8. Breech block handle
9. Magazine insert
10. Rear sight
11. Breech block catch (pawl)
12. Firing lock
13. Grip

D26/3

A

B

C

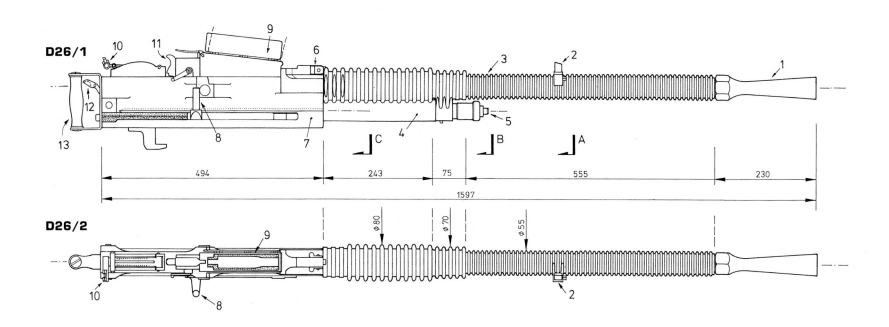

D26/1

D26/2

494   243   75   555   230

1597

Ø80   Ø70   Ø55

D27 'Lewis-type' 7.7mm machine gun

D27/1 Profile (scale 1:12.5)

D27/2 Front view (scale 1:12.5)

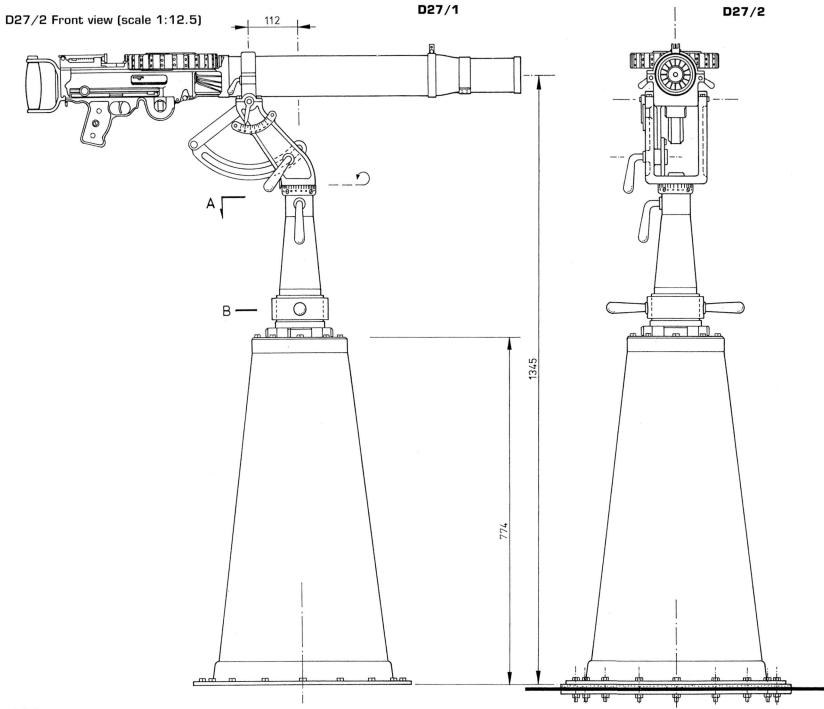

D27/1

D27/2

112

1345

774

A

B

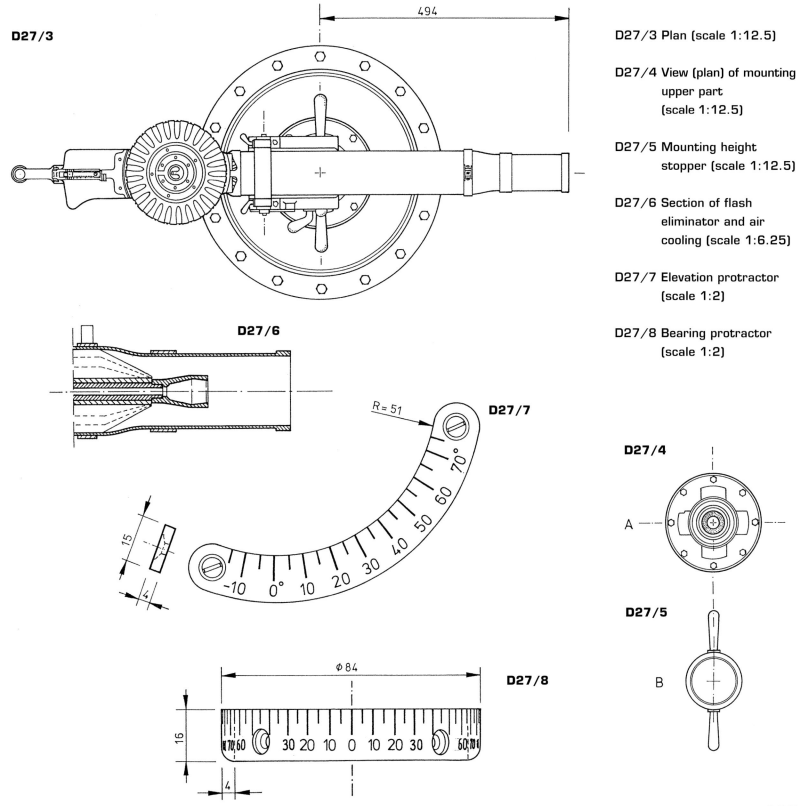

D27/3

494

D27/6

R = 51

D27/7

70°
60
50
40
30
20
10
0°
−10

15
4

D27/4

A

D27/5

B

Ø 84

16
4

70 60 30 20 10 0 10 20 30 60 70

D27/8

D27/3 Plan (scale 1:12.5)

D27/4 View (plan) of mounting
upper part
(scale 1:12.5)

D27/5 Mounting height
stopper (scale 1:12.5)

D27/6 Section of flash
eliminator and air
cooling (scale 1:6.25)

D27/7 Elevation protractor
(scale 1:2)

D27/8 Bearing protractor
(scale 1:2)

187

D28 25mm ammunition box for 240 rounds (scale 1:25)

D28/1 Profile

D28/2 Front view

D28/3 Plan

D28/4 Box with open cover

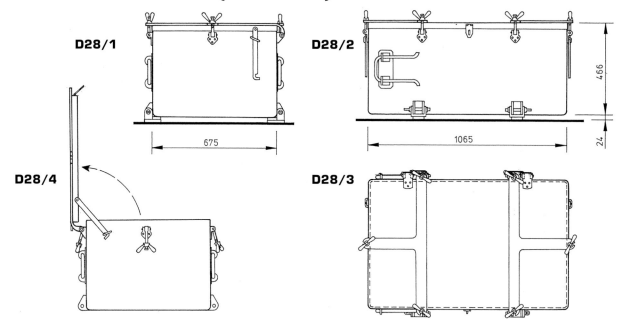

D28/1

D28/2

D28/4

D28/3

D29 25mm ammunition box for 240 rounds (scale 1:25)

D29/1 Profile

D29/2 Front view

D29/3 Plan

D29/4 Box with open cover
      (detail)

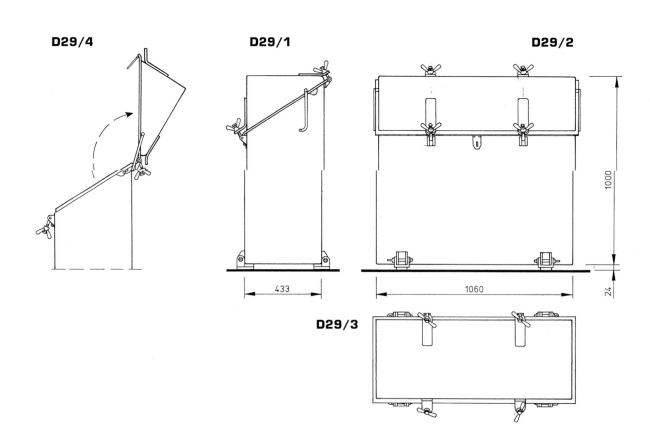

D29/4

D29/1

D29/2

D29/3

D30 13.2mm ammunition box for 960 rounds (scale 1:25)

D30/1 Profile
D30/2 Front view
D30/3 Plan

D31 Ammunition box deck fixture

D31/1 Profile (scale 1:2.5)
D31/2 Plan (scale 1:2.5)

D31/3 Axonometric view (no scale)

1 Ammunition box
2 Box assembly rig
3 Deck assembly rig
4 Pin
5 Washer
6 Cotter pin
7 Square washer

D31/1

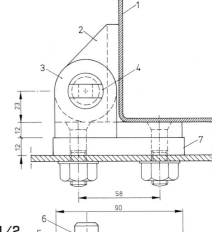

D31/2

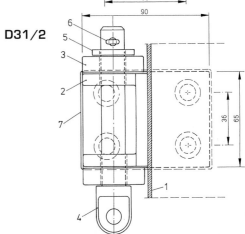

D31/3

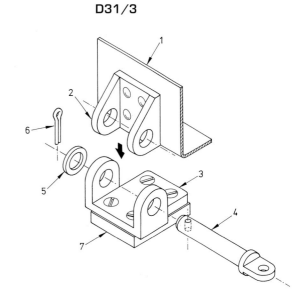

D30/1

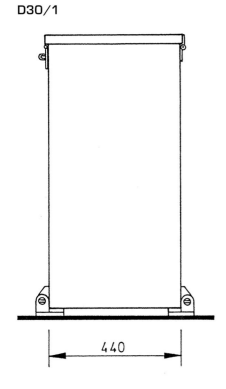

440

D30/2

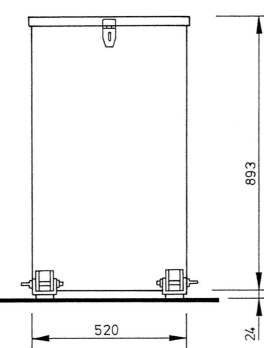

893

24

520

D30/3

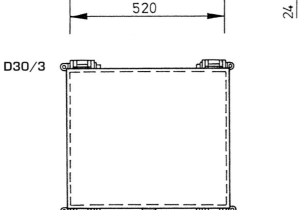

E FIRE CONTROL

E1 Top of pagoda tower bridge structure after main modernisation, 1933 (scale 1:37.5)

E1/1 Rear-view section of main 6m rangefinder mounting

E1/2 Plan of top rangefinder column (level XI–XIV)

E1/3 Plan of rangefinder platform

1 6m rangefinder tower
2 Auxiliary rangefinder sighting arm
3 Top light and lighting rood (arrester) stay in forward part of rangefinder platform (level XIV)

4 Circle platform
5 Fore platform
6 Rangefinder tower rollers
7 Voice pipe
8 Electric wires

9 Ventilator
10 Hatch
11 Turning limiter
12 Heat resistant steel sheet

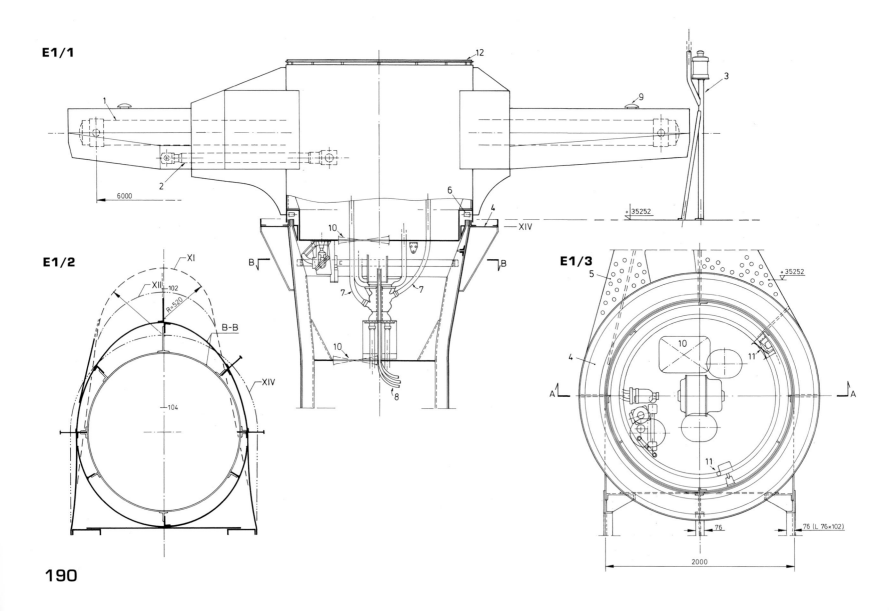

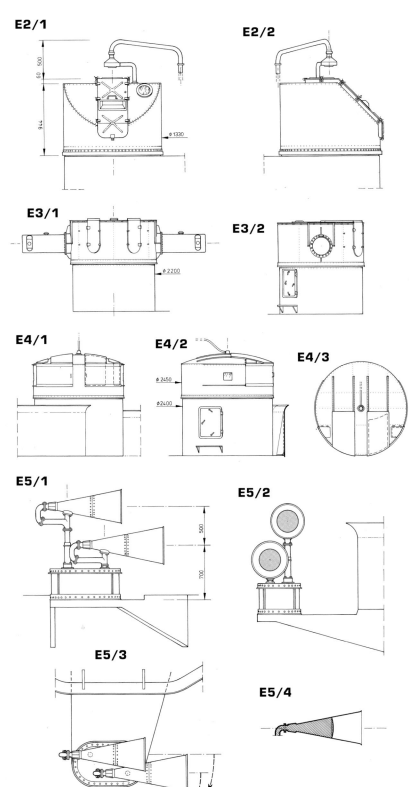

E2/1

E2/2

E2/3

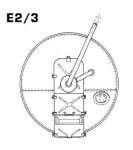

E2/4

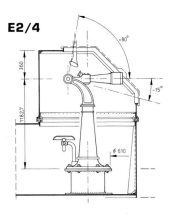

E3/1

E3/2

E3/3

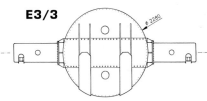

E4/1

E4/2

E4/3

E5/1

E5/2

E5/3

E5/4

E2 Protected look-out position tower equipped with 12cm binoculars (scale 1:37.5)

E2/1 Front elevation

E2/2 Profile

E2/3 Plan

E2/4 Section: 1 voice tube (only for towers on level IX and X)

E3 4.5m HA rangefinder fitted on aft part of signal platform (level VI) (scale 1:75)

E3/1 Front elevation

E3/2 Profile

E3/3 Plan

E4 '91-shiki' Kosha Sochi HA-gun fire director (scale 1:75)

Two turrets fitted on both sides of signal platform (level VI).

E4/1 Front elevation of tower (view from ship's side)

E4/2 Profile (view from stern)

E4/3 Plan

E5 Type-22 surface-search radar '22 Go Dentan Kai 4' (scale 1:37.5)

Horns-type antenna, fitted in August 1944 on both sides of air-defence command platform (level XII).

E5/1 Starboard profile

E5/2 Front view of starboard mount

E5/3 Plan of starboard mount

E5/4 Section of horn

Note: upper horn for receiving, lower for transmitting

E6 110cm
searchlight
controller
(scale 1:50)

E6/1 Profile

E6/2 Front view

E6/3 Plan

E7 12cm
observation
and direction
controller
(Kansoku-Kyo)
(scale 1:50)

E7/1 Profile

E7/2 Front view

E7/3 Plan

E8 Secondary-gun
fire director
(Fukuho Hoiban
Soyoun Sochi)
(scale 1:50)

E8/1 Profile

E8/2 Front view

E8/3 Plan

E9 Target course
and speed
controller
(scale 1:50)

E9/1 Front view

E9/2 Plan

E9/3 Perspective (no scale)

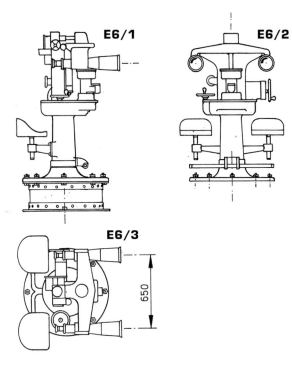

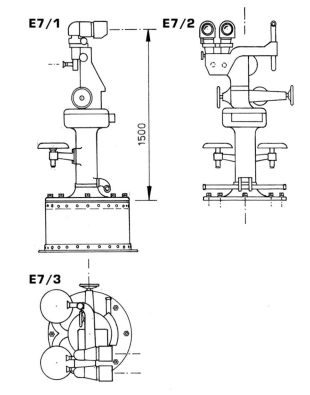

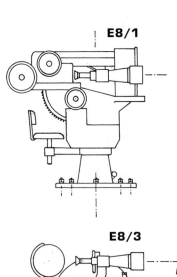

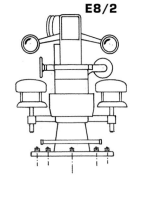

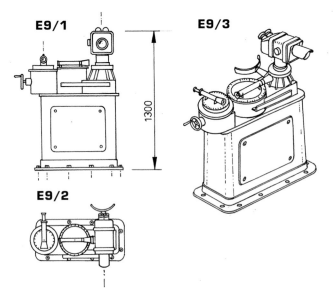

E10 Target-tracing installation (scale 1:50)

E10/1 Front view
E10/2 Plan
E10/3 Perspective (no scale)

E11 Target-course-and-speed computer ('13 shiki Sokuteki Ban') (scale 1:50)

E11/1 Profile
E11/2 Plan

E12 Machine gun fire director '95-shiki Kiju Shageki Sochi' (scale 1:50)

E12/1 Port profile
E12/2 Plan

E13 Type-21 air-search radar (21 Go Dentan Kai 2)

'Mattress-type' antenna, fitted in July 1943. The antenna consisted of combined transmitting and receiving arrays of 10mm diameter copper bars.

E13/1 Front elevation (scale 1:50)

E13/2 Profile (scale 1:50)

E13/3 Plan (scale 1:50)

E13/4 Section in detail (scale 1:20)

1 Receiving-transmitting array (10mm diameter bars)
2 Insulators of arrays
3 Insulators of installation wires
4 Wire screen grid, 40mm x 40mm module
5 Support plates for insulators
6 Antenna frame
7 Hole in screen gird for wires
8 Receiving array
9 Transmitting array
10 Footplate
11 Handrail

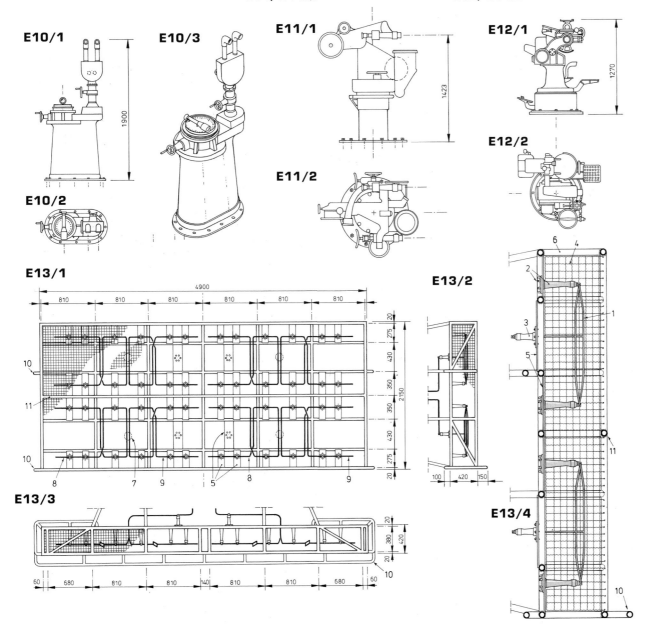

E10/1 **E10/3**

E10/2

E11/1

E11/2

E12/1

E12/2

E13/1

E13/2

E13/3

E13/4

E14 Type-13 air-search radar '3 shiki 1 Go Denpa Tanshingi 3 Gata'

Installed in August 1944 on both sides of funnel.

E14/1 Profile
(scale 1:37.5)

E14/2 Front elevation
(scale 1:37.5)

E14/3 Rear view
(scale 1:37.5)

E14/4 Plan
(scale 1:37.5)

E14/5 Section of pillar
(scale 1:18.75)

1 Receiving array
(10mm diameter bar)
2 Transmitting array
(10mm diameter bar)

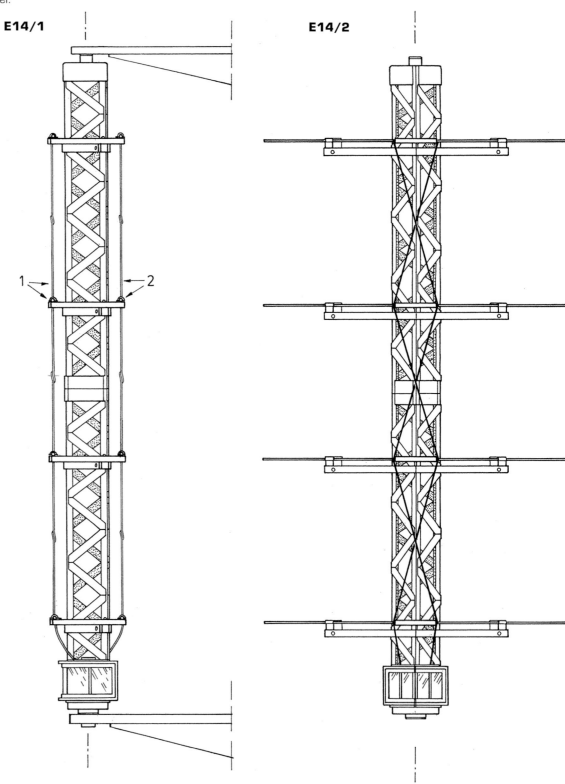

E14/1

E14/2

1

2

E14/3

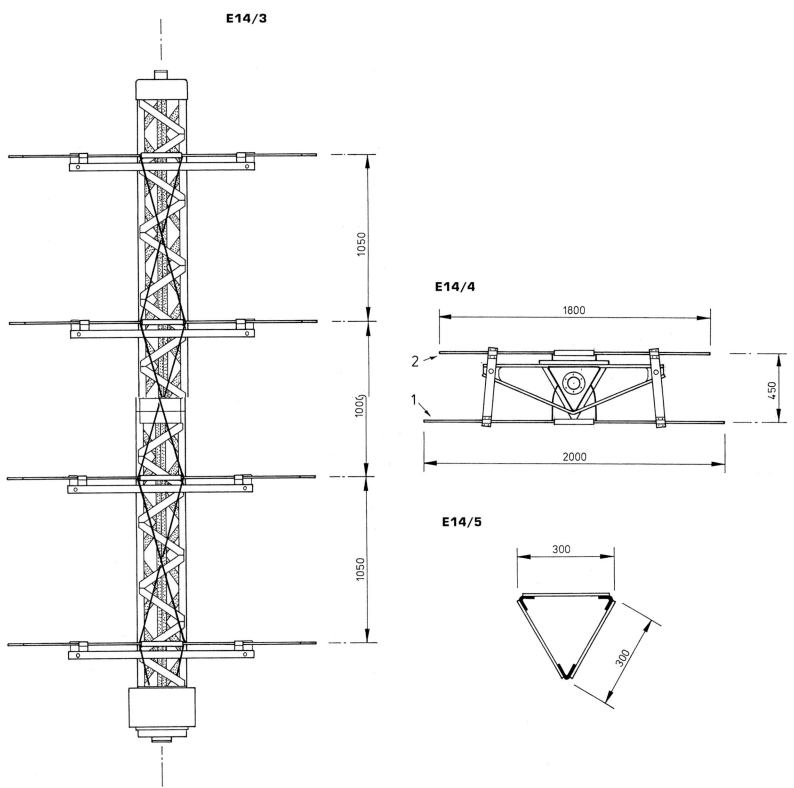

1050

1050

1050

E14/4

1800

450

2000

2

1

E14/5

300

300

195

E15 HA fire control installation '94-shiki Kosha Sochi' (scale 1:37.5)

Consisted of: 4.5m rangefinders, 3.5m rangefinders and '94-shiki Kosha Shagekiban' computer, which was located under pagoda superstructure in lower fire control room.

E15/1 Front view
1 Training telescope
2 Vertical inclination telescope
3 4.5m HA rangefinder base
4 Lateral inclination telescope
5 Elevation telescope
6 Elevation handwheel
7 Training handwheel
8 Vertical inclination handwheel
9 Lateral inclination handwheel
10 Range transmission device

E15/2 Plan of 4.5m rangefinder and 'Kosha Shagekiban' computer
1 Furure range dial
2 Range correction
3 Illumination switch
4 Own speed correction
5 Parallax correction
6 Vertical deflection balancing wheel
7 Vertical angle dial
8 Training angle dial
9 Lateral deflection balancing wheel
10 Compass repeater
11 Projector lamp
12 Projector lamp switch
13 Coordinates converter projector
14 Fuse reader
15 Fuse correction
16 Level target correction
17 Fuse dial
18 Range drum
19 Range change rate dial
20 Auxiliary switch for range mark
21 Range change rate chart

CREW:
A Rangefinder observer
B Range transmitter
C Training pointer
D Vertical inclination pointer
E Lateral inclination pointer
F Elevation pointer
G Spotter
H Director officer (data transmission and firing orders)

OPERATORS:
I Computer officer
J Correction setter No 2: own speed and parallax
K Vertical deflection setter
L Lateral deflection setter
M Compass receiver following compass repeater
N Lateral inclination correction setter
O Vertical inclination correction setter
P Correction setter No 1: fuse setting and level target
R Setter of range and range change rate

DATA TRANSMISSION:
IV Vertical inclination angle
II Lateral inclination angle
R   Range
E   Elevation angle
T   Training angle
ET Total elevation value
TT Total training value
FST Fuse setting time, directly to fuse setting machine
GT Gun turret

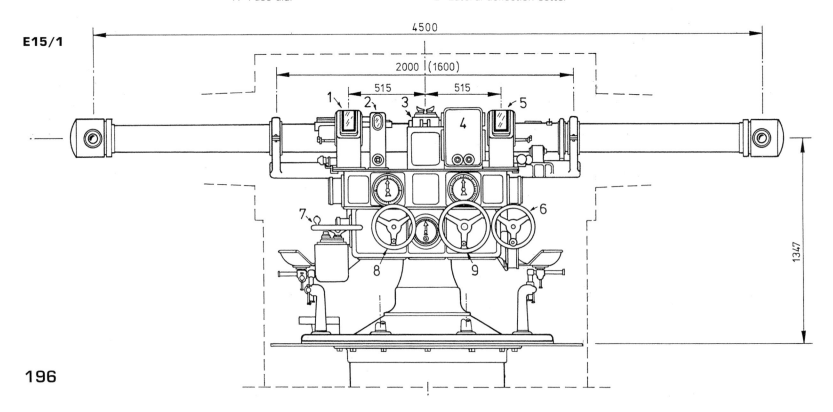

E15/1

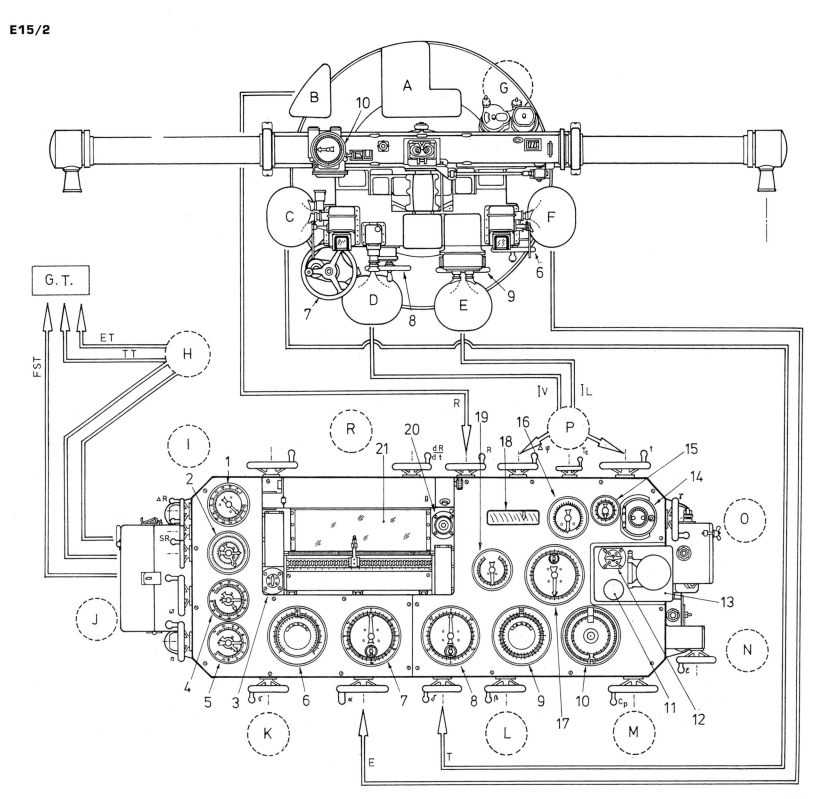

E16 Binoculars

E16/1 Typical binocular mounting (scale 1:12.5)

E16/2 8cm binoculars (scale 1:10)

E16/3 12cm binoculars (scale 1:10)

E16/4 6cm binoculars (scale 1:10)

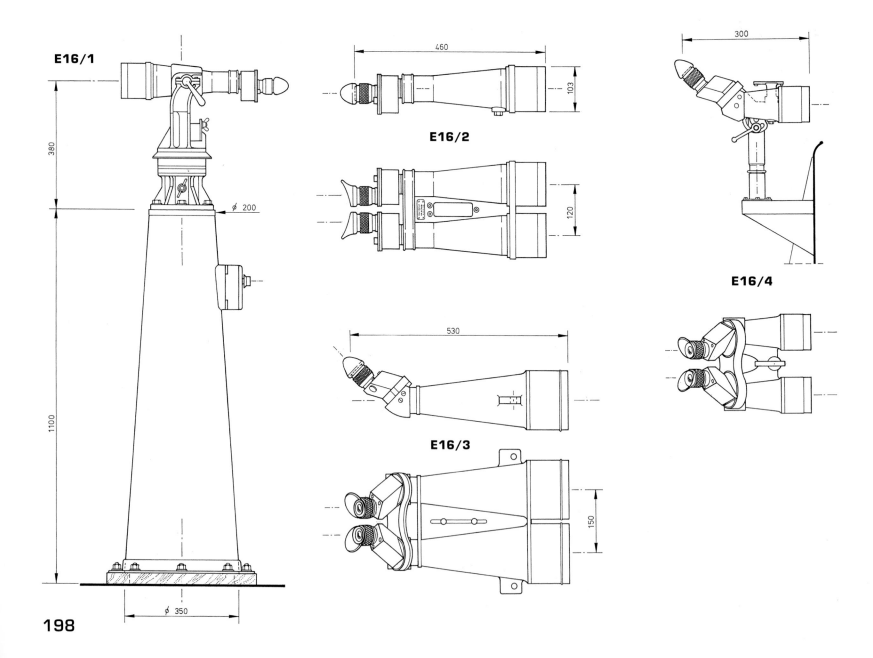

198

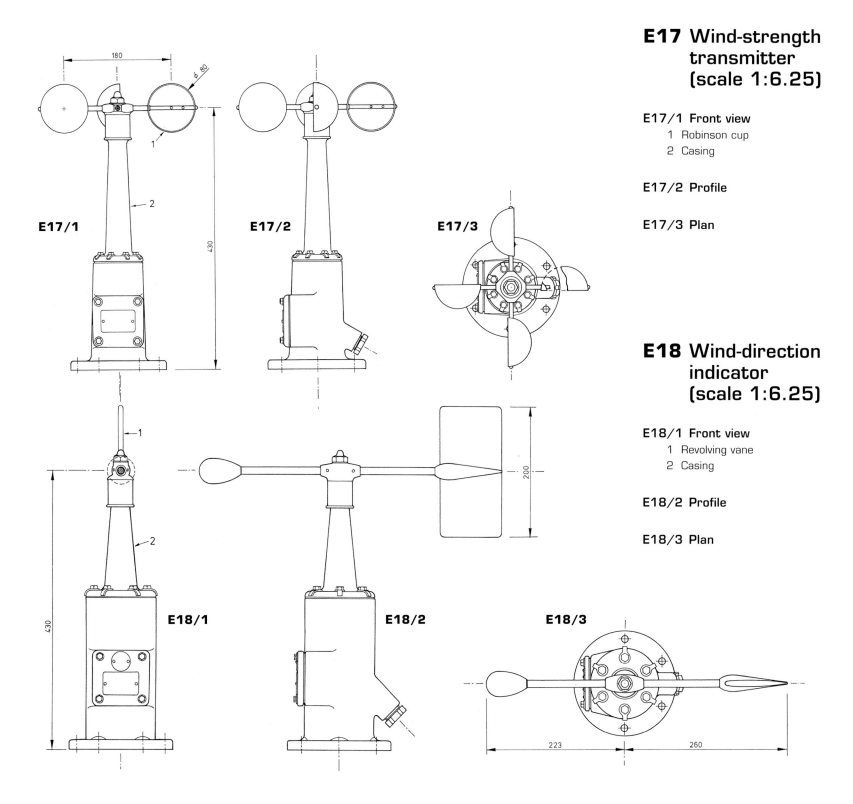

E17 Wind-strength
transmitter
(scale 1:6.25)

E17/1 Front view
  1 Robinson cup
  2 Casing

E17/2 Profile

E17/3 Plan

E18 Wind-direction
indicator
(scale 1:6.25)

E18/1 Front view
  1 Revolving vane
  2 Casing

E18/2 Profile

E18/3 Plan

E17/1   E17/2   E17/3

E18/1   E18/2   E18/3

F GROUND TACKLE (scale 1:100 except where stated)

F1 Forecastle after main modernisation, May 1933 (frames FP-45)

F1/1 Side view (starboard)

F1/2 Plan

1 Gold chrysanthemum crest
2 Jackstaff (removable part)
3 Tripod: jackstaff stanchion and support for dressing and awning lines
4 Towing fairlead
5 Tripod: stanchion for aerials and awning lines (both sides)
6 Folded awning stanchions
7 Centreline awning stanchions
8 Hawse pipe
9 Paravane roller fairlead
10 Roller chock for paravane lines
11 Dressing line
12 Aerials (antennae)
13 Awning lines
14 Draught marks
15 Side scuttle with securing bars
16 Eye
17 Welded side plates
18 Riveted side plates
19 Handrail
20 Clamps
21 Hole in hull: pipe for paravane cables
22 Scupper pipe
23 Auxiliary derrick
24 Leadsman's platform
25 Anchor cable
26 Stopper
27 Cable holder with brake handle
28 Naval pipe
29 Auxiliary anchor
30 Fore capstan
31 Bollards
32 Hatch
33 Skylight
35 Vents
36 Deck cleat
37 Deck eye
38 Scupper
39 Reels
40 Capstan removal reels storage
41 Chaffing plate
42 Sounding platform
43 8m sampan on davits

F1/1

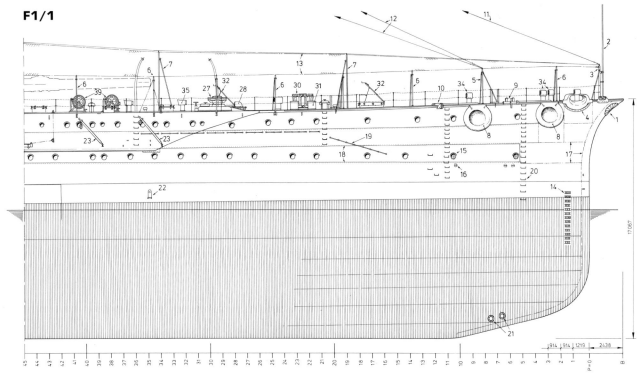

F1/2

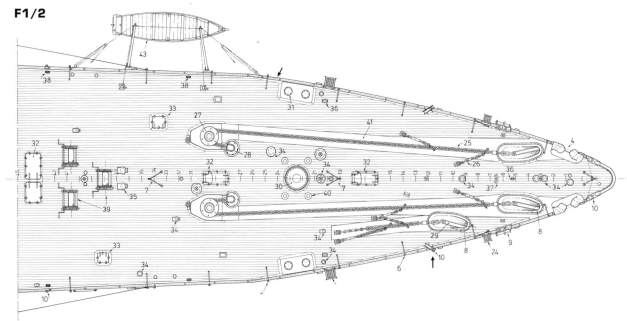

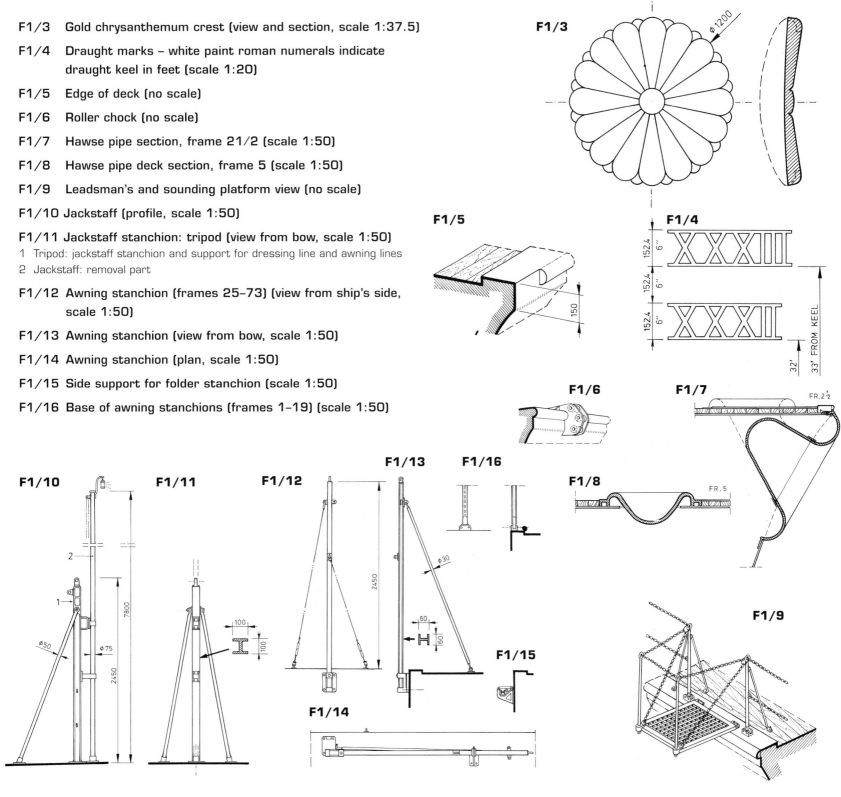

F1/3   Gold chrysanthemum crest (view and section, scale 1:37.5)

F1/4   Draught marks – white paint roman numerals indicate draught keel in feet (scale 1:20)

F1/5   Edge of deck (no scale)

F1/6   Roller chock (no scale)

F1/7   Hawse pipe section, frame 21/2 (scale 1:50)

F1/8   Hawse pipe deck section, frame 5 (scale 1:50)

F1/9   Leadsman's and sounding platform view (no scale)

F1/10 Jackstaff (profile, scale 1:50)

F1/11 Jackstaff stanchion: tripod (view from bow, scale 1:50)
1   Tripod: jackstaff stanchion and support for dressing line and awning lines
2   Jackstaff: removal part

F1/12 Awning stanchion (frames 25–73) (view from ship's side, scale 1:50)

F1/13 Awning stanchion (view from bow, scale 1:50)

F1/14 Awning stanchion (plan, scale 1:50)

F1/15 Side support for folder stanchion (scale 1:50)

F1/16 Base of awning stanchions (frames 1–19) (scale 1:50)

201

F2 8.5-ton main anchor, from Imperial Japanese Navy official anchor design, Stockless type (scale 1:50)

F2/1 Front view
F2/2 Profile
F2/3 Plan of anchor head
F2/4 Section of lower part
F2/5 Transverse section
F2/6 Stopper block (no scale)

1 Anchor ring
2 Shank
3 Anchor head
4 Block
5 Head pin
6 Block screw

F3 Main anchor equipment

F3/1 Anchor cable (scale 1:25)

1 Enlarged stud link
2 Studless long link
3 Swivel
4 Lugged joining shackle
5 Anchor ring
6 Shank

F3/2 Deck stopper (profile, scale 1:25)

F3/3 Deck stopper (plan, scale 1:25)

1 Stopper lug
2 Joining shackle
3 Bottle screw
4 Blake's slip

F3/4 Electric capstan (profile, scale 1:50)

F3/5 Electric capstan (plan, scale 1:50)

1 Scroll plate
2 Hood plate
3 Sprocket and snugs
4 Brake handwheel
5 Naval pipe: cover
6 Cover over brake
7 Ramp to chaffing plate

F2/1

F2/2

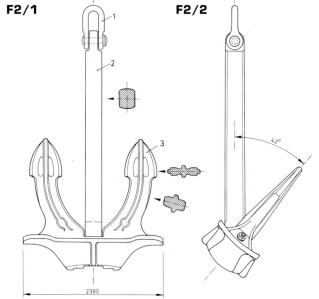

F2/3

F2/4

F2/6

F2/5

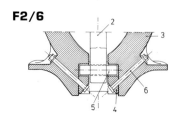
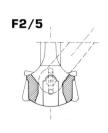

F3/5

F3/4

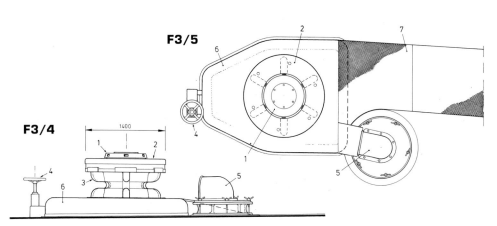

F3/2

F3/3

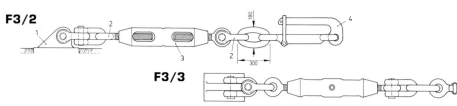

F3/1

F4 Forecastle electric capstan (scale 1:50)

F4/1 Plan

F4/2 Profile
1 Sockets for capstan bars
2 Portable whelp
3 Position of removable roller
4 Pawl
5 Pawl plate
6 Locating pin for capstan bars and portable whelp
7 Crown plate

F5 After capstan (scale 1:50)

F5/1 Plan

F5/2 Profile
1 Crown plate
2 Capstan bar socket
3 Pawl
4 Pawl plate

F6 Bollards (scale 1:50)

F6/1 Profile

F6/2 Plan

F7 Stern anchor (fitted on both hull sides) (scale 1:42)

F7/1 Front view

F7/2 Profile

F4/1

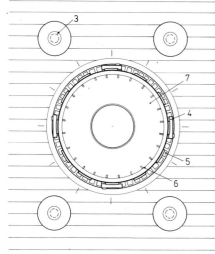

F4/2

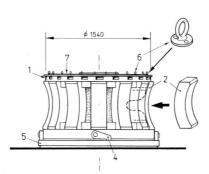

F6/1

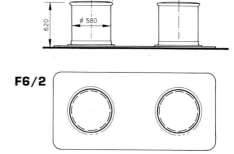

F6/2

F7/1   F7/2

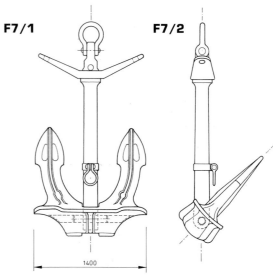

F5/1

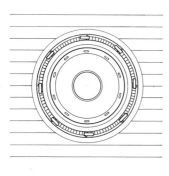

F5/2

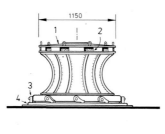

G FITTINGS (scale 1:200 except where stated)

G1 Forecastle deck fittings, May 1933 (frames 44–114)

G1/1 Plan

G1/2 Starboard view

1 14m (46ft) swinging boom
2 Mushroom vents
3 Closed deck hole
4 Reel
5 Washdeck locker
6 Electric winch
7 Paravane – deck stowage
8 Skylight
9 Hatch
10 Deck hand truck
11 Bollards
12 Fairlead
13 Scupper
14 Electric winch for 20m aircraft derrick
15 Awning stanchion
16 14m swinging boom stanchion
17 Folded derrick for moving paravane
18 Rails for aircraft trolley
19 Position of 9m cutter on davits
20 Position of 6m sampan on davits
21 Deck washer
22 HA gun crew loading exercise machine
23 10m auxiliary boom
24 Davit
25 Scupper exhaust hole
26 Scupper pipe

G1/1

G1/2

14 15 2 8 24 22 6 2 16 15 7 15 4 15

24 23 1

26 25 25

114 112 110 108 106 104 102 100 98 96 94 92 90 88 86 84 82 80 78 76 74 72 70 68 66 64 62 60 58 56 54 52 50 48 46 45 44

G1/3

FR.64

G2/1

G2/2

G3

G2/3

G4 Forecastle deck fittings, 1 May 1933 (frames 112–180) (scale 1:200)

G4/1 Plan

G4/2 Starboard elevation

1 Aircraft elevator movable platform
2 Rails and ramps for aircraft trolley
3 Ramp platform
4 Turntable
5 Ventilator superstructure
6 Skylight
7 Hatch
8 Mushroom vents
9 Electric winch
10 Deck hand truck
11 Deck closed hole
12 Scupper
13 9m cutter on davits
14 Deck position of 6m sampan
15 Deck position of 8m sampan
16 Deck washer
17 Washdeck locker
18 11m motor boat deck stay position
19 17m pinnace deck stay position
20 Positions of elevator movable columns
21 Deck reel
22 Awning stanchion
23 Scupper pipe
24 Scupper exhaust hole
25 Heavy oil hose shed

G4/1

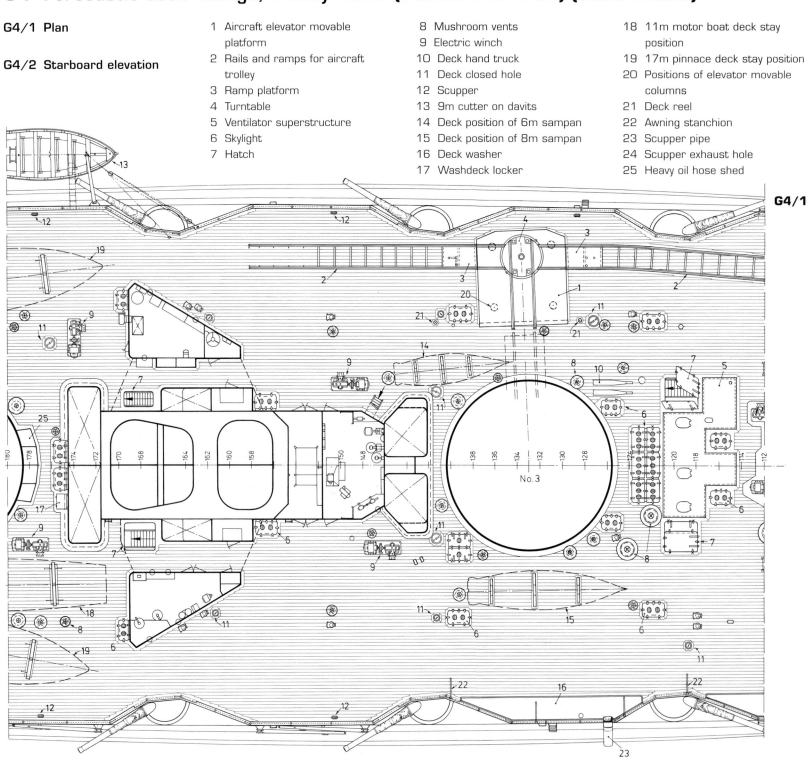

G5 Elevator for lifting aircraft with catapult cradle onto deck trolley to level of loading on the catapult

G5/1 Transverse section of hull and elevator (scale 1:200)

G5/2 Port side view of elevator with rails ramps (scale 1:200)

G5/3 View from stern direction of elevator in position of aircraft loading (scale 1:200)

G5/4 Section of ramp (scale 1:100)

G5/5 Detail of ramp (no scale)
1 Elevator platform lower position
2 Elevator columns
3 Elevator machine room
4 Shield of machine room
5 Upper (loading) position of elevator platform
6 Rail
7 Removable tripod-support of ropes for moving the trolley with aircraft from deck level to elevator platform
8 System of ropes used with deck electric winch to moving aircraft onto trolleys

G4/2

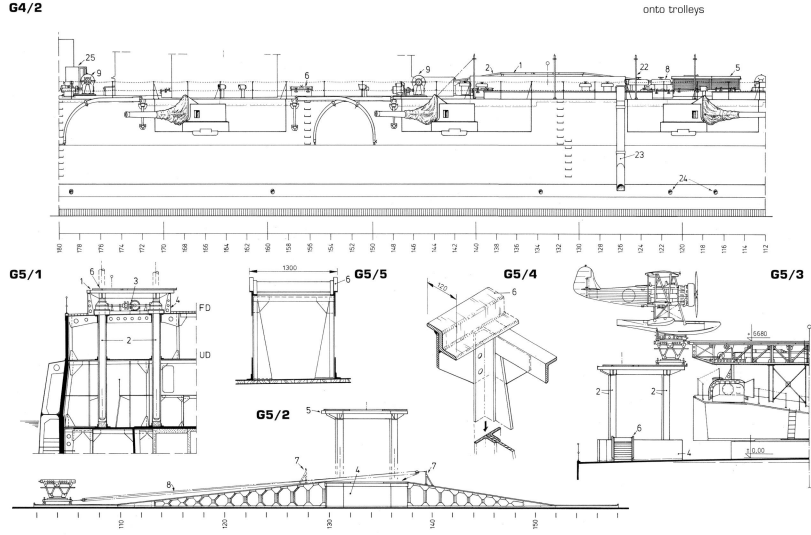

G6 Forecastle deck and upper deck fittings, May 1933 (frames 180–248) (scale 1:200)

G6/1 Plan
G6/2 Starboard view
G6/3 View from frame 200 towards bow

1 17m steam pinnace (old type) with boat cradles position
2 17m motor pinnace (with rounded rear cab) with boat cradles position
3 11m motor boat with boat cradles position
4 12m motor launch with boat cradles position
5 9m cutter with cradles position
6 9m cutter on davits (only in harbour or at anchorage)
7 Engine (cargo) hatch
8 Deck hand truck
9 Washdeck locker
10 Skylight
11 Ventilator fans
12 Sea-water tank
13 20m rear derrick
14 Rear derrick support
15 Hatch
16 Mushroom vents
17 Scupper
18 Covered deck hole
19 Oil-fuel hose hanger
20 Bollards
21 Fairlead
22 Awning stanchion
23 Accommodation ladder
24 Stay position of upper deck davits
25 Small fairlead
26 Scupper exhaust hole
27 Scupper pipe
28 Lifebuoy

G6/1

No.5   No.4

G6/3

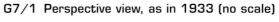
G7 Accommodation ladder

G7/1 Perspective view, as in 1933 (no scale)

G7/2 Plan of upper and lower platforms of accommodation ladder (scale 1:50)

G7/3 Detail of platform's wood gretting (no scale)

G7/4 Ladder working davit, after 1935 (rest of equipment without changes)

G6/2

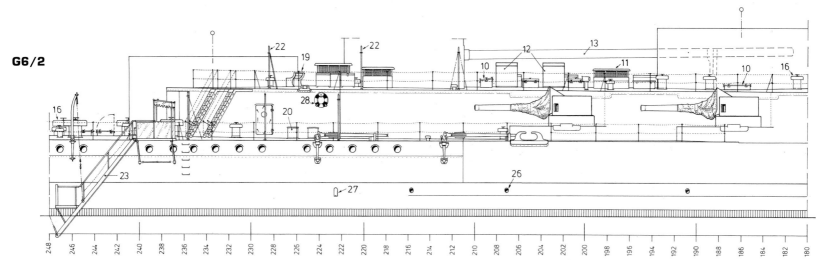

G7/4

IFR. 250

G7/1

G7/3

G7/2

2070   1290

1950   1110

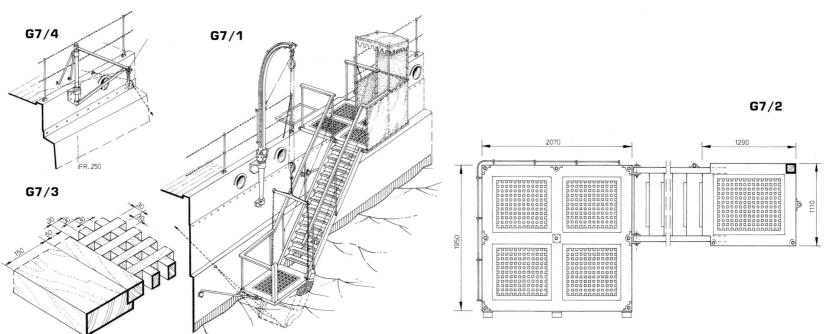

G8 Stern deck (upper deck), as in 1933 (short-stern hull) (scale 1:200)

G8/1 Plan

G8/2 Starboard view

1 Hatch
2 Skylight
3 Reel
4 After capstan
5 Mushroom vents
6 Ventilators
7 Covered deck hole
8 Bollards
9 Scupper
10 Awning and antenna support (tripod)
11 Ensign staff
12 Awning stanchion
13 Lifebuoy
14 After anchor
15 Fairlead
16 Leadsman's platforms
17 Folding part of ensign staff
18 Ensign staff tripod – stanchion–support of dressing line and awning lines
19 Gold 'hiragana' inscription 'Fu' (identical on both sides of ship)
20 Stern watertight door, the remains of the sternwalk removed during ship's construction (both sides)
21 Starboard rudder (port identical)
22 3,505mm-diameter (11ft 6in) propeller. Propellers sense of rotation in forward motion was (looking from stern): starboard propellers clockwise, port side propellers counter-clockwise

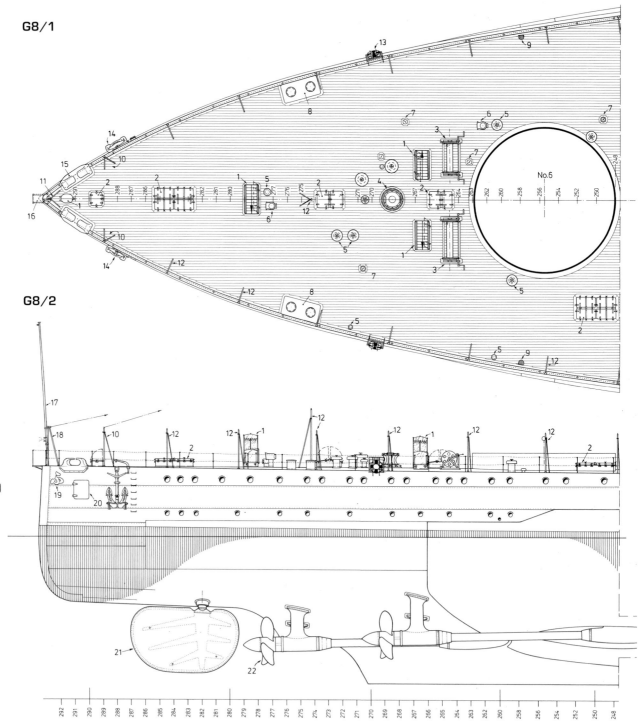

G9 Lifebuoy
(scale 1:50)

G9/1 Profile

G9/2 Front view

G9/3 Perspective (no scale)

G10 Gold 'hiragana' inscription 'Fu' on both sides of stern
(scale 1:50)
(on starboard and port sides only inscription 'Fu')

G11 14m (46ft) swinging boom

G11/1 Profile of work position
(scale 1:200)

G11/2 View of boom edge
(no scale)

1 Swinging boom arm
2 Lizards
3 Jacob's ladders
4 Lifeline
5 Topping line
6 Limiter wire
7 Tripod – boom stanchion

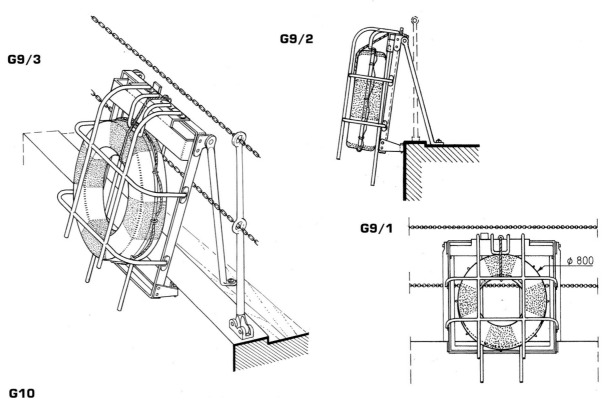

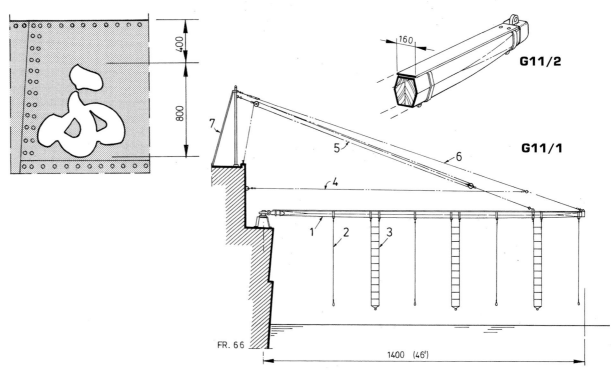

G12 Starboard side view after second phase of main modernisation, March 1935 (scale 1:200)

G12/1 Starboard view
   (frames 41–88)

G12/2 Starboard view
   (frames 110–148)

G12/3 Profile of scupper pipe
   (only on starboard side)

G12/4 Starboard view
   (frames 178-230)

G12/5 Profile of fairlead –
   mounting on the bulge
   upper edge

G12/6 Plan of fairlead

G12/7 Details of edge of
   upper deck (frames
   186–214) (no scale)

1 Upper bulge surface
2 Deck edge
3 Deck wood planking

G12/1

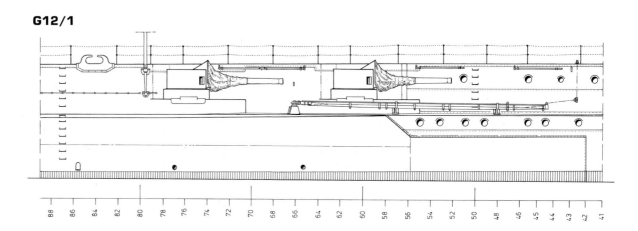

G12/2   **G12/3**

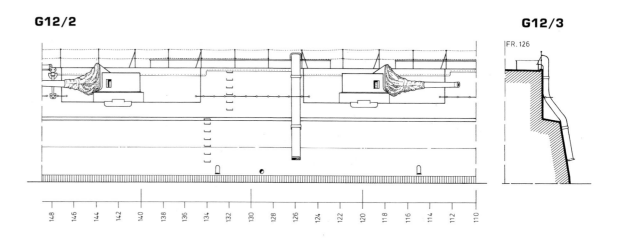

G12/6

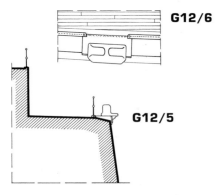

G12/5

G12/7

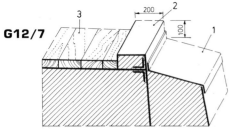

G12/4

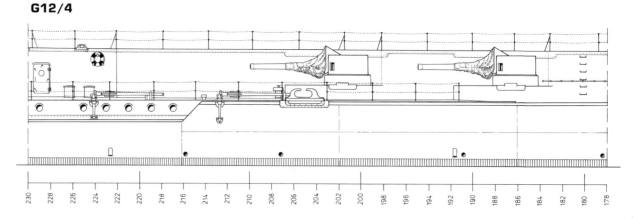

G13 Ventilator fans fitted on both sides of barbette No 2 36cm gun turret (scale 1:200)

G13/1 Plan

G13/2 Profile

G13/3 View from stern

G14 Starboard fore side view, April 1938 (scale 1:200)

Note: second hawse pipe was removed and hole covered by steel plate, the upper limit of red-brown colour was heightened

G15 Detail of join between the side wall of casemate deck and No 4 main gun barbette (on both sides) (no scale)

G13/1

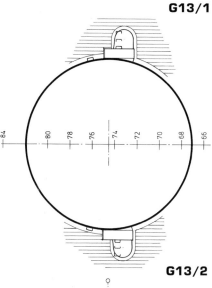

G13/2

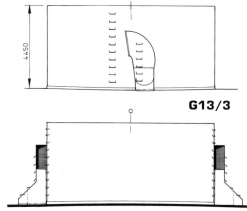

G13/3

G15

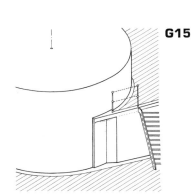

G14

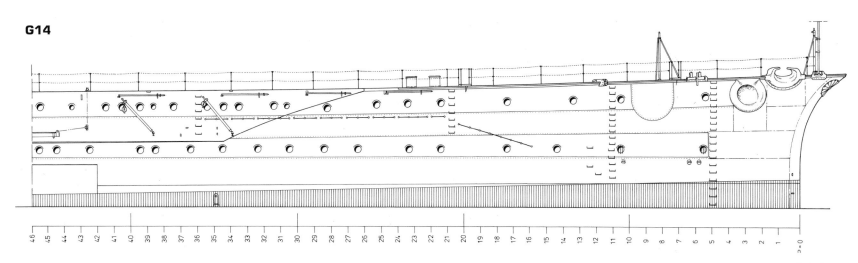

G16 Stern part of hull, March 1935 to 1940, after extension of stern (scale 1:100)

G16/1 Plan

G16/2 Starboard side view

G16/3 Port side view

G16/4 View from stern from
frame 242 on barbette
No 5 main guns and
rear 15cm gun
casemates

G16/5 Plan of barbette No 5
turret with ventilators

1 Dressing line
2 Antenna wire
3 Tripod – stanchion of awning and
antenna wires
4 Awning stanchion
5 Bulge-sponson – fitted as aircraft
crane engine room but not used
before 1941
6 Skylight
7 Hatch

G16/4

G16/5

G16/1

G16/2

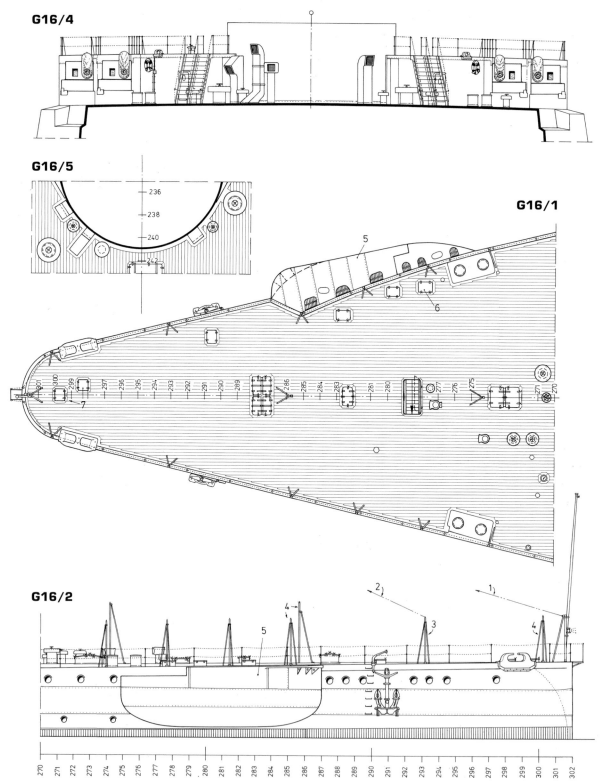

G16/3

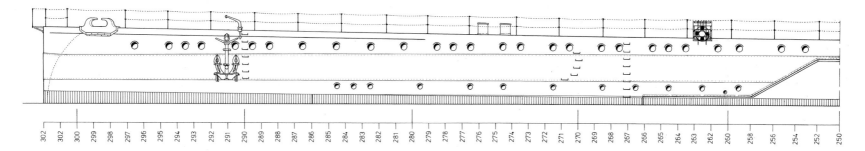

302 302 300 299 298 297 296 295 294 293 292 291 290 289 288 287 286 285 284 283 282 281 280 279 278 277 276 275 274 273 272 271 270 269 268 267 266 265 264 263 262 260 258 256 254 252 250

G17 Views of ship's side in 1944 (fragments) (scale 1:200)

Note: Removal in 1937–38 refit of fore pair of secondary casemate 15cm guns (No 1 and No 2 turrets)

Degaussing cable fitted in 1942

Lower (below UD) side scuttles closed

Platform-sponson of crane stay position fitted

G17/1 Fore starboard side (fragments)

G17/2 Port side view of stern part

G17/1

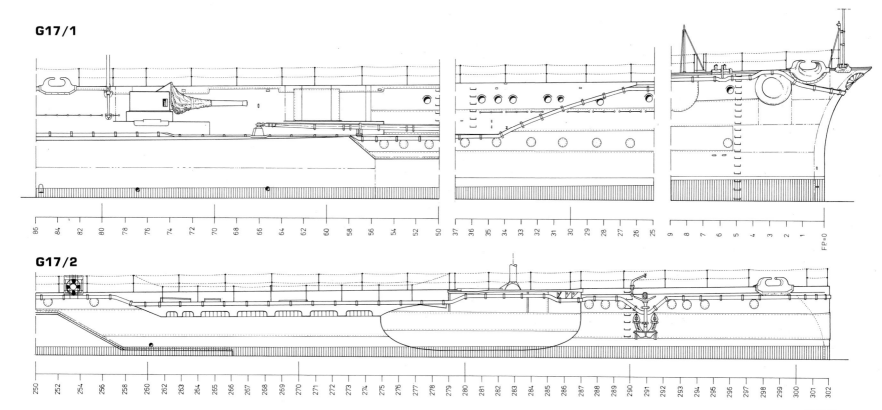

86 84 82 80 78 76 74 72 70 68 66 64 62 60 58 56 54 52 50   37 36 35 34 33 32 31 30 29 28 27 26 25   9 8 7 6 5 4 3 2 1 FP=0

G17/2

250 252 254 256 258 260 262 263 264 265 266 267 268 269 270 271 272 273 274 275 276 277 278 279 280 281 282 283 284 285 286 287 288 289 290 291 292 293 294 295 296 297 298 299 300 301 302

G18 Aircraft equipment on stern deck of hull fitted in 1940–1 modernisation

G18/1 Plan of aircraft deck
(scale 1:200)

G18/2 Port side elevation
(scale 1:200)

1 19.5m catapult type 'Kure shiki 2 Go 5 Gata'
2 Catapult turntable
3 Turntable for rails
4 Deck rails
5 Deck covered by linoleum sheets
6 Brass strip (width 30mm) – support for linoleum joints
7 Aircraft crane stay platform
8 Aircraft crane stay position
9 Deck cover plate of crane column
10 Washdeck locker
11 Hatch
12 Skylight
13 Ventilator
14 Bollards (new position)
15 Crane hand operating
16 12m ensign staff and antenna support
17 Scupper

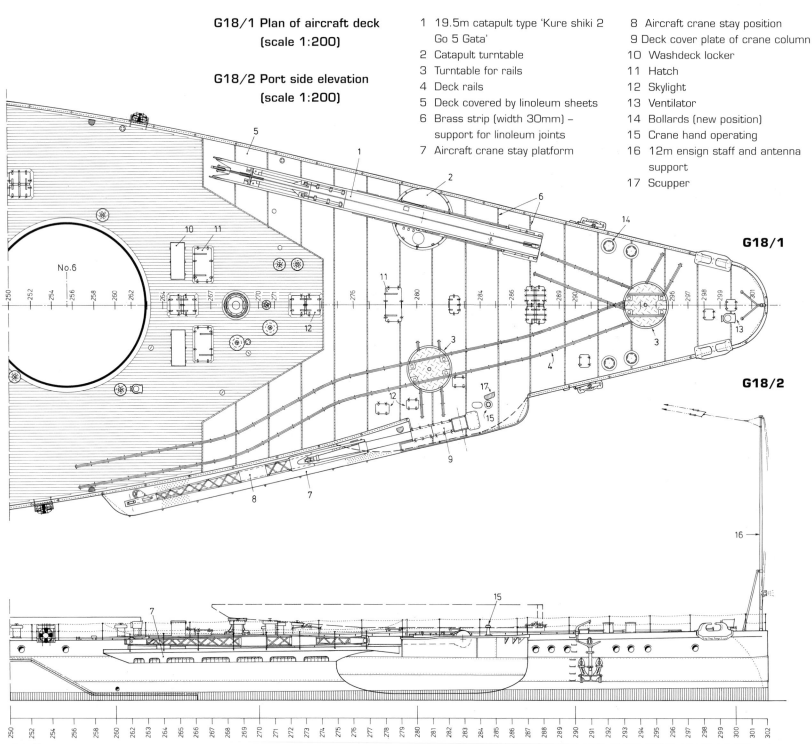

G18/1

G18/2

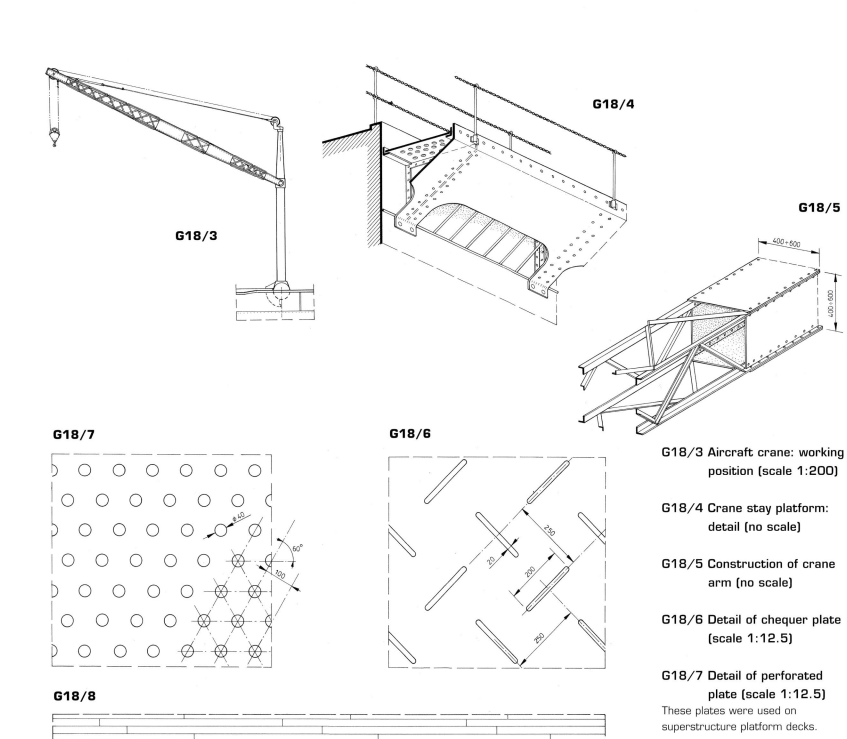

G18/3

G18/4

G18/5

400÷600

400÷600

G18/7

Φ40

60°

100

G18/6

250

20

200

250

G18/8

G18/3 Aircraft crane: working
position (scale 1:200)

G18/4 Crane stay platform:
detail (no scale)

G18/5 Construction of crane
arm (no scale)

G18/6 Detail of chequer plate
(scale 1:12.5)

G18/7 Detail of perforated
plate (scale 1:12.5)
These plates were used on
superstructure platform decks.

G18/8 Scheme of deck
planking (4.5–5.5m-long
17.7cm-wide teak wood)
(Scale 1:100)

217

G19 Typical reels (scale 1:50)

G19/1 Profile of 1,000mm- 1,750mm- and 2,250mm-wide reels

G19/2 1,000mm-wide reel (fore deck) (front view)

G19/3 1,000mm-wide reel (fore deck) (plan)

G19/4 1,750mm-wide reel (rear deck) (front view)

G19/5 2,250mm-wide reel (rear deck) (front view)

G19/6 Side disk of rear reels

G19/7 Reel from sides of No 1 turret barbette (profile)

G19/8 Reel from sides of No 1 turret barbette (front view)

G20 Paravane (scale 1:50)

G20/1 Plan

G20/2 Profile with deck cradle

G20/3 Front view

G20/4 Section with view on deck cradle

G20/5 Section A-A

G21 Typical electric deck winch (scale 1:40)

G21/1 Front view

G21/2 Plan

218

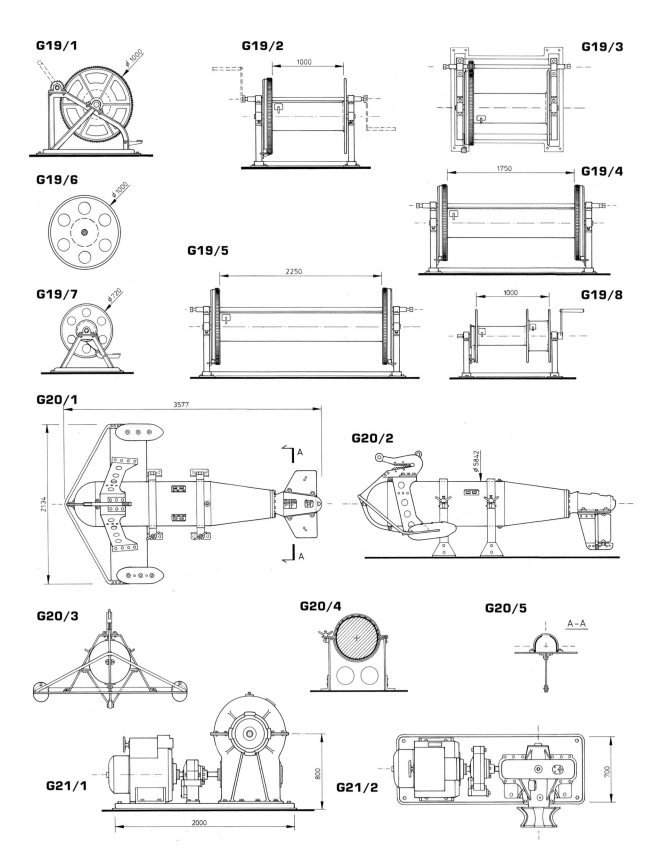

G22 Folded guard rails (scale 1:25)

G22/1 Front view
G22/2 Front view (stanchion with stay)
G22/3 Profile
G22/4 Plan

1 Guard rail stanchion
2 Guard rail of chain
3 Spurnwater
4 Stanchion stay
5 Scupper
6 Deck planking

G22/5 Section of deck (FD) between casemate turrets
G22/6 Section of deck (FD) above casemate turret
G22/7 Section of deck (UD) of lengthened part of hull
G22/8 Base of stanchion (view from ship's side) (scale 1:12.5)

G22/9 Base of stanchion (profile, scale 1:12.5)
G22/10 Axonometric view of base (no scale)

G23 Typical closed deck holes (the largest also an escape hole) (no scale)

G23/1 Front view
G23/2 Profile
G23/3 Plan

G23A Typical fairlead (scale 1:50)

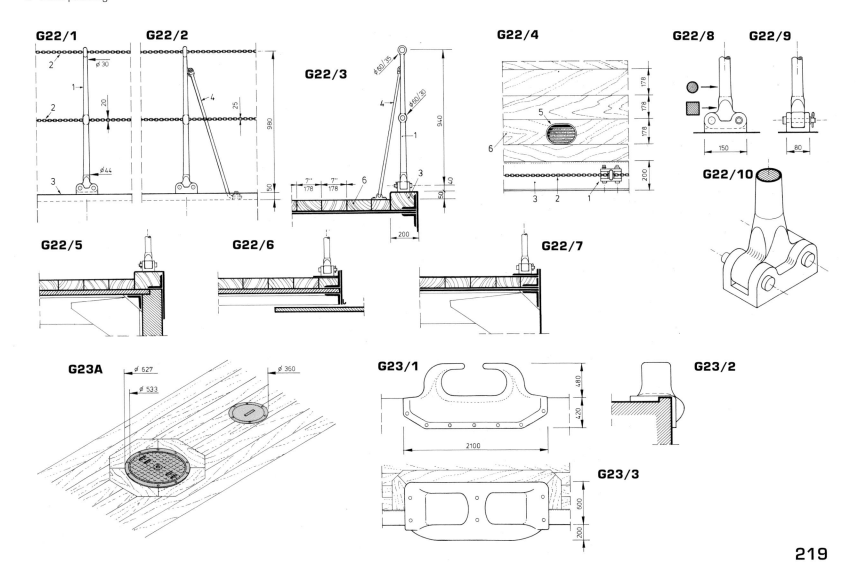

G24 Davits

G24/1 Davit of 6m or 8m sampan (only port sides) (scale 1: 100)

G24/2 Davit of 9m cutter (fitted on both sides of hull) (scale 1:100)

G24/3 Davit of 9m cutter (frames 105, 148, 157 and 173)

G24/4 Davit of 9m cutter (fore of pairs from UD) (scale 1:100)

G24/5 Davit of 9m cutter (rear of pair from UD) (scale 1:100)

G24/6 Davit of accommodation ladder (until 1935) (scale 1:100)

G24/7 Head of davit (profile, scale 1:2)

G24/8 Head of davit (profile of another type, scale 1:25)

G24/9 Head of davit (front view, scale 1:25)

G24/10 Typical davit block (scale 1:25)

G24/11 Davit base (profile, scale 1:25)

G24/12 Davit base (front view, scale 1:25)

G24/13 Detail of davit construction

G24/1 **G24/2** **G24/3**

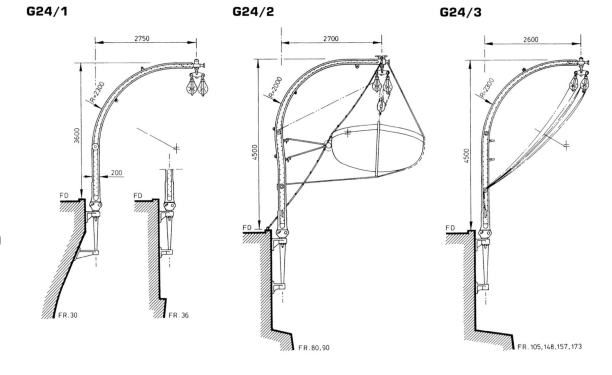

G24/4 **G24/5** **G24/6**

G24/7

G24/8

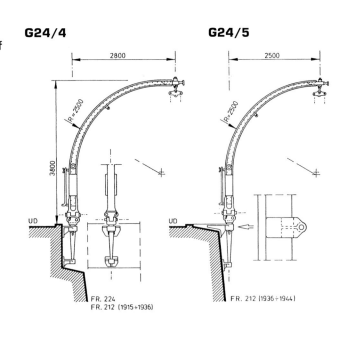

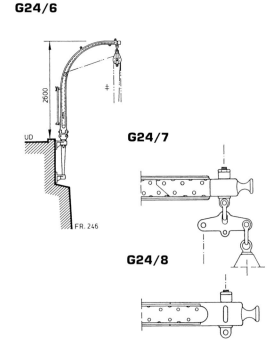

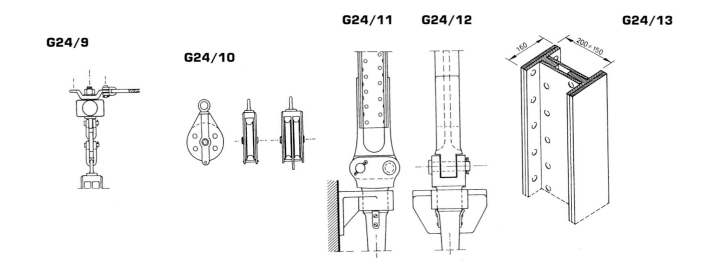

G24/9

G24/10

G24/11   **G24/12**

G24/13

160   200÷150

G25/1

G25/2

G25 Roller fairlead
     for paravane
     (scale 1:25)

G25/1 Front view
G25/2 Profile
G25/3 Plan
G25/4 Section

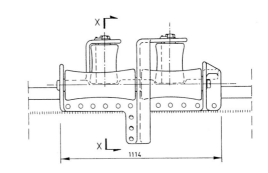

X

X

1114

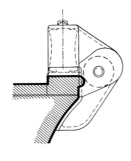

G25/3

G25/4

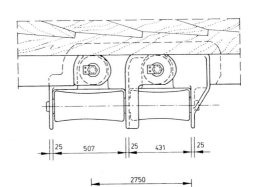

25   507   25   431   25

2750

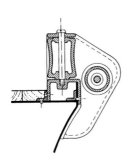

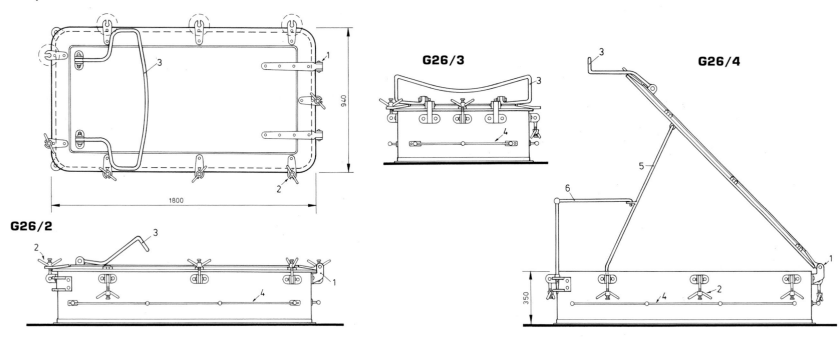

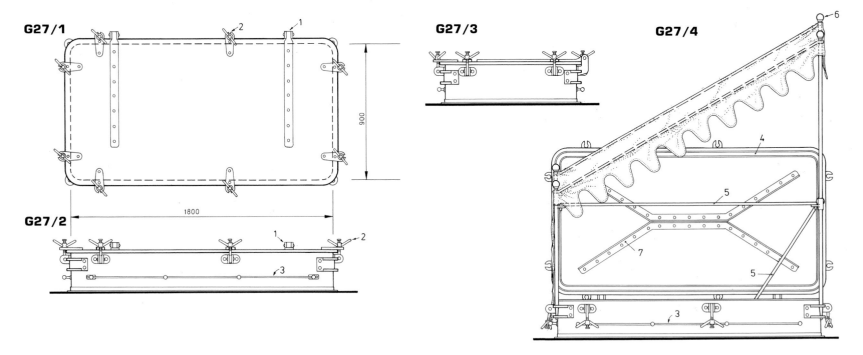

222

G26 Deck hatch (type used on fore deck) (scale 1:25)

G26/1 Plan
G26/2 Profile
G26/3 View from bow
G26/4 Profile with open hatch
1 Hinge
2 Butterfly nut
3 Flat bar
4 Canvas support
5 Hatch cover stay
6 Handrail

G27 Deck hatch (type used on rear deck (UD) (scale 1:25)

G27/1 Plan
G27/2 Profile
G27/3 Front view
G27/4 Open hatch with canvas roof
G27/5 Perspective of open hatch
1 Hinge
2 Butterfly nut
3 Canvas support
4 Hatch cover washer (gummi)
5 Handrail
6 Brass balls
7 Cover reinforcement (of angle bars)

G28 Typical skylights with scuttles protected by steel bars (after 1941 by steel covers) (scale 1:30)

G28/1 Plan of 1,200mm-wide skylight
G28/2 Plan of 1,000mm-wide skylight
G28/3 Profile
G28/4 Plan of skylight fitted at superstructure wall
G28/5 Profile of skylight fitted at superstructure wall
G28/6 Plan of skylight with scuttles protected by steel covers (all skylights after 1941)
G28/7 Profile of cover with protected scuttles

G29 Skylight without scuttles (types 700mm x 800mm and 800mm x 1,000mm) (scale 1:15)

G29/1 Plan
G29/2 Profile
G29/3 Section
G29/4 Frosted glass windows of skylights (all types) (no scale)

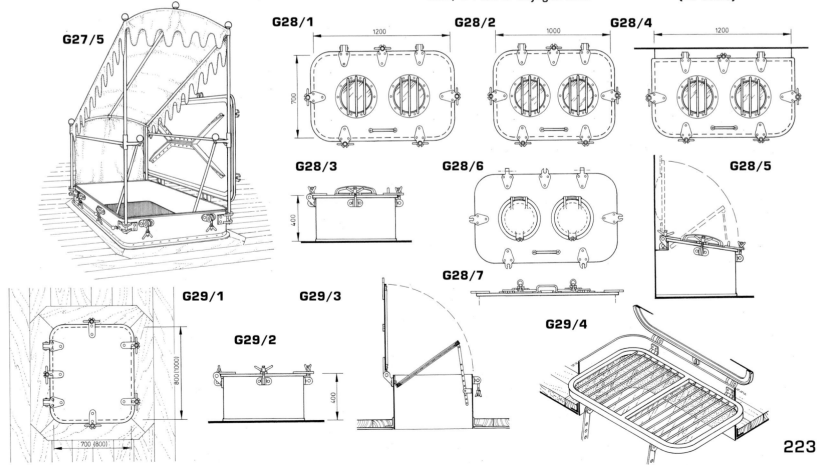

G27/5

G28/1   G28/2   G28/4
1200   1000   1200
700

G28/3   G28/6   G28/5
400

G28/7

G29/1   G29/3   G29/4
800 (1000)

G29/2
400

700 (800)

223

G30 Larger skylight (main types) (scale 1:30)

G30/1 Skylight before No 2 main gun turret (plan)

G30/2 Skylight before No 2 main gun turret (profile)

G30/3 Skylight from stern deck (frame 250, and frame 287 until 1935) (plan)

G30/4 Skylight from stern deck (frame 250, and frame 287 until 1935) (profile)

G30/5 Skylight from stern deck (frame 287 after 1935) (plan)

G30/6 Skylight from stern deck (frame 287 after 1935) (profile)

G30/7 Skylight from stern deck (frame 273) and boat deck (FD) (plan)

G30/8 Skylight from stern deck (frame 273) and boat deck (FD) (profile)

G30/9 Skylight from stern deck (frame 265) (plan)

G30/10 Skylight from stern deck (frame 265) (profile)

1 Hinge
2 Butterfly nut
3 Frosted glass windows
4 Stanchion for holding open watertight cover
5 Window lifting bar
6 Dividing plate

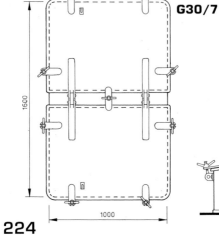

G30/1

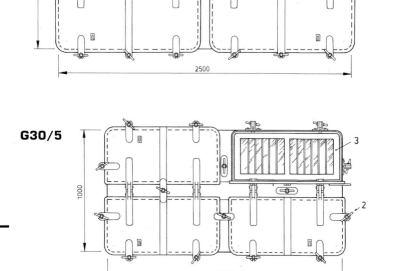

G30/9

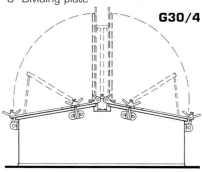

G30/5

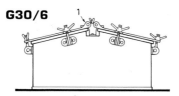

G30/4

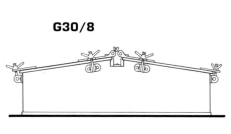

G30/2

G30/7

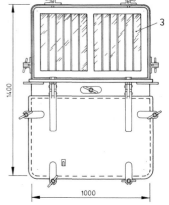

G30/3

G30/6

G30/8

G30/10

G31 Typical mushroom vents (scale 1:50)

G31/1 Mushroom vents fitted on forecastle and upper decks

G31/2 Mushroom intake vents

G31/3 Mushroom vents (intake) from bow and stern deck (stripe indicates direction to bow)

G31/4 Mushroom vents, from 1915–3

G31/5 General view of mushroom vent (no scale)

G31/1

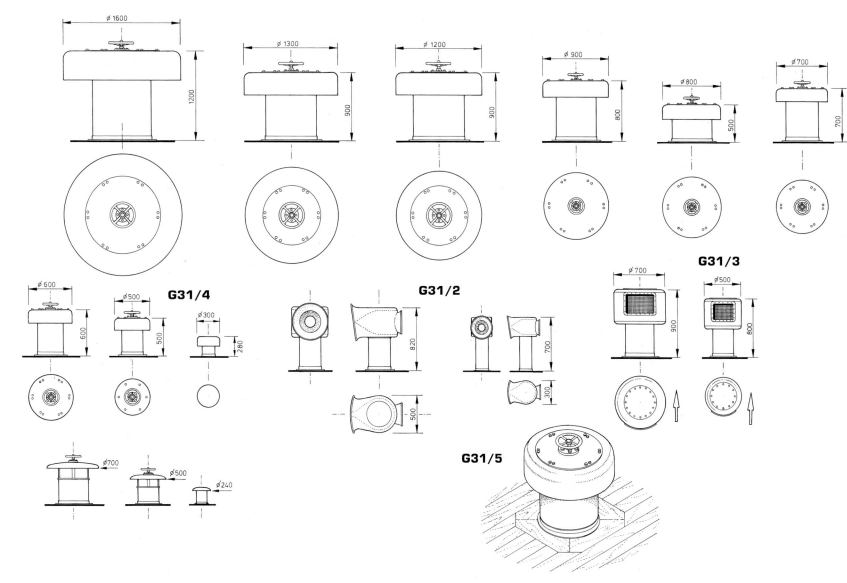

G31/4

G31/2

G31/3

G31/5

G32 110cm searchlight used 1915-30 (scale 1:50)

G32/1 Profile

G32/2 Front view

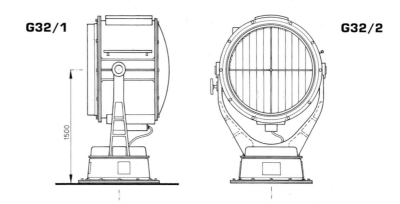

G32/1

G32/2

G33 110cm searchlight used 1925–37 in scheme designated 'A' (fitted on pagoda tower rear platform and rear platform of funnel) (scale 1:50)

G33/1 Left profile

G33/2 Front view

G33/3 Plan

G33/4 Right profile

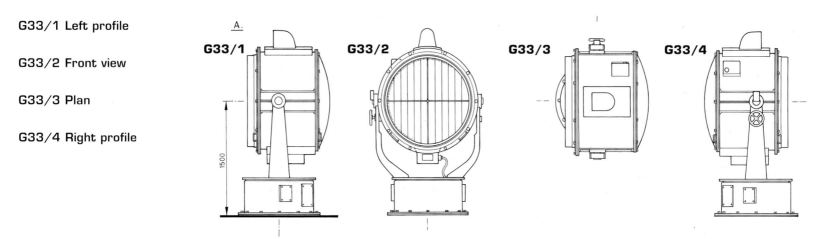

A.

G33/1   G33/2   G33/3   G33/4

G34 110cm searchlight 'Su-shiki' used 1933–41 in scheme designated 'B' (scale 1:50)

G34/1 Left profile

G34/2 Front view

G34/3 Right profile

G34/4 Plan

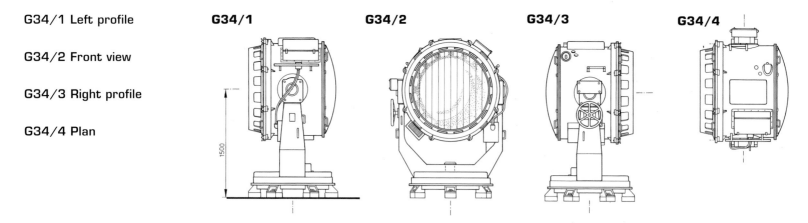

G34/1   G34/2   G34/3   G34/4

G35 110cm searchlight '92 shiki' used after 1938 in scheme designated 'C' (scale 1:25)

G35/1 Left profile

G35/2 Front view

G35/3 Right profile

G35/4 Plan

G35/5 Rear cover

G35/6 Plan of searchlight base

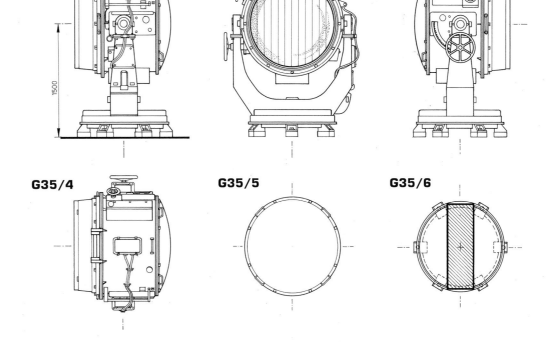

G35/1   G35/2   G35/3

G35/4   G35/5   G35/6

G36 Arrangement of 110cm searchlights (designated in text 'A', 'B' and 'C') on funnel platforms during years 1933–44

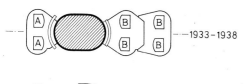
1933–1938

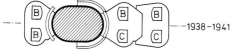
1938–1941

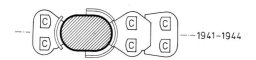
1941–1944

G37 60cm searchlight used mainly for signalling (fitted on both sides of pagoda tower) (scale 1:50)

G37/1 Left profile

G37/2 Front view

G37/3 Right profile

G37/4 Plan

G37/5 Rear cover

G37/6 Detail of fore frame mounting (no scale)

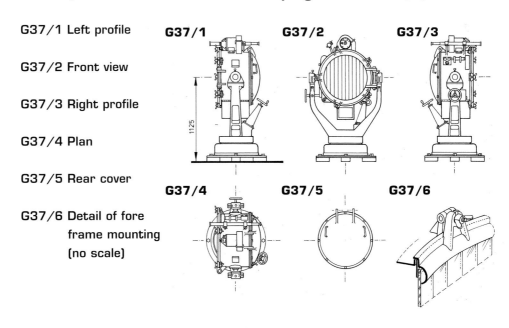

G37/1   G37/2   G37/3

G37/4   G37/5   G37/6

G38 30cm deck lamp (scale 1:25)

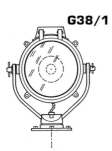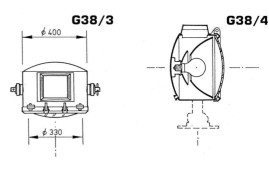

G38/1 Front view
G38/2 Right profile
G38/3 Plan
G38/4 Section

G39 Signalling lamp (fitted on both sides of battle bridge platform) (scale 1:25)

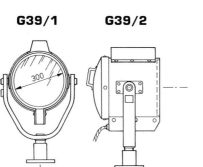

G39/1 Front view
G39/2 Profile

G40 2kw daylight signal lantern (fitted on signal yards on both sides of searchlight control platform – level X of pagoda tower) (scale 1:20)

G40/1 Side view
G40/2 Plan

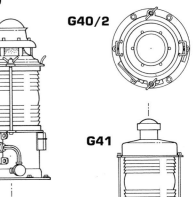

G42 Side scuttle (scale 1:20)

G42/1 Side scuttle (inner view)

G42/2 Section

G42/3 Front view of side scuttle from superstructure

G42/4 Front view of side scuttle from ship sides (stern part of middle deck compartments and superstructure)

G42/5 Front view of side scuttle from ship sides (upper deck and main deck compartments)

1 Scuttle or port
2 Scuttle frame
3 Deadlight
4 Rubber sealing ring
5 Sidelight glass
6 Sidelight frame
7 Butterfly clips
8 Clip lug
9 Save-all
10 Hinge
11 Back of deadlight
12 Rigol
13 Ship side plating
14 Arrow indicating direction to bow

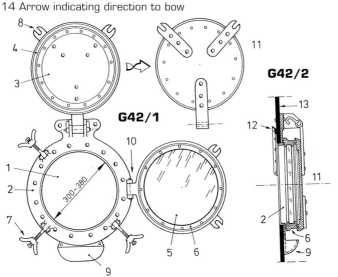

G41 Typical lantern (scale 1:20)

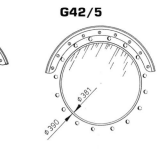

G43 Watertight door from rear of casemate deck (frame 230)

G43/1 Watertight door open (scale 1:37.5)
G43/2 Outer surface of door (scale 1:37.5)
G43/3 Section (scale 1:37.5)
G43/4 Section of clip (scale 1:5)
G43/5 View of clip (scale 1:5)
G43/6 Section of hinge (scale 1:5)
G43/7 View of hinge (scale 1:5)

G44 Typical watertight door (scale 1:37.5)

G44/1 Open door (with circle or square upper part, on
      square form as on lower part) (scale 1:37.5)
G44/2 Section (scale 1:37.5)
G44/3 Outer surface (scale 1:37.5)
G44/4 Watertight door (from lower parts of superstructure)
      (scale 1:37.5)
G44/5 Section of clip (scale 1:5)
G44/6 View of clip (scale 1:5)

1 Clip
2 Wedge on face of door
3 Hinge
4 Angle bar door frame (both sides of bulkhead)
5 Rubber seal
6 Bulkhead
7 Rigol
8 20cm diameter door scuttle
9 Colour sign (white)
10 Door handle (both sides)
11 Inner reinforcement
12 Stamping reinforcement (middle inner, upper and lower outer)

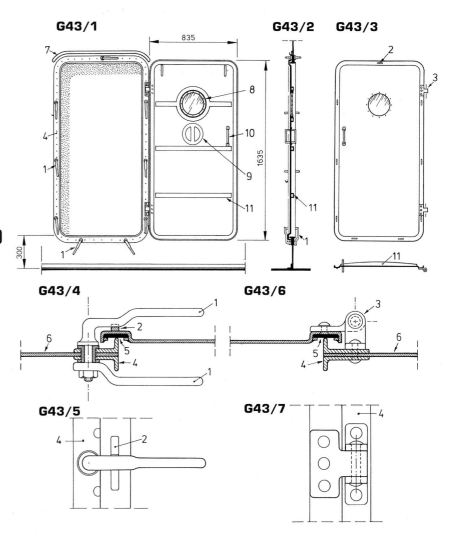

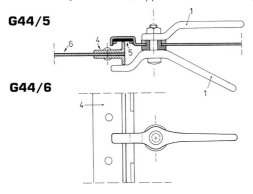

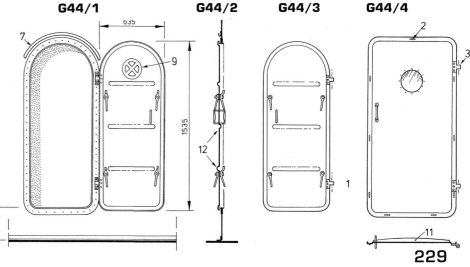

229

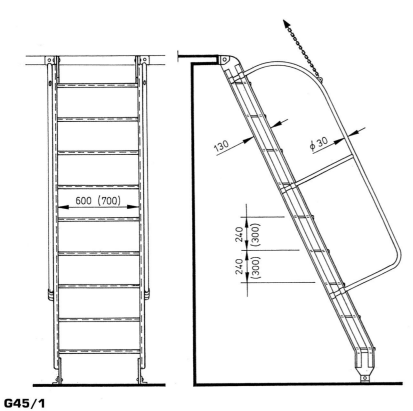

G45 Typical ladders (scale 1:37.5)

G45/1 Ladder from UD to FD, from FD to superstructures, from lower to middle platforms of superstructure

G45/2 Ladder from upper parts of superstructure

G45/3 Ladder from superstructure walls

G45/4 Ladder from funnel, from inner spaces

G45/1

G45/2

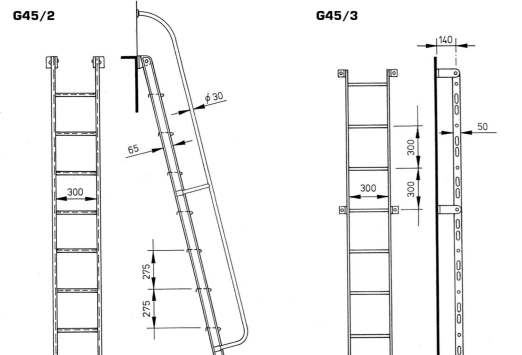

G45/3

G45/4

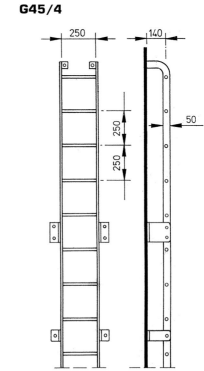

H AIRCRAFT EQUIPMENT

H1 Catapult 'Shiki 2 Go 5 Gata' (Type 2 Model 5) fitted on stern deck during refit 1940–41 (scale 1:50)

Note: For the catapult used 1933–40, see drawings of No 3 main gun turret

H1/1 Starboard elevation and deck trolley with catapult cradle

H1/2 Plan of catapult and trolley

H1/3 Rear view of catapult and base ring

H1/4 Front view of the deck trolley

H1/5 Axonometry of catapult structure (no scale)

H1/6 Perspective view of fore part (no scale)

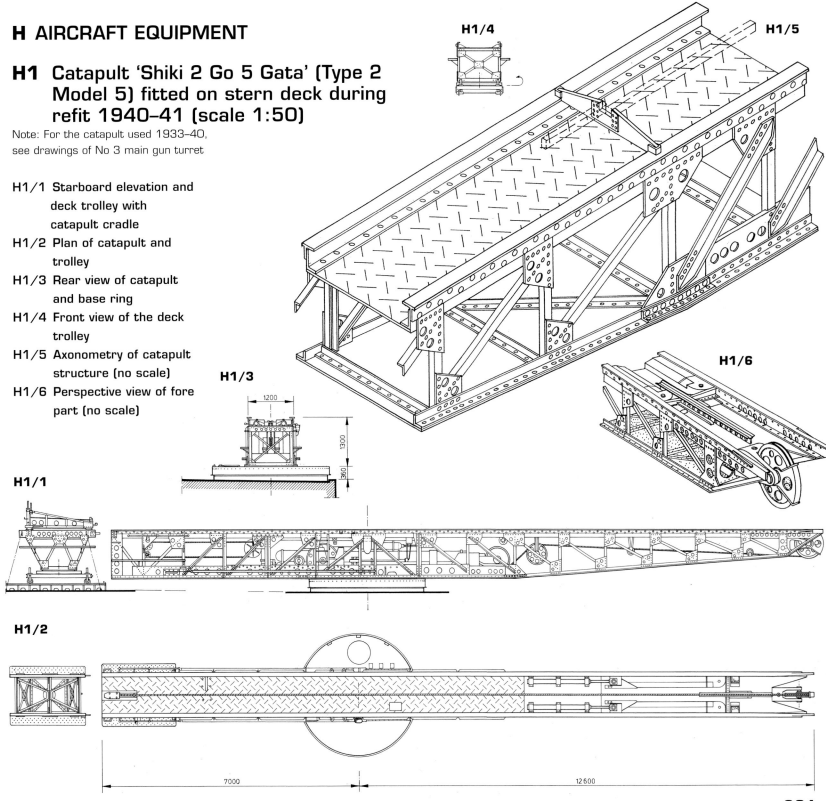

H2 Turntable for aircraft deck rails
(scale 1:50)

H2/1 Plan

H2/2 Profile

1 Non-rotating girder
2 Rotating platform of turntable
3 Stopper for trolley
4 Stopper of turn
5 Rails

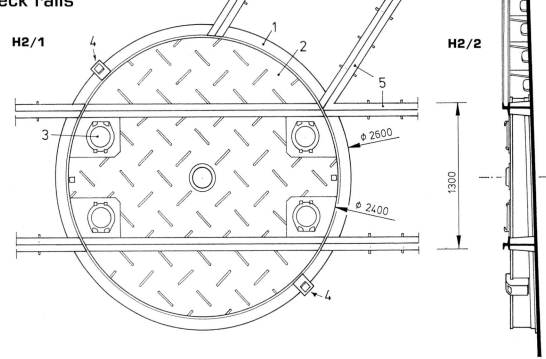

H3 Aircraft deck rails
(scale 1:12.5)

H3/1 Deck rails (section)

H3/2 Rail base with height
       dependent on deck chamber
       (for identical rail level);
       height about 200–250mm

1 Rail
2 Rail base
3 Deck level
4 Hole

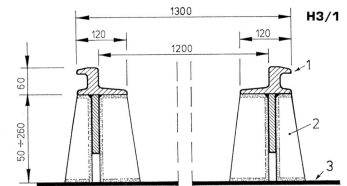

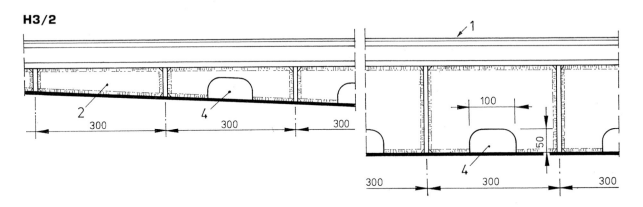

H4 Catapult cradle
for single
floatplane
(E4N2, E8N2
and F1M2)
(no scale)

H5 Trolley for
floatplane
transport on
deck rails and
ramps to
elevator, used
1933–44

(axonometric view)

(no scale)

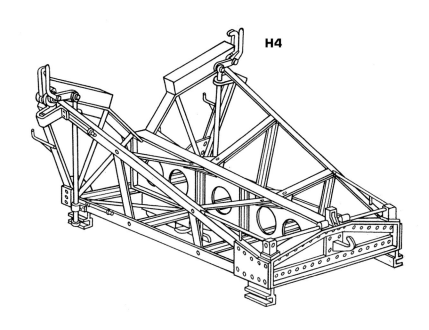

H4

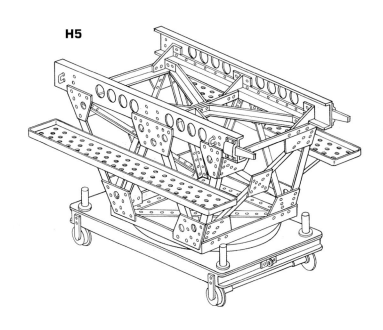

H5

J   AIRCRAFT

J1   Nakajima E4N2 Navy Type 90-2 Reconnaissance floatplane, May 1933–February 1937 (scale 1:100)

J1/1   Profile view

J1/2   Front view

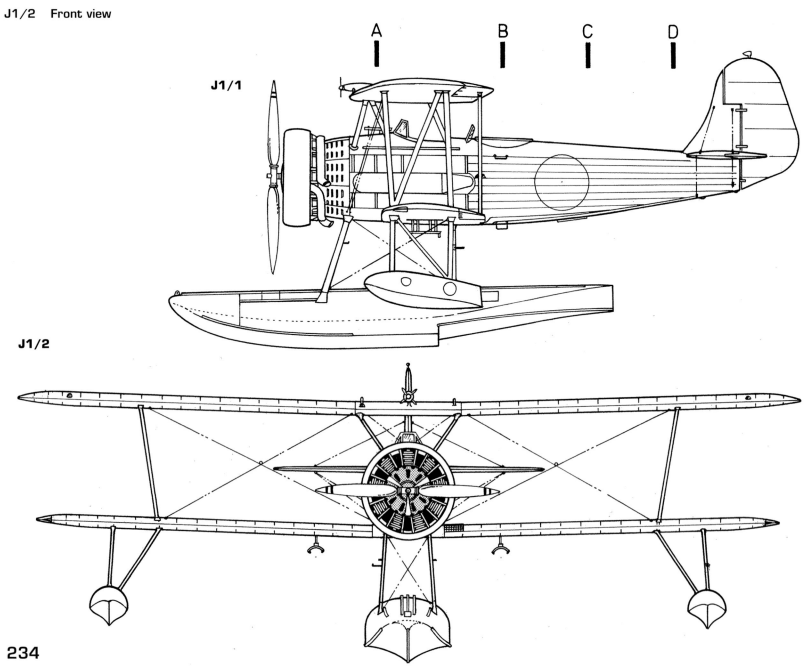

234

J1/3 Plan

J1/4 Sections

J1/5 Fore part
Black colour of couling,
silver-and-light-grey body

J1/6 Back part
Red 'hinomaru', fin and tail
plane. Black colour
inscription. White colour
inscription (FU-SA-U) on
upper part of tail plane

J1/7 Upper wing of aircraft
No 2, black inscription
(FU-SA-U) with red
'hinomaru'

J1/8 Upper wing of aircraft
No 3

J1/9 Upper wing of aircraft
No 1 (fragment)

J1/10 Lower wing underside
inscription of No 2 (No
1 and No 3 identical
except for number)

J1/11 White stripes on red
tailplane for rear
gunner

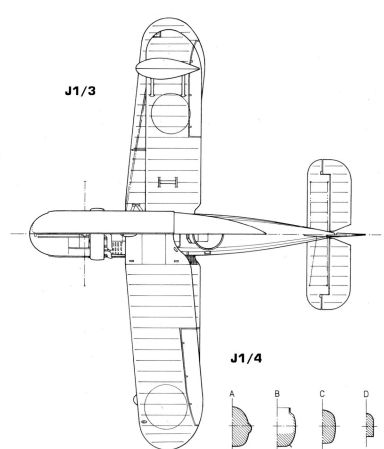

J1/3

J1/4

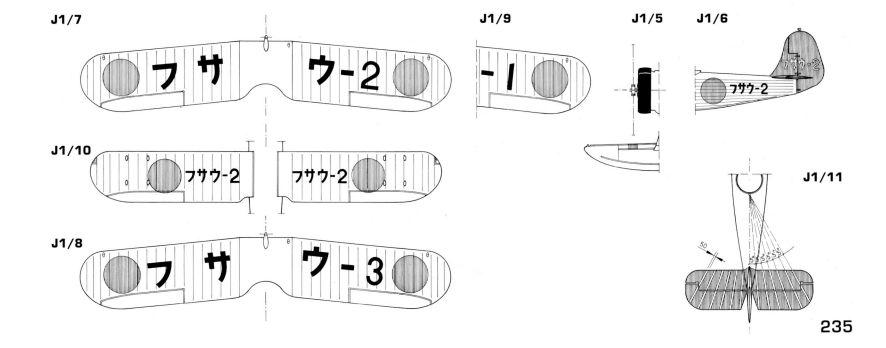

J1/7

J1/9   J1/5   J1/6

J1/10

J1/8

J1/11

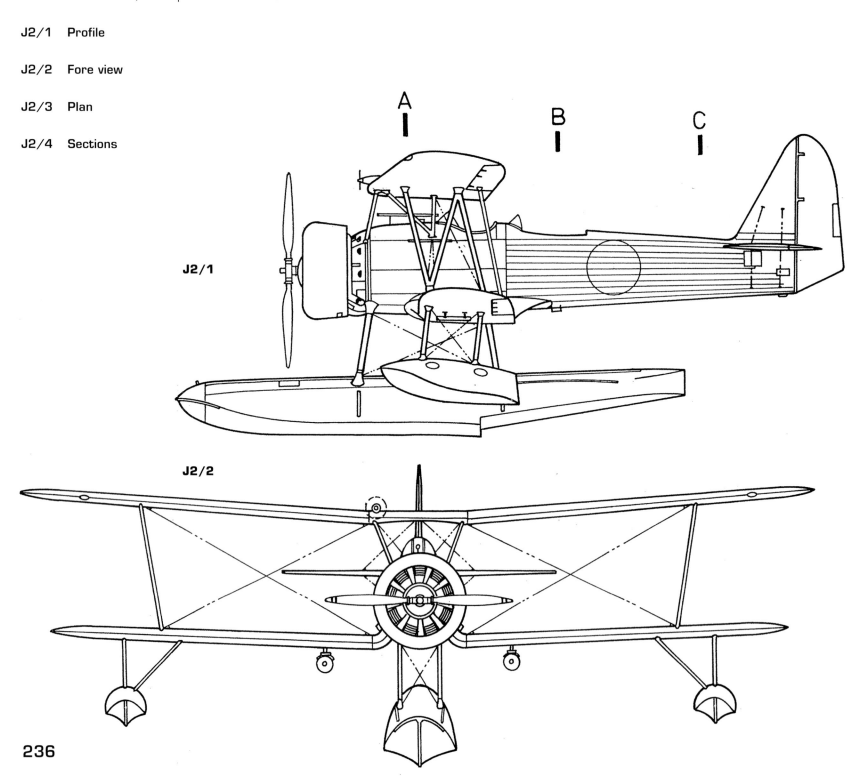

J2 Nakajima E8N2 Navy Type-95 reconnaissance floatplane (scale 1:100)

Allied codename 'Dave'; used April 1938–end of 1942

J2/1 Profile

J2/2 Fore view

J2/3 Plan

J2/4 Sections

A

B

C

J2/1

J2/2

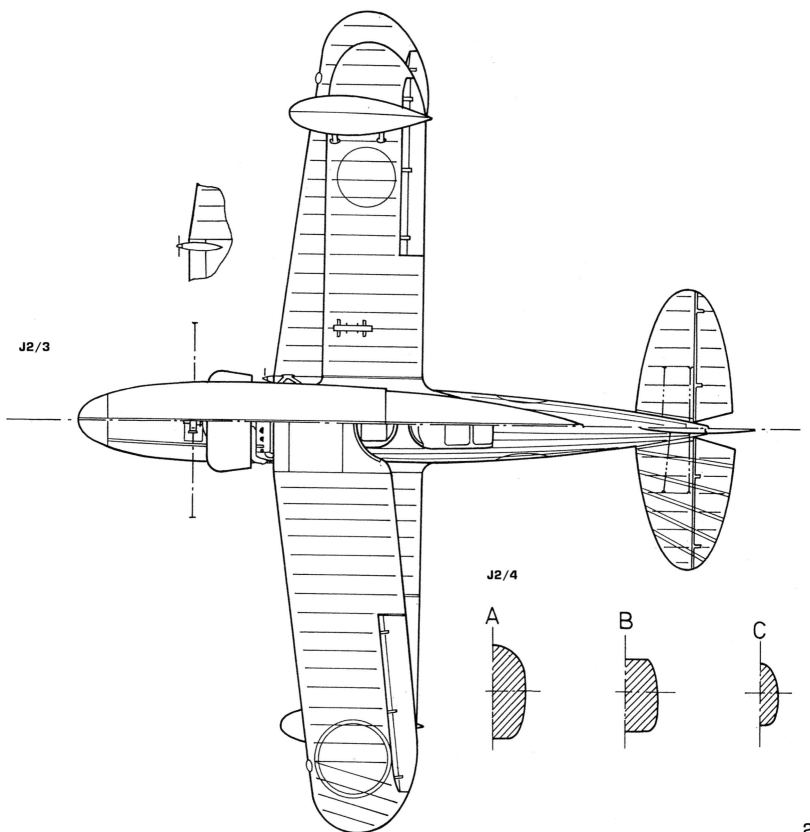

J2/3

J2/4

A   B   C

J3 Mitsubishi F1M2 Navy 'Type-O' (zero) reconnaissance floatplane (scale 1:100)

Allied codename "Pete"; used since early 1943

J3/1 Profile

J3/2 Fore view

J3/3 Plan

J3/4 Sections

J3/5 Triple-bladed propeller

J3/6 60kg bomb

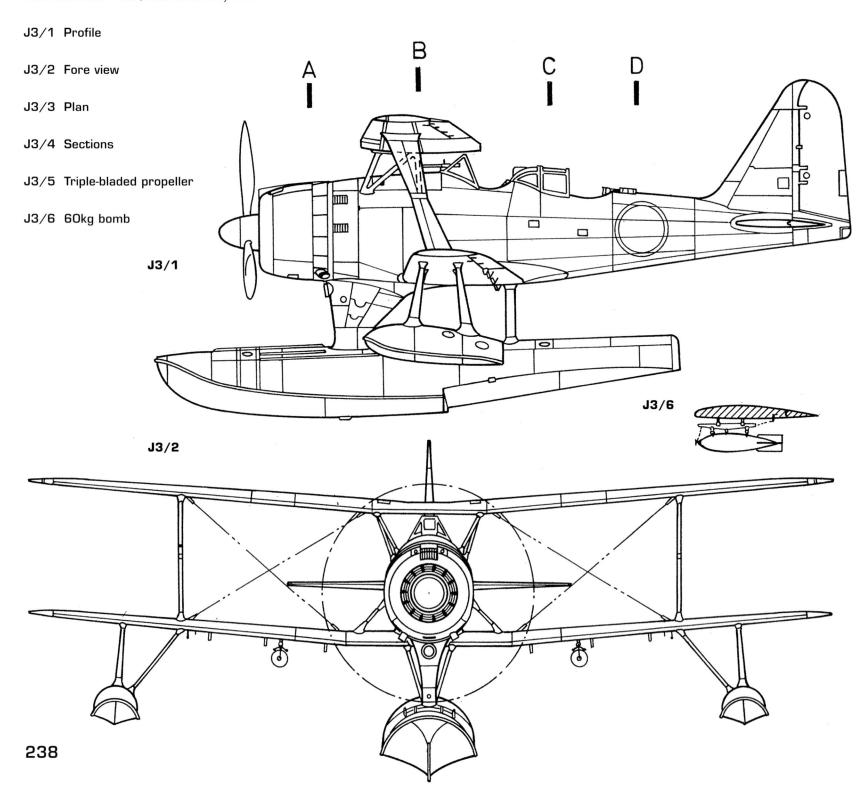

J3/1

J3/2

J3/6

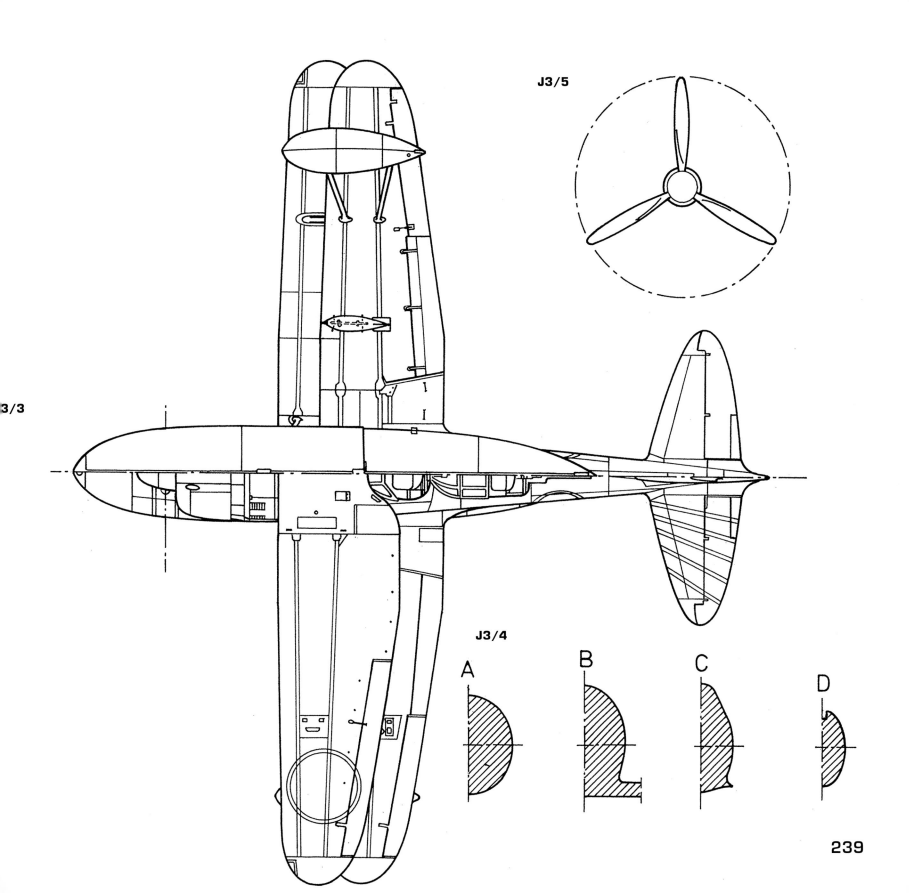

J3/5

J3/3

J3/4

A   B   C   D

239

K   BOATS

K1   17m steam pinnace – ceremonial barge (scale 1:100)

Two boats with white hulls and cabins, red-brown underwater hull surface, black upper part of funnel; used 1915–30.
One boat painted grey (hull, cabins, funnel) and unpainted wood deck; used 1933–34 (stowed on port side of boat deck)

K1/1   Profile (paint scheme 1915–33)

K1/2   Plan

K1/1

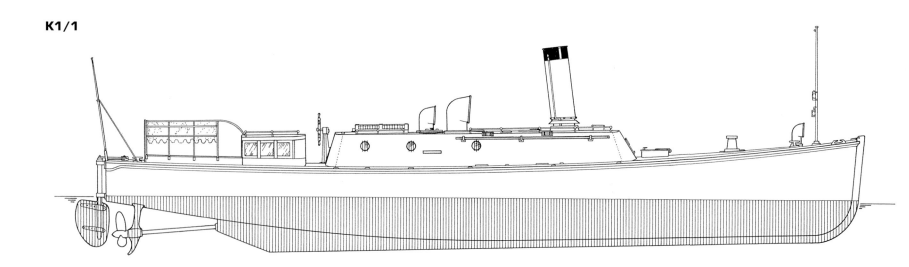

K1/2

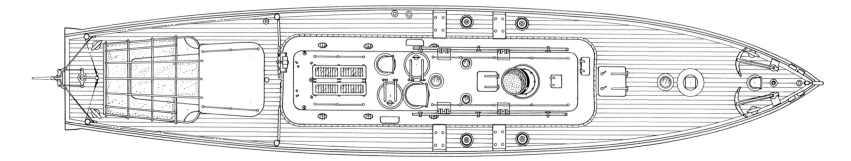

K2   17m motor pinnace – ceremonial barge (scale 1:100)

Used March 1935–February 1937; on port side of boat deck (replaced 17m steam pinnace).

Note: On board stowage: funnel, mast, ensign staff, jackstaff, lights stanchion, vent intake, glass windscreen were removed and stowed on boat deck. This scheme included 17m pinnaces in 1915–37

K2/1   Profile

K2/2   Plan

K2/1

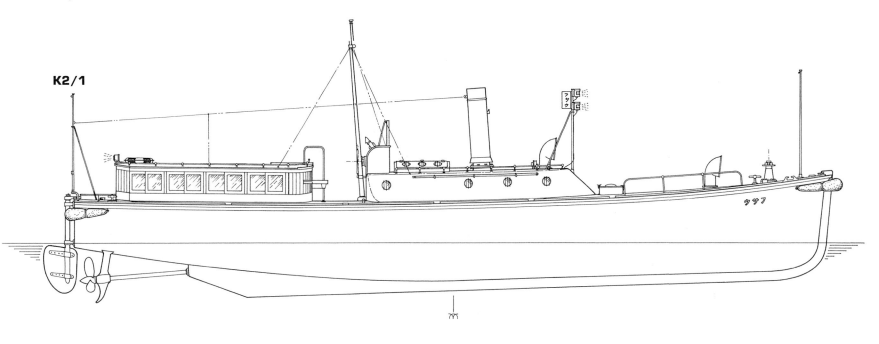

K2/2

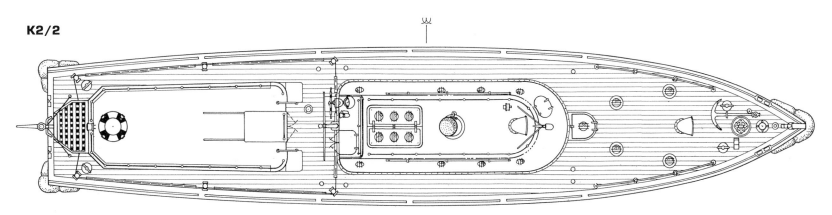

K2/3   Internal profile

K2/4   Internal plan

K2/5   Body plan

K2/6   Section (frame 5, with view to stern)

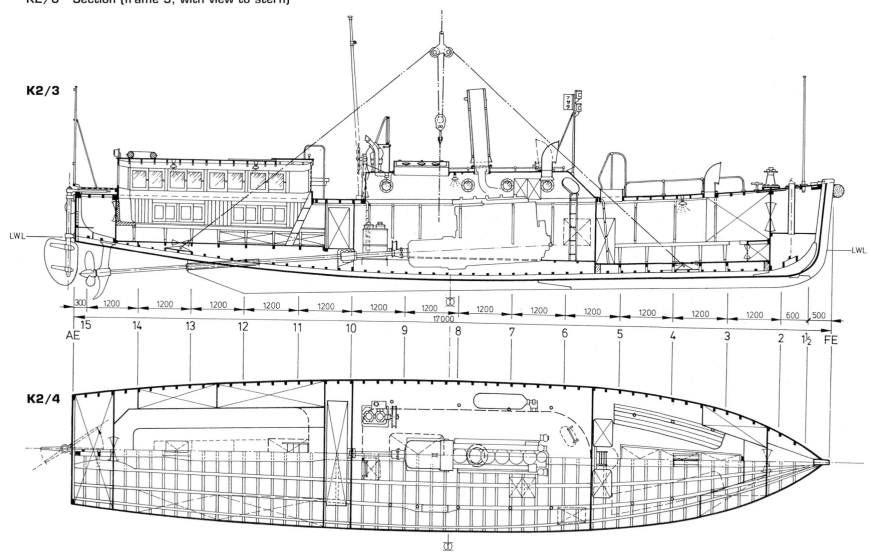

K2/3

LWL

LWL

300 | 1200 | 1200 | 1200 | 1200 | 1200 | 1200 | 1200 | 1200 | 1200 | 1200 | 1200 | 1200 | 1200 | 600 | 500

17 000

15 14 13 12 11 10 9 8 7 6 5 4 3 2 1½ FE

AE

K2/4

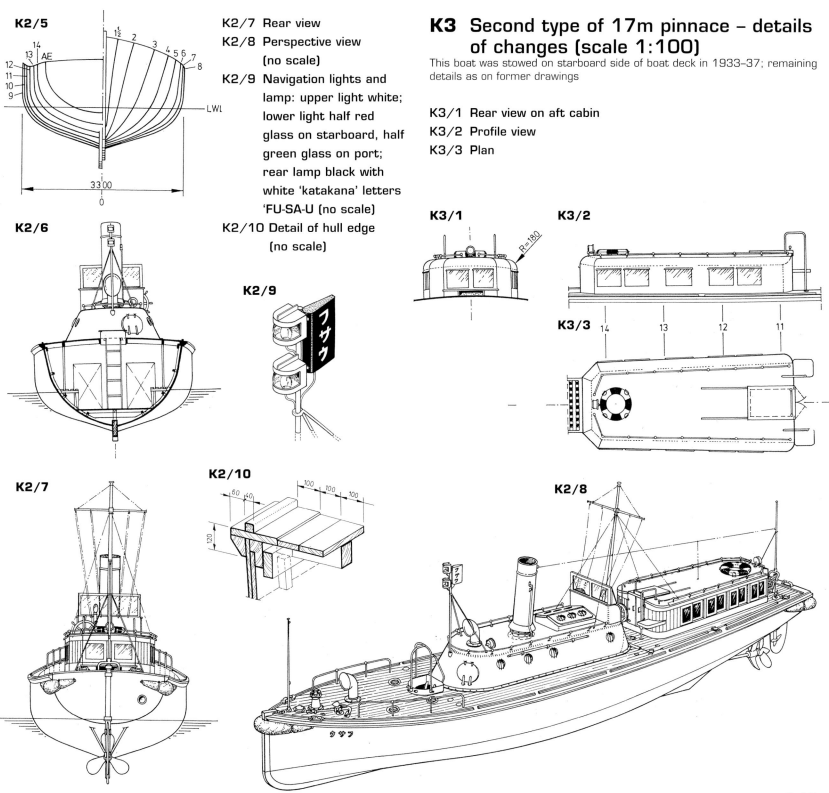

K2/5

14
13 AE
12
11
10
9
1½ 2 3 4 5 6 7 8
LWL

33·00
0

K2/6

K2/7

K2/10

60 40 100 100 100
120

K2/7 Rear view
K2/8 Perspective view
       (no scale)
K2/9 Navigation lights and
       lamp: upper light white;
       lower light half red
       glass on starboard, half
       green glass on port;
       rear lamp black with
       white 'katakana' letters
       'FU-SA-U (no scale)
K2/10 Detail of hull edge
       (no scale)

K2/9

フサウ

K3 Second type of 17m pinnace – details
      of changes (scale 1:100)

This boat was stowed on starboard side of boat deck in 1933–37; remaining
details as on former drawings

K3/1 Rear view on aft cabin
K3/2 Profile view
K3/3 Plan

K3/1

R=180

K3/2

K3/3

14   13   12   11

K2/8

フサウ

クサフ

243

K4 11m 60hp motor boat (scale 1:75)

K4/1   Side elevation

K4/2   Plan

K4/3   Detail of canvas rack (no scale)

K4/3

K4/1

K4/2

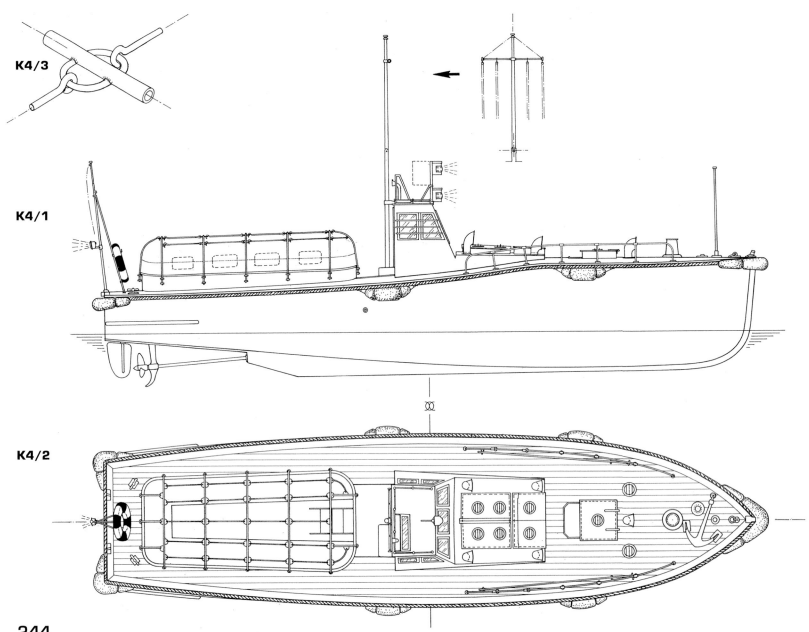

K4/4   Internal profile

K4/5   Internal plan

K4/4

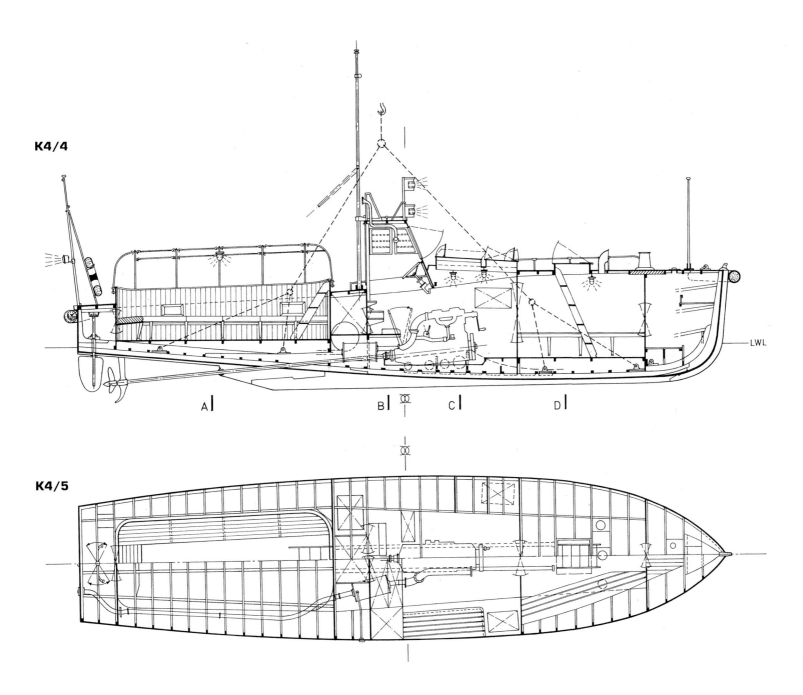

A   B   C   D

LWL

K4/5

K4/6 Body plan

K4/7 Sheer elevation

K4/8 Waterline plan

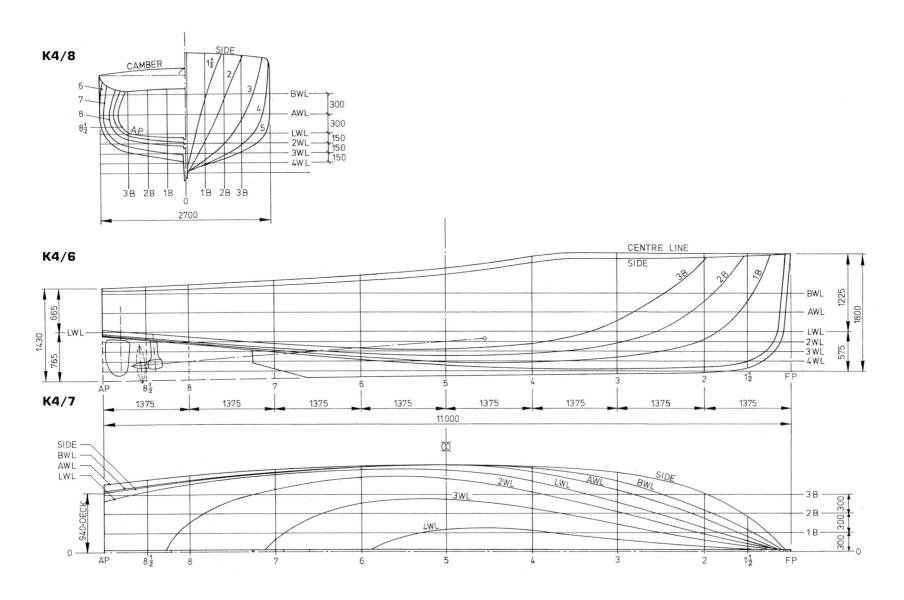

K4/8

CAMBER

SIDE
1½
2
3
6
7
8
8½
AP
4
5

BWL
AWL
LWL
2WL
3WL
4WL

300
300
150
150
150

3B 2B 1B 0 1B 2B 3B

2700

K4/6

CENTRE LINE
SIDE
3B 2B 1B

BWL
AWL
LWL
2WL
3WL
4WL

1225
1800
575

1430
665
765

LWL

AP 8½ 8 7 6 5 4 3 2 1½ FP

K4/7

1375 1375 1375 1375 1375 1375 1375 1375

11000

SIDE
BWL
AWL
LWL

2WL
LWL
AWL
BWL
SIDE

3WL

LWL

940-DECK

0

AP 8½ 8 7 6 5 4 3 2 1½ FP

3B
2B
1B
0

300 300 300 300

K4/9–12 Sections (scale 1:37.5)

K4/13 Cradle (no scale)

K4/9

A

K4/10

B

K4/12

D

LWL

LWL

K4/11

K4/13

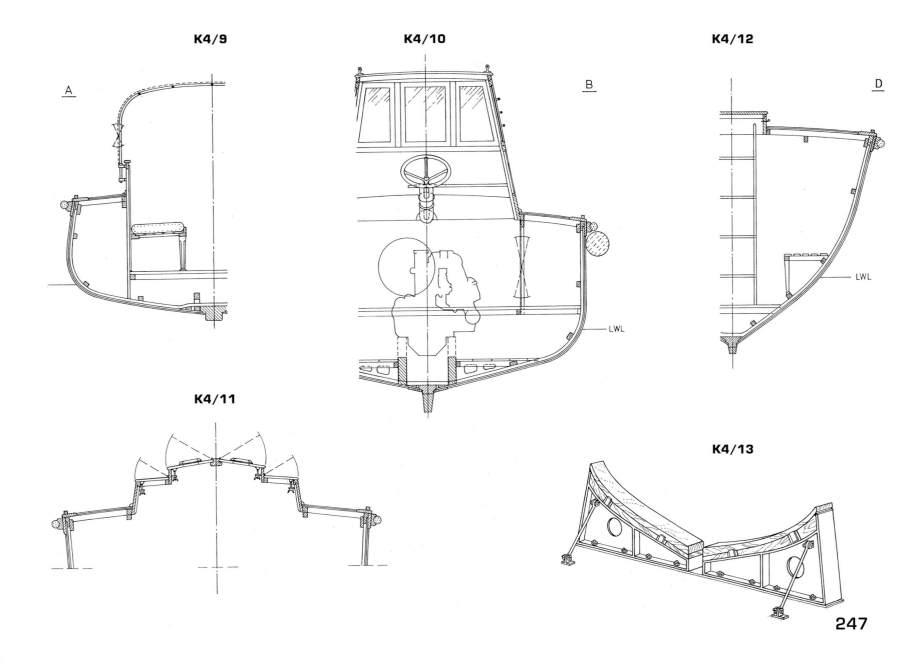

K5　12m 30hp motor launch

K5/1　Internal profile (canvas rack was used only sporadically) (scale 1:75)

K5/2　Plan (scale 1:75)

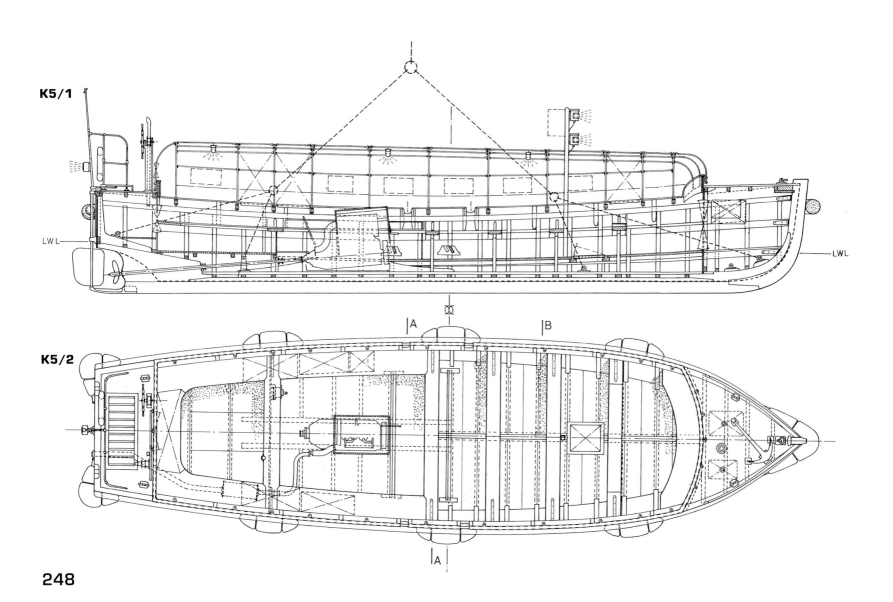

K5/1

LWL

LWL

K5/2

K5/3   Body plan (scale 1:75)

K5/4   Sheer elevation (scale 1:75)

K5/5   Waterline plan (scale 1:75)

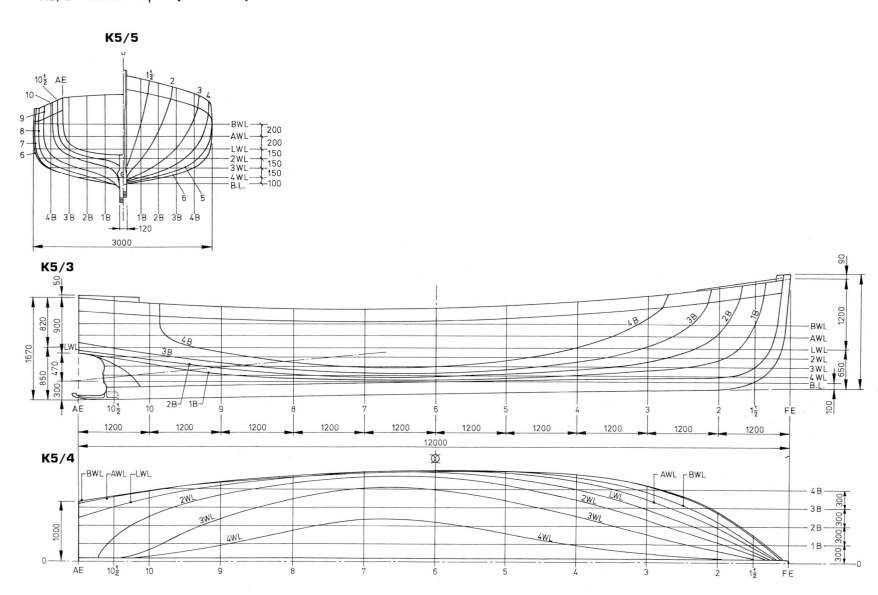

K5/6   Section of middle part
       (scale 1:37.5)

K5/7   Detail of section:
       dolphin fender
       (scale 1:18.75)

K5/8   Section 'B-B'
       (scale 1:18.75)

K5/9   Typical cradle
       (no scale)

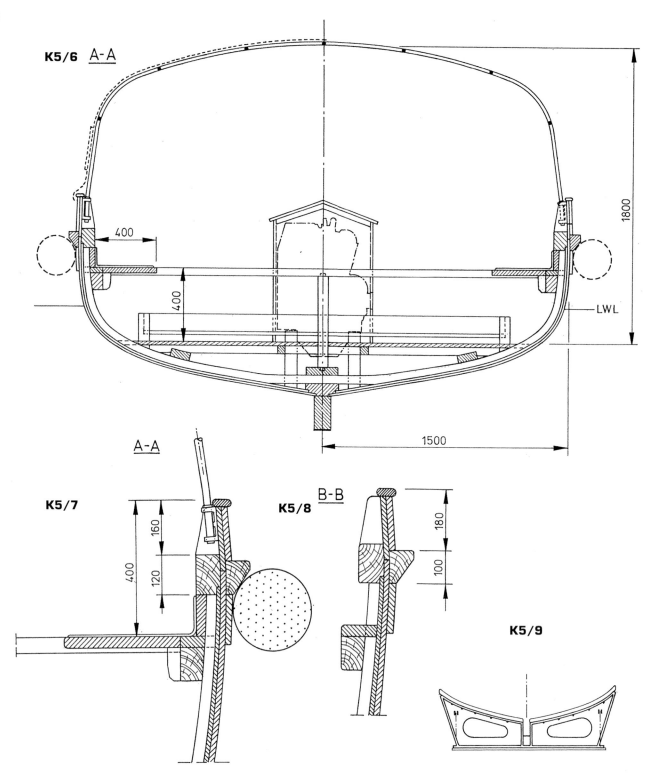

K5/6 A-A

1800

400

400

LWL

1500

A-A

K5/7

400

160

120

K5/8 B-B

180

100

K5/9

K6 9m cutter

K6/1   Profile view (scale 1:50)

K6/2   Internal profile (scale 1:50)

K6/3   Plan (scale 1:50)

K6/1

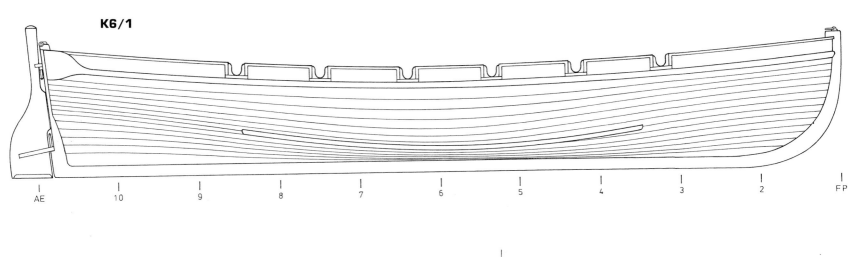

AE   10   9   8   7   6   5   4   3   2   FP

K6/2

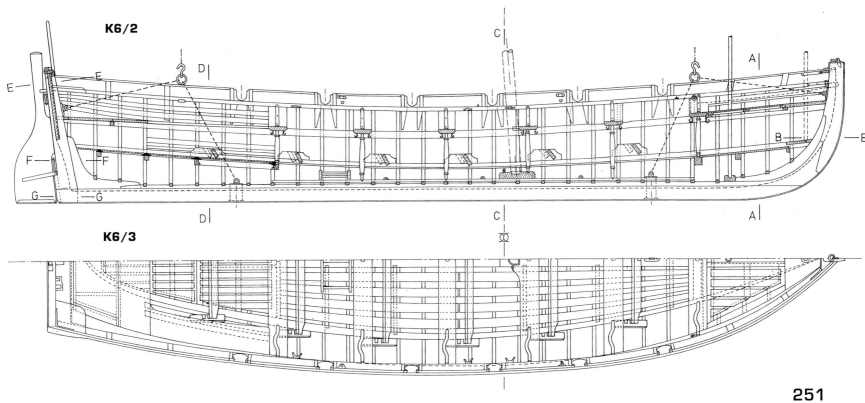

K6/3

251

K6/4   Body plan

K6/5   Sheer elevation (scale 1:50)

K6/6   Waterline plan (scale 1:50)

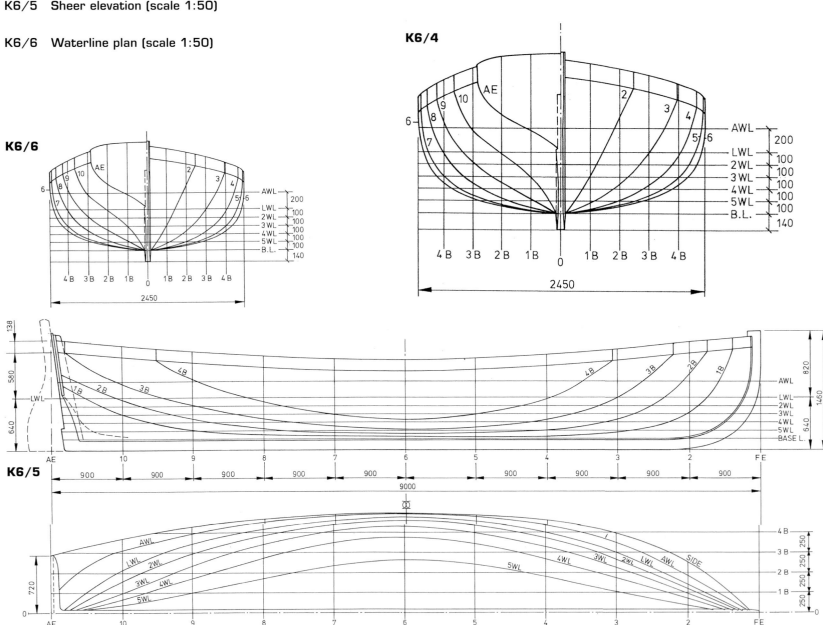

K6/7–13 Sections
    (scale 1:25)

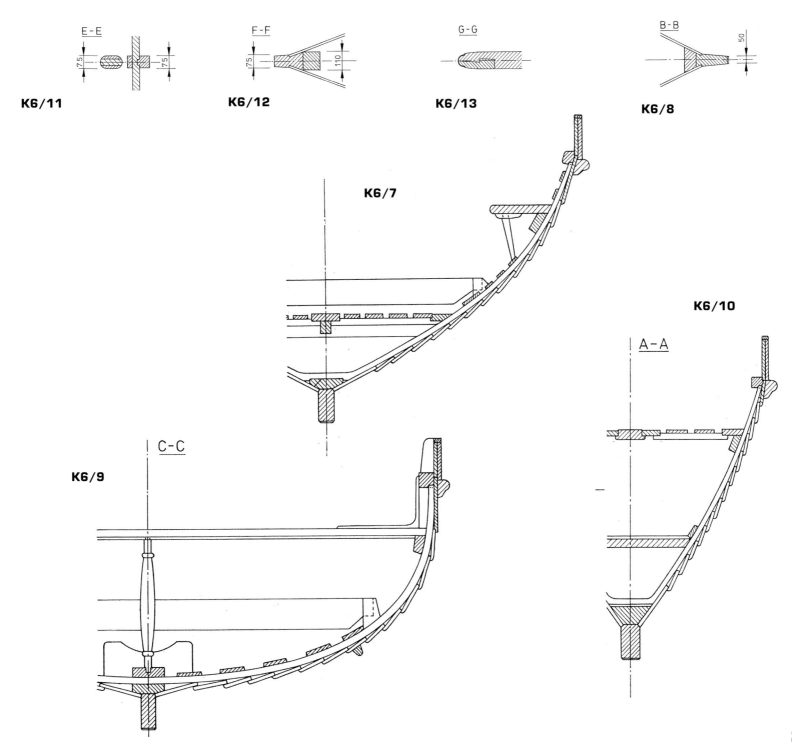

E - E

K6/11

F - F

K6/12

G - G

K6/13

B - B

K6/8

K6/7

K6/10

A - A

C - C

K6/9

K7   8m (27ft) sampan (scale 1:50)

K7/1   Profile view   K7/4   Section of middle part

K7/2   Internal profile   K7/5   Rudder

K7/3   Plan

K7/1

K7/2

8229

K7/5

K7/3

K7/4

1900

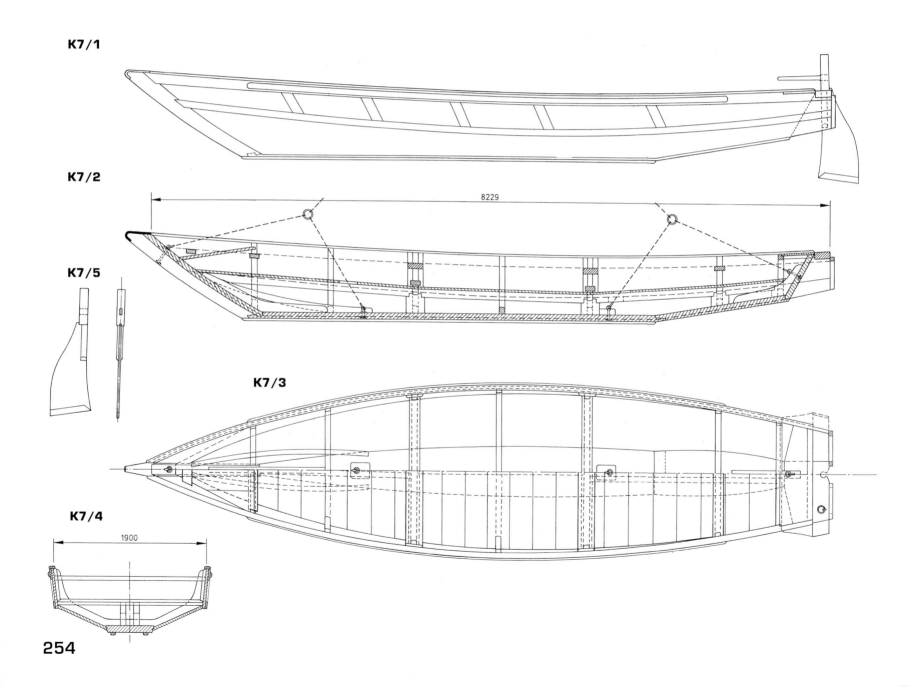

254

K8 6m (20ft) sampan (scale 1:50)

K8/1 Profile view

K8/4 Section of middle part

K8/2 Internal profile

K8/5 Rudder

K8/3 Plan

K8/1

K8/4

K8/2

K8/5

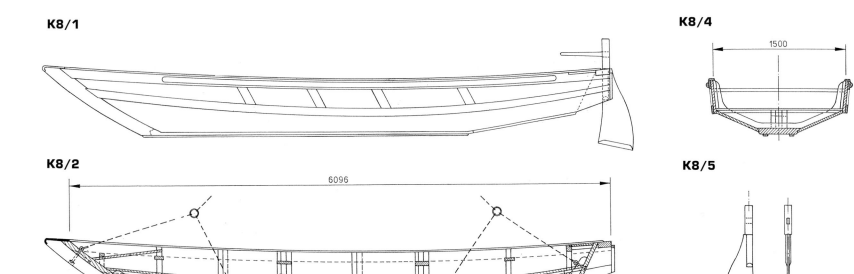

6096

1500

K8/3

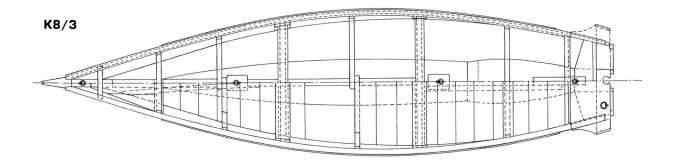

BIBLIOGRAPHY

Breyer, Siegfried, *Battleships and Battlecruisers 1905-1970* (London, 1973)

Breyer, Siegfried, *Grosskampfschiffe 1905-1970* (Munchen, 1978)

Campbell, John, *Naval Weapons of World War Two* (London, 1985)

Dulin R, Garzke W, *Battleships-Aksis and Neutral Battleships in World War II* (Annapolis, 1976)

Field J A, Jr, *The Japanese at Leyte Gulf: The Sho Operation* (Princeton, 1947)

Flisowski, Zbigniew, *Burza nad Pacyfikiem* (*Storm over the Pacific*) (Warszawa, 1994-96)

Fukui, Shizuo, *Fighting Ships of the Imperial Japanese Navy* (Tokyo, 1969)

Fukui, Shizuo, *Japanese Naval Vessels Illustrated,* Vol 1 *Battleships and Battle Cruisers* (Tokyo, 1974)

Fukui, Shizuo, *Japanese Naval Vessels 1869-1945: Fukui Shizuo Collection* (Tokyo 1994)

Hori M, *Die Japanische Flotte* (Tokyo, 1960)

Society of Japanese Naval Architects, *Designs of Imperial Japanese Navy Vessels* (Tokyo 1980)

Jentshura H, Jung D, and Mickel P, *Die Japanischen Kriegschiffe 1869-1945* (Munchen, 1970)

The Koku-Fan, *The Japanese Warships of the Pacific War* (Tokyo, 1972)

Gardiner, Robert, *Conway's All the World's Fighting Ships 1906-1921,* and *1922-1946* (London, 1992 and 1995)

Gardiner, Robert, *The Eclipse of the Big Gun: The Warship 1906-45* (London, 1992)

The Maru Graphic No 11 *The Imperial Japanese Navy Battleships* (1970)

The Maru Graphic No 4 *Japanese Battleships* (1972)

Maruzen Co, *Maru Special* No 11 *Battleships Fuso and Yamashiro* (!975)

Maruzen Co, *Maru Special* No 113 *Battleships Fuso-class and Ise-class* (Tokyo, 1986)

Maruzen Co, *Maru Special: Mechanisms of Japanese Battleships and Battle Cruisers*

(Tokyo, 1980)

Morison, S E, *The Battle of Surigao Strait* (US Naval Institute Proceedings, 1958)

Morison, S E, *History of the United States Naval Operations in World War II* (Boston, 1955-62)

Macdonald, C, *Japanese Battleships and Cruisers* (London, 1971)

Macintyre D, *The Battle for the Pacific* (London, 1966)

Mori Tsunehide, *Random Japanese Warship details* (Tokyo, 1990)

Mori Tsunehide, *Japanese Cruisers* (Tokyo, 1993)

Mori Tsunehide, *Japanese Destroyers* (Tokyo, 1995)

Matsumoto Kitaro, *Design and Construction of the Battleships Yamato and Musashi* (Tokyo, 1961)

Naval Institute Press, *Japanese Naval Vessels of World War Two – as seen by US Naval Intelligence* (Annapolis, 1987)

Roskill S W, *The War at Sea*, Vol III (London, 1954-56)

Sekai-no Kansen, *Japanese Warships*, No 257 (Tokyo, 1972)

Sekai-no Kansen, *Japanese Combined Fleet at Its Zenith*, No 489 (Tokyo, 1994)

Watts A J, *Japanese Warships of World War II* (London, 1971)

Woodward C V, *The Battle of Leyte Gulf* (New York, 1947)

Yoshimura Akira, *Build the Musashi!* (Tokyo, 1991)

JOURNALS

'Sekai-no Kansen' *Ships of the World*
Maru
Maru War and Person
Warship
Warship International

MICROFILM

Reports of the US Naval Mission to Japan – Washington

Unpublished materials from private Japanese sources